LAUS VIRTUTIS ACTIO

GOULD CAROLUS DAVIS

Management of Artificial Lakes and Ponds

REINHOLD BOOKS IN THE BIOLOGICAL SCIENCES

Consulting Editor
PROFESSOR PETER GRAY
Department of Biological Sciences
University of Pittsburgh
Pittsburgh, Pennsylvania

MANAGEMENT OF

Artificial Lakes and Ponds

GEORGE W. BENNETT
Head, Aquatic Biology Section
Illinois Natural History Survey
Urbana, Illinois

New York
REINHOLD PUBLISHING CORPORATION
Chapman & Hall, Ltd., London

Foreword

In the struggle for existence that occupies the time of all successful living things, there is constantly the pressure on the part of an organism to increase its numbers, and the opposite pressure of competing organisms to reduce its numbers. This is done unconsciously, as far as we know, by all living things but man. Man, though, is so peculiarly endowed by nature with reason, and the ability to think of the future and to plan for it, that this matter of changing the numbers of living things becomes an obsession with him.

Much of man's activity, either indirectly or directly, is aimed at manipulating populations. He increases the numbers of wheat plants, and decreases the numbers of Hessian flies. He increases the numbers of sheep and decreases the numbers of those organisms which parasitize sheep. He increases the numbers of grouse or rabbits and then concerns himself with the diseases which attack these game species. He wishes to increase the numbers of lake trout and at the same time he searches for methods to destroy the sea lamprey.

From the beginning of time man has used other organisms in his ascendency to his present state. Early expressions of culture which have come down to us include arrow points and hammer heads for the capture of game, and spears and hooks for the capture of fishes.

In man's attempt to manipulate populations, the art of fish and game management had its roots. But a new phenomenon has appeared within the present century, and much of it after the first two decades had passed. This has been the changing of the *art* of management to the *science* of management. As we have learned more about fish and game, we have found that these organisms often react in an empirical, predictable way, and the old wives' tales and rules of thumb of just a little while ago have been found to be erroneous unless they happened to be based on what we now know as scientific fact.

The knowledge which we have of a field such as fish management becomes so hidden in the literature, and sometimes so abstruse to the non-specialist, that it must be brought together and interpreted by someone who is conversant with the field. This is what Dr. Bennett has done in his book.

There is certainly a need for organized information on fish management. According to a survey recently published by the United States Fish and Wildlife Service, more than twenty-five and one-quarter million Americans fished in 1960. They spent about 2.7 billions of dollars in this activity.

That the need is growing is indicated by a similar survey conducted in 1955, which showed that at that time there were about twenty-one million fishermen who spent more than 1.9 billions of dollars. During the period 1955-1960 the number of fishermen in America increased by an average of almost one million per year.

Therefore the present book should have a great audience, and the facts which it contains should be of importance and of value to a great many people. The author has found it necessary to simplify many terms, and define many things in this book, for there is no profession of sport fishermen. People with this delightful addiction may vary from those handy with a shovel to those skilled with an electron microscope. They start fishing when they can hardly hold a pole, and, at the other end of the age span, stop only when they can again hardly hold a pole. To most of these people this book should be in part or in the whole a valuable tool.

And there will be more interested people as time goes on, for the already large number of Americans who fished in 1960 is bound to increase.

HARLOW B. MILLS

Urbana, Illinois
May, 1962

Preface

Any book that is written and published probably stems from the belief of the author that there is a need for such a book. Therefore it seems only fair that the preface should let the reader know for whom the book is intended. This one was planned as a general reference for the professional fishery biologist, and for the recreation expert assigned to the task of producing hook-and-line fishing in the artificial impoundments of parks and forest preserves. It will interest fishermen who wish to be informed on lake-management matters, and should serve as a baseline from which research biologists in warm-water fisheries launch further investigations. Students of aquatic biology and fishery management will find both theory and practice here, as well as references for further reading on many subjects.

A sincere effort has been made to recognize and acknowledge those researchers whose activities have contributed to a well-balanced theory of management and to avoid the pitfalls of oversimplification in management. Out of respect for biological variability, I usually have avoided specific directions, such as, for example, how to stock a lake. Rather, I have tried to show the range of *reasonable* stocking and its relationship to the range of potential results. Our purposes will have been satisfied if the reader gains enough insight into what might happen and why, to appreciate the danger of fish management by cookbook methods, and hence seeks to make use of the general principles of management as well as the sources of information available in the realistic solution of management matters that may come his way as a professional biologist and citizen.

The organization of the present book was devised to achieve its purposes. First a brief, concise view of fish culture is presented to place the modern approach to the management of artificial lakes and ponds in a proper perspective. Next, artificial aquatic habitats are distinguished from natural bodies of water, are described, and, as much as is feasible, categorized. Then, the ecological interrelationships of fishes and lake habitats are investigated and the implications for the professional manager are discussed. After a reasonably thorough treatment of such large concepts as carrying capacity, productivity, growth, reproduction, competition, and predation, the book comes to grips with the theory and techniques of management per se. Now, the complex problems of fishing mortality and natural mortality are handled before concluding with chapters on sensory perception and behavior in sport fishing and the commercial aspects of this most popular of all outdoor sports.

No attempt has been made to avoid technical matter, although technical terminology has been reduced to a minimum and the mathematical approach to population dynamics has been relegated to a list of papers, many of which will be available in the nearest university library. For the convenience of the student and individual pond owner who will be using the book, important terms and concepts are defined when they are first presented. No scientific names of fishes appear in the nine chapters of this book; however, the scientific names as well as the common names of all fishes mentioned may be found in the Appendix. A few scientific names other than those of fishes appear in the text, most of which are the names of aquatic plants as given by Fassett.*

Any author who completes a book is indebted to many people. In this respect, I have been very fortunate in receiving the counsel of all of the members of the Aquatic Biology Section of the Illinois Natural History Survey. I am particularly indebted to Drs. William C. Starrett, R. Weldon Larimore, and Donald F. Hansen of our Section editorial committee for giving of their own time to read and criticize this manuscript.

Dr. Harlow B. Mills, Chief of the Illinois Natural History Survey, has contributed greatly through his encouragement, his suggestions for improving certain areas in each of the nine chapters, and through his special ability to recognize and point out the author's bias regarding several controversial subjects.

Mr. Royal B. McClelland, Executive Secretary of the Illinois Federation of Sportsmen's Clubs and Editor of Illinois Wildlife magazine, has read the manuscript through the eyes of a fisherman and lake owner, and has suggested changes to make the book more understandable and readable.

Much of the original planning for subject matter included in Chapter 6 came from discussions with Mr. Sam A. Parr, Executive Assistant for the Illinois Department of Conservation, and Mr. W. W. Fleming, Director of Fish and Game, Indiana Department of Conservation. This chapter on theories and techniques of management was later presented to Mr. William J. Harth, Superintendent of Fisheries, Mr. Al Lopinot, Chief Fishery Biologist of the Illinois Department of Conservation and to other professional fishery biologists with the Department for general discussion at the 1961 meeting of Illinois aquatic and fishery biologists. I am grateful for the suggestions offered at this meeting.

* Fassett, N. C., "A Manual of Aquatic Plants," with revised Appendix by A. C. Ogden, University of Wisconsin Press, Madison, Wisconsin (1957).

Many people furnished invaluable cooperation as lake and pond owners willing to allow the collection of fish and fishing in their waters. These cooperators would number more than a hundred. Of these, I have space to mention a few: Mr. William Utterback and Mr. David Malcomson, each of whom owns a number of gravel-pit ponds and who not only allowed us to use these ponds for research but gave of their own time to assist in research activities; Mr. Faye H. Root, Assistant Professor of Camp and Park Management at the University of Illinois Robert Allerton Estate near Monticello, who has arranged for our use of 4-H Club ponds and has given cooperation in many ways; and Mr. Max McGraw, owner of the Fin 'n Feather Club, who has built special ponds for research and has furnished creel and management data from ponds and lakes on the club property for our use.

I especially wish to acknowledge the valuable assistance of Miss Mary Frances Martin, Technical Assistant and Secretary for the Section of Aquatic Biology, who was always willing to help in various phases of this work, and of others who have typed material, a page at a time. My wife, Mary Ellyn, read the manuscript at each stage of progress for spelling, punctuation, and meaning.

I do want to express my appreciation to Dr. Peter Gray and Messrs. Ross, Chastain, and Hart of the Reinhold editorial staff for their constant encouragement and assistance in improving my manuscript.

GEORGE W. BENNETT

Urbana, Illinois
April, 1962

Contents

Foreword   v

Preface   vii

CHAPTER 1. HISTORY OF FISH MANAGEMENT   1

Early Pond-Fish Culture   2
The Development of Hatcheries   3
Early Attempts at Management   5
The Importance of Studying Total Populations   7
Pond Management   8
Reservoir Management   9
    Early Investigations   9
    Fish Cycles in Reservoirs   10
    Recent Advances in Management   11
      Phases of Operation   11
      Reducing Undesirable Populations   12
What is in the Future?   12
Literature   13

CHAPTER 2. ARTIFICIAL AQUATIC HABITATS   15

The Farm Pond   17
    Purposes of Farm Ponds   17
    Engineering Considerations for Farm Ponds   18
When is a Pond a Lake?   20
Artificial Lakes for Domestic Uses   20
    Water-Supply Reservoirs   21
Navigation Pools   22
Lateral Levee Reservoirs   22
Multi-Purpose Reservoirs   22
Ponds and Lakes with Excavated Basins   24
    Gravel-Pit Lakes   24
    Strip Mine Lakes   26
    Quarry Lakes   27

Lakes Built for Recreation 28
Planning an Artificial Lake or Pond 29
    Watershed, Run-off, and Water Manipulation 30
Thermal Stratification and Loss of Oxygen 31
    Seasonal Thermal Stratification 31
    Variations in Thermal Stratification 33
    Fall Overturn 33
    Attempts to Upset Stratification 34
Thermal Stratification and Reservoir Outlets 34
Other Factors Affecting Thermal Stratification 36
Biological Productivity of Water 38
Lake Size and Productivity 39
Literature 40

CHAPTER 3. INTERRELATIONSHIPS OF FISHES AND LAKE HABITATS 42

Sewage Pollution and Fertility 43
pH and Chemistry of Water 44
Effects of Water Temperature on Fish 45
Effects of Turbidity 46
Oxygen and Carbon Dioxide 48
Winterkill and Summerkill 49
    Winterkill 49
        1. Aeration of Water Under Ice 51
        2. Aeration of Water Above Ice 51
        3. Pumping of Well Water 51
        4. Snow Removal 52
        5. Lamp Black 52
        6. Circulation of Bottom Water 52
    Results of Partial Winterkill 53
    Summerkill 54
Other Dangers of Impoundments 56
    Loss of Ponds Because of Burrowing Animals 56
    Wind Action 56
    Dangers from Insecticides 57
Literature 57

CHAPTER 4. CARRYING CAPACITY, PRODUCTIVITY, AND GROWTH 59

Carrying Capacity and Standing Crop 60
    Surface Area 61
    Experimental Testing 61
    Factors Affecting Poundage 62
        Fertilization 63

Chemical Basis for Fertility 63
Kinds of Fishes 63
Growing Season 69
Other Factors Related to Standing Crop Size 69
Fish of Useful Sizes 70
Fish Production 71
Definition of Production 71
Food Conversion 72
Relation to Standing Crop 73
Estimating Production 74
Relative Plumpness of Fish 75
Methods of Measuring Condition 76
Coefficient of Condition 76
Index of Condition 76
Condition Factor of E. M. Corbett 77
Condition Factor of Cooper and Benson 78
Condition Cycles 78
Condition and Growth Rate 79
Use of Condition in Management 79
Growth 79
Effects of Starvation 81
Growth of Fish in New Waters 81
Factors Affecting Rate of Growth 82
Interpretation of Growth from Fish Scales 85
Literature 89

CHAPTER 5. REPRODUCTION, COMPETITION, AND PREDATION 91

Reproduction 92
Reproductive Potential of Fishes 92
Spawn Production and Number of Spawners 94
Age and Sexual Maturity 96
Sex Ratios 96
External Sex Characteristics 97
Spawning 97
Hybridization 99
Selective Breeding 101
Unsuccessful Reproduction 103
Stocking 103
Fishes Used 104
The Bass-Bluegill Combination 104
Other Combinations of Fishes 107
Changes in Fishing 110

Stocking for Improvement of a Population   110
Stocking to Improve a Food Chain   112
Failures in Stocking Fish   113
Predation   115
The Role of Predation in Fish Management   115
Competition   118
Competition for Food   118
Competition for Space   119
Competition for Specific Habitats   123
Starvation   123
Inter- and Intraspecific Competition   123
Reproduction, Competition, and Predation   124
Balance   125
Literature   127

CHAPTER 6. THEORIES AND TECHNIQUES OF MANAGEMENT   130

Fish Sampling   130
Reasons for Sampling Fish Populations   131
Sampling Methods   132
Gill Nets   133
Trammel Nets   133
Seines   133
Hoop Nets, Wing Nets, and Trap Nets   134
Minnow Seine Sampling   135
Minnow Seine Method of Pond Analysis   136
Spot Poisoning   137
Boat Shocking   137
Angling   139
Management Techniques   140
Complete Fish Population Removal   140
Population Removal by Draining   140
Population Removal by Rotenone Treatment   142
Selective Poisoning   147
DDT and Other Insecticides   147
Toxaphene   148
Sodium Cyanide   149
Sodium Sulfite   149
Fish Population Adjustment   150
Use of Nets and Seines   150
Partial Poisoning   150
Timing in Partial Poisoning   151
Shoreline vs. Sectional Treatment   152

Artificial Fluctuation of Water Levels 155
Effects Upon the Exposed Lake Bottom 158
Effects Upon Rooted Aquatic Vegetation 158
Effects Upon Invertebrates 159
Effects Upon Fishes and Other Vertebrates 159
Types of Drawdowns 161
Lake Fertilization 162
Manganese 164
Lime 164
Potassium 164
Phosphorus 165
Nitrogen 165
Other Functions of Fertilizers 165
Dangers From the Use of Fertilizers 166
Aquatic Vegetation and Control Measures 168
Types of Aquatic Plants 169
Algae as a Basic Food 170
Dangerous Algae 171
Nuisance Algae 171
Control of Algae 172
Loss of Fish Production Through Rooted Vegetation 172
Sudden Plant Die-Offs 173
Role of Aquatic Vegetation in Management 176
Control of Higher Aquatic Vegetation 177
Literature 177

CHAPTER 7. FISHING AND NATURAL MORTALITY 181

Population Estimation 181
Forces Acting Upon a Fish Population 182
Fishing Mortality 183
Angling Compared to Natural Predation 183
Yields and Standing Crop 184
Maximum Yields and Length of Growing Season 185
Underfishing 187
Overfishing 189
Fishing Pressure vs. Yield 190
Types of Fishing Pressure 193
Factors Related to Rate of Catch 195
Role of Commercial Fishing in Sport-Fish Management 196
Natural Mortality 199
Causes of Natural Death 199
When Do Fish Die? 200

Scavengers   201
Length of Life of Fishes   201
Problems of Measuring Natural Mortality   202
Fishing Mortality, Natural Mortality and Recruitment   207
Restrictions and Mortality   208
  Size Limits   208
  Creel Limits   209
  Closed Seasons   209
Literature   210

CHAPTER 8.   FISH BEHAVIOR AND ANGLING   212
Vision   213
  Color Vision   213
  Underwater Vision   214
  Changing Pigmentation   216
  Direct Observation and Sun Orientation   217
  Light Sensitivity   217
Hearing   218
  Sound Location   218
  Sound Production   219
Odor Perception and Taste   219
  Location of Taste Organs   220
  Some Uses of Odor Perception   221
    Schooling   221
    Fright Reaction   221
    Identification of Common and Uncommon Odors   222
    Odor as an Aid in Migration   222
    Odor as an Aid in Homing   224
Temperature Perception and Responses   224
  Sensitivity to Temperature Change   225
  Mortalities Caused by High Temperatures   225
  Temperature Acclimation   226
  Preferred Temperatures   227
Behavior Patterns   229
  Some Types of Behavior Patterns   229
    Social Groupings   229
    Seasonal Rhythm   230
    Daily Activity   231
  Responses to Specific Stimuli   232
  Hyperactivity as a Lethal Factor   233
  "Stay at Home" Fish   233
  Homing and Home Range   234

Theories of Migration in Fishes   236
Responses of Fishes to Angling   237
Factors that Influence Biting   238
   Water Temperatures   238
   Water Transparency   240
   Diurnal Effects   241
   Rising and Falling Water Levels   241
   Barometric Pressures and Fishing Tables   242
   Resistance of Fish to Being Caught   243
   Fisherman "Know-how"   245
Literature   246

CHAPTER 9. COMMERCIAL ASPECTS OF SPORT FISHING   249

Interest in Angling   251
  Supplying the Needs of the Sport Fisherman   251
   Costs Assigned to an End Product, Usually Fish 252
   Supplying Fishermen's Baits   253
   Earthworms and Other Invertebrates   253
   Minnows   254
Fishing for Sale   254
  "Executives" Fishing and Hunting Clubs   255
  Fishing-Lake Investments   255
  Trespass-Rights Fishing   256
  Catch-Out Ponds   257
  Ponds in Which Fish Are Artificially Fed   259
  Floating Fishing Docks   261
  Fish for Sale   263
  Fish Management Service   265
Literature   266

Appendix   267

Index   271

1 ～～～

History of Fish Management

Fish management can be defined as the art and science of producing sustained annual crops of wild fish for recreational and commercial uses.[31] But, this activity is not synonymous with fish farming, or the production either of hatchery fish for put-and-take fishing or fish fry and fingerlings for the purpose of stocking. Nor does it consist merely of regulations to control the take of kinds, numbers, and sizes of fish (as when limits are placed upon fishing seasons) any more than it is restricted to "habitat improvement" per se.

Nonetheless, fish management makes use of knowledge gleaned from fish farming, the products of the hatchery, legal assistance to regulate fishing, and methods of habitat modification. However, these facets of fishery husbandry and knowledge can be employed only when integrated into a master plan that eliminates physical and physiological barriers to the well-being of the fishes selected for management. Thus, as stated above, *fish management* is defined as *the art and science of producing sustained annual crops of wild fish for recreational and commercial uses.* The reasons that we have stressed the words "art" and "science" should soon be apparent.

Dr. T. H. Langlois[29] in his studies of fish production in Lake Erie has illustrated the complexity of factors influencing the fish in an aquatic habitat by demonstrating that turbidity and plankton abundance control the size of surviving year classes of important commercial fishes. We can see from Dr. Langlois' study that the crop of fish available for capture in any given year was not related to fishing intensity in past seasons, but instead to the amount of topsoil carried into the lake during some preceding year when the fish being studied were hatching. Although naturally no amount of legal regulation of the fishery can be expected to change such a cause-and-effect relationship, the results themselves might be changed by intensive soil conservation practices on the land in the watersheds tributary to Lake Erie. This points up the importance and com-

1

plexity of fish management; however, its history is bound up with the broader term "fish culture."

We might somewhat arbitrarily divide fish culture and management into three time periods—a division that has its greatest relevance to the student of fish management. The first, which stretches from its earliest development in the pre-Christian era to about 1900 A.D., is characterized by classical fish culture. The second, which roughly covers the period from 1900 to the 1930's, represents the first gropings (often blind and erroneous ones) toward the manipulation of wild populations. The third, which began in the 1930's and extends to the present time, is identified with the development of modern ideas and methods related to managing "wild" fish in natural and artificial waters.

Thus, fish management as an integrated science is rather recent, and it may be said to have had its beginnings when fishery biologists began to study fish populations as composite units. Nevertheless, to recognize the importance of what went before, one must consider the historical records of pond-fish culture that began with the earliest historical writings.

EARLY POND-FISH CULTURE

In almost all written history there are references to fish ponds or fish culture. A study of these records reveals that the Chinese were well versed in raising fish many years before the time of Christ. Also, it can be seen that the Romans copied the techniques of this art at a very early time, although they probably added nothing to the knowledge of fish culture that existed in the ancient Chinese civilization.

Pond-fish culture spread through Europe during the Middle Ages. The first carp ponds were built in Wittingau (Czechoslovakia) in 1358, and for the next 400 years in Europe this was the center for raising pond fish.[36] During this period, fish culture became quite complex. For example, carp culture very early demanded specialized holding areas, such as spawning and hatching ponds (where fry were allowed to grow during the first summer) and growing and fattening ponds. Further, in the fall, carp had to be moved to deep wintering ponds. Special strains of carp were developed, much as various strains of domestic animals have been produced. Thus, from the 15th to the 18th centuries, with this growth in complexity, men, such as North,[37] Baccius,[1] and others, presented detailed techniques for raising pedigreed carp and other common fish useful for food. These investigations have been continued up to the present, and much progress has been made in an understanding of the many facets composing the pond habitat for fish.

Since pond-fish culture in Europe represented food production, it supplied a cash crop that was harvested much as any other farm crop. However, this type of "farming" has not been profitable in North America until very recently [27] because of an early and extensive development of the commercial fishing of wild fresh-water and marine populations which provided a more than adequate amount to supply domestic demands. For example, the commercial yield of fresh-water fishes from the Illinois River (Illinois) alone was 24 million pounds in 1908; [45] the catch was composed mostly of carp, buffalo fish, and catfish and was largely shipped by rail to eastern markets. In fact, it is interesting to note that special strains of carp imported to this country from Europe in the 1880's soon reverted to the original wild type. However, in the period since 1908, the fisheries of the Great Lakes and coastal marine waters have largely supplanted those of inland rivers and smaller lakes, so that now the commercial operations in inland rivers are much reduced, except those for catfish which always have a ready market.

THE DEVELOPMENT OF HATCHERIES

A normal outgrowth of European fish-culture practices brought to this country by immigrants was the development in the U.S. of hatcheries to supplant the natural production of young wild fish. The earliest hatcheries were privately operated, usually for the production of trout. Dr. Theodatus Garlick, the Rev. Dr. John Bachman, and Seth Green were all operating private hatcheries prior to 1865. [50] In 1872, at the urging of the American Fish-Culturists' Association, the Congress of the United States enlarged the duties of the newly formed Fish Commission to include the propagation of fish.* In 1875 both federal and state governments were operating hatcheries for the artificial production of fish. The late nineteenth and the early years of the twentieth centuries were marked by attempts at hatchery production and stocking of the kinds of fish useful for sport and food in the more important waters. However, many of these attempted introductions resulted in failure for the following reasons: a lack of understanding of physical and biological limitations, the release of the fish into habitats unsuitable for them, and their inability to survive predation and/or to compete with other organisms already present in the waters. These failures were due largely to the fact that at that time the science of fish ecology was practically unknown, while the art and science of fish culture was well advanced.

This was the heyday of the men engaged in the artificial propagation of fish. States vied with one another in the race to put out larger and larger numbers. "Paper fish" flourished in the reports of hatchery superintendents: numbers were important; little else mattered.

Moreover, in the late nineteenth century only a few trained professional

* U.S. Comm. of Fish Rept. 1872-73 (1874).

biologists were employed by State Conservation Departments; most of the limnologists and ichthyologists were attached to universities and were given little or nothing to say in formulating the programs of Conservation Departments. The scientists and fish culturists came together at the annual meetings of the American Fisheries Society. The latter probably looked upon the scientists as men having little practical use for anything except for the identification of some strange fish or aquatic bug; during this period, the university biologists were primarily engaged in taxonomy and distributional studies. Undoubtedly, some of the things the "practical men" said at the American Fisheries Society meetings mildly irritated the biologists, but not sufficiently to cause them to become crusaders. After all, at that time, they had little real information on the ecology of fishes, except in a broad, general way.

This divergence of beliefs was perhaps nowhere more clearly illustrated than in Illinois in the 1880's and '90's when Professor Stephen A. Forbes and his group of scientists were studying the biology of the Illinois River. Concurrently, the Illinois Fish Commission was working in this area, but with the primary objective of rescuing the fish stranded by the receding waters of early summer along the Illinois and Mississippi Rivers.

Forbes' emphasis is clear: he recognized the loss of fish as a natural phenomenon: [19] "As the waters retire, the lakes [*of the Illinois River bottoms*] are again defined; the teeming life which they contain is restricted within daily narrower bounds, and a fearful slaughter follows; the lower and more defenseless animals are penned up more and more closely with their predaceous enemies, and these thrive for a time to an extraordinary degree." Fish stranded in land-locked pools were either preyed upon by other, larger fish or by amphibians, reptiles, fish-eating birds or mammals; or if the pools dried completely, the fish died and decayed where they lay exposed. Since these victimized fish were mostly small ones, the products of the current reproductive season, Forbes and his colleagues recognized them as being in excess of the small number required to maintain the population at a constant level. They realized that this apparent waste was normal and had been occurring on the overflow lands of large rivers for many thousands of years.

The Illinois State Fish Commission, on the other hand, engaged crews of men with seines and wagons to rescue these fish for stocking in other lakes or for release in open water. These crews usually operated each year from the time the first fish became stranded in the spring, until the waters had receded to their usual summer low-water levels.[4]

Professor Forbes must have recognized that this program was entirely useless, not only because the fish were "expendable," but also because their survival was in doubt when they were seined up and transported during hot weather. Yet, judging from what was published at that time, there was no animosity between Professor Forbes and the State Fish Commissioners. Perhaps the former realized that the Commission was responding to the desires of the public.

It is against this background that we can visualize the important place hatcheries held in the minds of fish culturists at that time. The products of inland hatcheries were trout, salmon, whitefish, walleye, largemouth bass, smallmouth bass, northern pike, muskellunge, and several other species propagated for stocking in special locations. Since hatchery operators were thoroughly convinced of the worth of their product, they scarcely gave any thought to how fish managed to survive before the hatchery was developed.

Hatchery superintendents and fish- and game-department officials on both state and federal levels exerted considerable effort to convince the public that hatchery fish were needed to maintain populations of fish in the face of advancing civilization—a drive which gave great impetus to the hatchery movement. However, almost no effort was made to determine the final disposition of hatchery fish or to estimate the importance of the hatchery produce on the basis of fish stocked per acre of water. Since such questions were dangerous to the hatchery movement they were simply avoided. Even so, it is interesting to note that the hatchery movement was so successful that even today the otherwise uninformed layman inquires about recent stocking of the waters in which he plans to fish. In later sections of this book, we will see some of the important ways the hatching of fish is useful in fish management.

EARLY ATTEMPTS AT MANAGEMENT

In spite of the fact that the artificial propagation of fish in hatcheries continued to hold the center of the fisheries stage, some of the early investigations were not directly related to artificial fish propagation. These studies helped to pave the way for the modern concept of fish management which is the subject of this book. Before 1759, Hederström [21] recognized rings of growth on the vertebrae of fishes as representing annuli; later other biologists discovered the growth rings on the scales of fish, but Borodin [9] and Barney [2] were responsible for bringing a method of aging fish from scales to the attention of fisheries workers. Wiebe [49] and C. Juday, *et al.,*[28] were among the first to do comprehensive experiments with fertilizer materials in water and to measure the increase in plankton resulting therefrom. Surber [41] tested sodium arsenite as a chemical means for the control of aquatic vegetation. The first electric fish shocker for research purposes was developed by Burr.[10] Markus [33] investigated the relationship between water temperatures and the rate of food digestion in largemouth bass. Thompson [44] tagged fish and studied their migration in rivers.

Several early pond studies gave promise of things to come, such as that of Dyche [14] who observed that interspecific predation between largemouth bass and bluegills might favor bluegills rather than bass. Barney and Canfield [3] studied the fish production of an 0.22-acre pond over a period of 5 years and gathered some evidence that production and total standing crop were related to the lengths of the food chains of the fishes introduced. The first record of the use of the bass-bluegill combination was published in 1902.[39] Barney and Canfield [3] used largemouth bass, crappies, and bluegills, or bluegills alone prior to 1922.

A comprehensive inventory of current thinking on fishery management in 1938 was given by Carl L. Hubbs and R. W. Eschmeyer in their book, "The Improvement of Lakes for Fishing." [22] Dr. Hubbs, then head of the Michigan Institute for Fishery Research, and Dr. Eschmeyer, one of his students recognized for his independent thinking, pooled their experiences and hypotheses and built, with a strong assist from Leopold's concepts of game management, a thesis that populations of fish in lakes could be managed also. Actually, they had very little to go on, but they held with the assumption that if game habitat could be improved by the addition of cover on land, fish habitat must be deficient of cover under water and could be improved in the same manner. So the book begins with a section on improving cover, based on the theory that such cover was one of the larger needs.

Other subjects discussed were Managing Plant Growths, Bettering Spawning Conditions, Regulating the Fluctuations of Water Levels, Preventing Erosion and Silting, and many more. Under the topic Handling Populations with Stunted Growth, the authors suggest that one might do the following: (1) increase food (however, without suggestions as to how to go about it), (2) avoid overstocking, and (3) reduce the population by liberalizing size limits, season limits, and bag limits, as well as by destroying nests, by planting fish-eating game fishes and, as a last resort, by killing the entire population as Dr. Eschmeyer had already done at the time the book was published. In all, there were 20 types of fish-management practices described, none of which had yet been carefully tested.

Evidence that the authors were still affected by the earlier beliefs and operations is to be found under the subject Place of Lake Improvement in Fish Management:

"At least for the near future, lake improvement cannot be foreseen as a substitute for the long-recognized practices in fish management [restrictive and protective legislation, law enforcement, and the introduction of fish and the stocking of artificially propagated and reared fish.[32]] Methods of lake improvement would need to be enormously perfected, before this new practice, if ever, could be expected to replace the older means of maintaining the fish supply." (Bracketed matter mine.)

Hence, the book, "The Improvement of Lakes for Fishing" has its greatest importance in that it initiates a rather bold break with the past, points toward things to come, and presents a precise picture of current thinking in 1938; whereas, the actual lake-management data which it contains is of less significance.

IMPORTANCE OF STUDYING TOTAL POPULATIONS

An important step in the understanding of fish-management problems was the censusing of populations of fish by the poisoning or draining of lakes so that a population could be observed as a unit.[5, 16] Such a census was particularly enlightening when conducted on a lake population with past stocking and fishing records available, because, under such circumstances, the effects of stocking could be evaluated and good or poor fishing associated with a specific population. Almost immediately it became evident that there was never a shortage of fish; in fact, usually there appeared to be an overabundance of individuals, particularly of the fish of smaller sizes.

When many complete fish censuses became available, some of the causes for poor fishing were obvious: (1) an excess of undesirable fish, that is, the domination of these populations by species of no interest to anglers, whereas, proportionally, the number of acceptable fish was so small that the chance of catching them was remote; (2) an excess of desirable fish, that is, in populations containing only hook-and-line species, overpopulation led to stunting, so that few of them were large enough to interest fishermen. Thus, the causes for poor fishing were domination by undesirable fish and the overpopulation of desirable ones with consequent stunting. This type of information gave direction to attempts at fish management, something that had been lacking before.

At this time, several studies of entire populations helped to give us an understanding of certain aspects of population dynamics. Thompson,[45] who took periodic samples of the fish population of Lake Senachwine (Illinois) with wing nets and used the mark-and-recovery method of population estimation, came to the conclusion that the "fine" fish component of this population (consisting of largemouth bass, crappies, bluegills, and other centrarchids) totaled between 50 and 55 pounds per acre, regardless of whether the lake level was high and the area was 6000 acres in extent or whether it was reduced by drought to 3000 acres or less. Moreover, the poundage was constant from year to year, in spite of a cycle of size and numbers. In certain years there were ten times as many fish as in other years, but the average weight was only one tenth as great. This was a crappie-dominated cycle, wherein a dominant brood of crappies curtailed the survival of its own young and those of other species until this brood was decimated by natural mortality associated with senile degeneration. Then another dominant brood was produced and the cycle was repeated. The cycle shifted between high numbers of black crappies with low numbers of white crappies and bluegills, and moderate numbers of white crappies and bluegills with low numbers of black crappies. Hence this investigation demonstrated that, in spite of constancy of poundage, continual changes might be taking place among the fishes of certain populations.

One of the most significant studies, in that it helps to show the true position of hatcheries in the fish management picture, was that of Carbine,[12] who followed the spawning and hatching of nest-building centrarchids in Deep Lake (Michigan). Fry were sucked through glass tubing from nests guarded by males (to give identification of kind) and counted. On the basis of these counts and the number of occupied nests observed, Carbine estimated that the hatch of fish *per acre* in Deep Lake exceeded one-half million during a single spawning season. Thus, he was able to demonstrate that the hatching success of fishes in natural lakes was as high or higher than that observed in fish hatcheries.

POND MANAGEMENT

Several investigators working with fish in ponds demonstrated the capacity of fish populations to expand and contract in relation to the capacity of the habitat to support them [42] and the relationships between length of the food chains and poundages of fish supported.[46]

Probably the most extensive pond research unit in North America was developed between 1934 and 1944 by H. S. Swingle and E. V. Smith at the Alabama Polytechnic Institute (now known as Auburn University), Auburn, Alabama. This unit consisted of more than 100 ponds which could be drained and refilled; the ponds ranged in size from one tenth of an acre to more than one acre. These ponds were used for developing simple pond-management techniques which could be used by laymen for increasing the fish yield of farm ponds. Recommendations that worked well in the region of Auburn, Alabama, caught the interest of sports writers throughout the country, and many magazines of national circulation published articles on the Alabama methods of pond management. The U.S. Soil Conservation Service, foremost pond-sponsoring agency in the United States, and many State Conservation Departments, also put to use the recommendations of the Alabama biologists.

The national publicity on pond management stimulated such widespread interest in ponds that many states developed programs of pond research on their own. However, it soon became evident that the same kinds of fishes that produced satisfactory hook-and-line yields in Alabama ponds, when stocked in the "correct" numbers in ponds in other parts of the country, behaved in an entirely different manner. This was not only because the habitats and fish food complexes were different, but also because the behavior and physiology of the fishes varied within the limits of their natural range. Thus, the program of stocking fingerling bass and bluegills in a ratio of 1 to 10 or 15, and fertilizing the ponds with inorganic fertilizer—a program which produced a harvestable fish crop in the southeast—created overpopulation problems in the central states and was still less useful in more distant parts of the United States.

Fishery biologists began to study life histories of many common warm-water fishes and to test combinations other than that composed of large-mouth bass and bluegills, with the objective of finding new combinations that would work as well or better than the bass-bluegill combination. Soon nearly every state developed its own stocking recommendations for largemouth bass and bluegills, and many states recommended the stocking of bass or some other piscivorous species with one or several other omnivorous species, often not including the bluegill at all.[30, 34]

At the present time, there is still considerable variation in recommendations for many aspects of pond management throughout the United States. Most biologists believe that no combination of fishes is entirely satisfactory for producing sport fishing in a selected impoundment, yet any of several combinations may be reasonably useful for this purpose.

RESERVOIR MANAGEMENT

EARLY INVESTIGATIONS

The progress of fish management in large reservoirs has been detailed by Jenkins.[24] In the early 1920's, many large ones for flood control and hydro-electric power were constructed, and among the first studied was Lake Keokuk—a low-dam impoundment on the Mississippi River near Keokuk, Iowa.[13, 20]

As reservoir construction gained momentum in the 1930's, studies of these new reservoirs consisted primarily of inventories of plankton, bottom fauna, and fish,[35, 47] but provided, in addition to these inventories, opinions on how to improve the fish-producing capacities of the reservoirs.[48]

However, during the latter part of the 1930's, a number of reservoirs, previously superb for fishing, became poor. Consequently, some biologists concluded of these large reservoirs that, after an initial high productivity brought about by the decay and utilization of the organic matter present at impoundment,[11, 15] we could expect them to become aquatic deserts.

However, a team of fishery biologists, employed by the Tennessee Valley Authority to investigate the fish populations of TVA reservoirs,[18, 43] concluded that there was insufficient evidence to substantiate this belief.

FISH CYCLES IN RESERVOIRS

The work of the TVA in this direction was strengthened by the studies of others, and, in time, biologists, who had seen fishing in a number of new water-supply reservoirs change from excellent to very poor in a matter of a few years, were ready to predict a reservoir fishing cycle: [6]

"At the first spawning season (May-June) after the reservoir is filled and stocked with fish, the young of largemouth bass will be very abundant. These will grow rapidly to legal size and produce excellent bass fishing for about three years. Moderate numbers of young crappies, bluegills, and other sunfish and bullheads may be produced during the first spawning period. These will grow rapidly to large average sizes and add to the excellence of fishing.

"Carp, buffalo, and suckers, as well as some other fish present in the stream flowing into the impoundment will move into the lake in small numbers and produce some young the first season.

"During the first few years the reservoir will be clear except immediately following heavy rains, and the recreational attractions other than fishing, such as swimming and boating, will be at their maximum.

"Reduced recreational values will be apparent in about the length of time that the original spawn of bass survives (usually four to six years). By this time the bass fishing will be largely gone. Crappies and bluegills will be present in such large populations that they will have become small, stunted and unattractive to fishermen; carp and other rough fish will have multiplied so successfully that their bottom-feeding activities will continually stir up the bottom mud. The lake will remain turbid throughout the year, regardless of periods of dry weather, and will have lost much of its attractiveness to fishermen and bathers. Many of the aesthetic values of boating will be gone. The conditions will be entirely the result of changes in the relative abundance of certain fishes, and as the primary function of the reservoir is to supply water, and not recreation, almost nothing can be done to bring back conditions that were obtained in the early years of impoundment."

As a result of investigations of small impoundments not used for water supply, many examples were available by 1946 to show that the chemical treatment or the draining of such small impoundments to remove undesirable populations (such as those that developed in water-supply reservoirs) entirely eliminated "aquatic desert" conditions, and that once these impoundments were restocked with desirable fish they did become very productive. Thus, the theory of Ellis [15] that high fish production in the early years of impoundment resulted from organic decay in the new lake basin was largely disproved, since this cycle of production could be repeated as often as the reservoir was completely drained (or poisoned) and restocked with small numbers of fish.[7] In addition, the hypothesis of progressive loss of fertility that had been advanced could be attacked in some situations on the basis of the fact that the amount of flooded vegetation in a lake basin was too meager, in relation to the huge volume of water impounded, to produce a "hay infusion" that would result in an initial high fish production.

RECENT ADVANCES IN MANAGEMENT

In 1945 the Federal Office of River Basin Studies was formed. Within the framework of this organization, biologists could appraise the fishery resources of a river before a federal impoundment was built and thereby estimate the effect of the impoundment on that resource. Although these benefits or losses were incorporated in the cost-benefit ratios prepared by the U.S. Corps of Engineers, the predicted gains or losses of a fishery seldom influenced the decision to build a reservoir.

In 1944, Norris Reservoir (Tennessee) was opened to year-round fishing; the results were so encouraging that Tennessee dispensed with a closed season on all of its remaining reservoirs in 1945, as did Ohio that year and some additional states shortly thereafter.

After World War II there was a marked expansion of studies of fish populations in reservoirs, particularly in the states of Tennessee, Kentucky, Missouri, Oklahoma, Texas, and California. In many instances there seemed little to be done that would have any effect upon the fish population of a large reservoir, and the fishermen and biologists were forced to go along with fish population changes resulting from natural biological phenomena.[40]

Phases of Operation. By the late 1950's, reservoir management had been reduced to about five phases of operation: (1) *The manipulation of water levels to favor certain species and depress others.*[8, 17, 23, 26, 38, 50] (2) *The addition to reservoirs of certain species not originally present, in order to contribute directly to the creel or to "fill in" indirectly the trophic levels in the food chain of some important fish already present.* Good examples of the first type of addition are to be found in the introduction of the white bass and striped bass (the striped bass was isolated in the Santee-Cooper Reservoir and then added to Kentucky Lake). On the other hand, the introduction of the threadfin shad is an example of a "fill in" fish to improve food conditions for game fish.[25] (3) *The control of overabundant rough fish and/or forage fish to reduce their competition with game fish for food and space.* There was a need for more efficient methods of controlling these undesirable fish, of which the rough fish species were catostomids (buffalo fishes, carpsuckers, etc.), carp and other large cyprinids, and drum, and the forage fish, usually gizzard shad. (4) *An increase in the harvest of hook-and-line fish.* This was done through year-around open seasons, by heated fishing docks, the creation of temperature gradients, installation of brush piles, and by other means of attracting and holding fish in concentrations where fishermen could harvest them in the most efficient manner possible. (5) *Publicity so that the public would know "where to go and when" to catch fish.* Newspaper stories of catches stimulated interest and induced fishermen to go fishing, but newspapers should also furnish information on where fishes are being caught.

Reducing Undesirable Populations. In the management of large reservoirs, our greatest progress will probably come with the development of more efficient methods for the reduction of undesirable populations.

Recently, fishery management in water-supply reservoirs received a great stimulus through the granting by the Public Health Departments of some states, of permission to use rotenone for the control of undesirable fish in these reservoirs. The Public Health Department of the State of Oklahoma prior to 1954 permitted the use of rotenone to kill gizzard shad in a water-supply reservoir. Other states soon followed this lead (Illinois in 1956) until many states now sanction the use of rotenone for the removal of excessive populations of gizzard shad by partial poisoning, or for the poisoning of all fish in a reservoir with subsequent restocking of new populations of selected species.

In no case has the use of rotenone or the presence of dead fish for the short period before they are picked up and hauled away from the lake had any noticeable effect upon the water supply after it had been filtered and chlorinated. In many water-supply reservoirs where the rooting of rough fish had kept the water continuously muddy, the complete poisoning of these fish with rotenone stopped all mud-stirring activity and greatly reduced the task of water treatment because of the much-reduced problem of filtering-out suspended silt. Water-supply reservoirs, renovated and restocked with desirable fish, regained all of their former recreational values—fishing, swimming, boating, and aesthetics.

WHAT IS IN THE FUTURE?

The farm pond, originally used chiefly for livestock, has demonstrated its potential for recreation. Anglers have been quick to appreciate the excellent fishing from properly managed ponds, and some farmers have channeled this interest to supplement the farm income. Furthermore, local sportsmen or sportsmen's organizations are ready to pay well for outdoor recreation directly associated with these ponds. Thus, the pond-building movement continues to boom with recreational uses sharing equally with those of water supply.

Many communities still have inadequate water supplies for their residents and for commercial developments. Others that have adequate water today will find they need supplemental water sources in the future. Thus within the near future, most of the available small sites for artificial impoundments in the more thickly populated sections of the country will be in use. In most instances these water-supply reservoirs will be available for public recreation.

The U.S. Corps of Army Engineers has created reservoirs or has plans for impoundments on nearly every stream in the United States with any record of primary or secondary flood damage. Many of these planned reservoirs may not be built within the immediate future, but enough will be authorized to spread a network of reservoirs throughout the drainage basins of all major rivers. These reservoirs will be created primarily for flood control, but nearly all will have conservation pools that will be used extensively for aquatic recreation.

As hunting becomes progressively more restricted and localized, opportunities for fishing will continue to increase and become more widely distributed. The development of management methods for impoundments will be intensified, but along lines of greater sport production, rather than for the production of fish for food.

In the following chapters I have detailed the known characteristics and dynamic processes of warm-water fish populations. These must be thoroughly understood and appreciated before one can apply management. While the principles of warm-water populations are broad, any application to a selected population is specific, and hence requires understanding not only of these general principles but also of all the ramifications of a current situation.

LITERATURE

1. Baccius, G., "A Treatise on the Management of Fresh Water Fish," London, J. Van Voorst, 1841.
2. Barney, R. L., *Am. Fish. Soc. Trans.*, **54**, 168-177 (1924).
3. Barney, R. L., and Canfield, H. L., *Fins, Feathers and Fur*, **30**, 3-7 (1922).
4. Bartlett, S. P., "Rept. Bd. Ill. Sta. Comm., Oct. 1, 1890 to Sept. 30, 1892," Springfield, 1893.
5. Bennett, G. W., *Ill. Nat. Hist. Surv. Bull.*, **22**, 357-376 (1943).
6. Bennett, G. W., *Ill. Wildl.*, **1**(2), 8-10 (1946).
7. Bennett, G. W., *N. A. Wildl. Conf. Trans.*, **12**, 276-285 (1947).
8. Bennett, G. W., *N. A. Wildl. Conf. Trans.*, **19**, 259-270 (1954).
9. Borodin, N., *Am. Fish. Soc. Trans.*, **54**, 178-184 (1924).
10. Burr, J. G., *Am. Fish. Soc. Trans.*, **61**, 174-182 (1931).
11. Cahn, A. R., *Am. Fish. Soc. Trans.*, **66**, 398-405 (1937).
12. Carbine, W. F., *N. A. Wildl. Conf. Trans.*, **4**, 275-287 (1939).

13. Coker, R. E., *Bull. U.S. Bur. Fish.*, **45**, 141-225 (1930).
14. Dyche, L. L., *Kan. St. Dept. Fish and Game Bull.*, **1**, 1-208 (1914).
15. Ellis, M. M., *Am. Fish. Soc. Trans.*, **66**, 63-75 (1937).
16. Eschmeyer, R. W., *N. A. Wildl. Conf. Trans.*, **3**, 458-468 (1938).
17. Eschmeyer, R. W., and Jones, A. M., *N. A. Wildl. Conf. Trans.*, **6**, 222-239 (1941).
18. Eschmeyer, R. W., and Tarzwell, C. M., *Jour. Wildl. Mgt.*, **5**(1), 15-41 (1941).
19. Forbes, S. A., *Sta. Lab. Nat. Hist. Bull.*, **15**(9), 537-550 (1925).
20. Galtsoff, P. S., *Bull. U.S. Bur. Fish.*, **39**, 347-438 (1924).
21. Hederström, H., *Rön Fiskars Älder. Handl. Kunal. Vetenskapsakademin* (Stockholm) **20**, 222-229 (1759). Rep. in *Inst. Freshwater Res.* (Drottningholm) **40**, 161-164 (1959).
22. Hubbs, C. L., and Eschmeyer, R. W., *Inst. for Fish. Res. Bull.*, **2**, 1-233 (1938).
23. Hulsey, A. H., *Proc. Ann. Conf. SE Assoc. Game & Fish Comm.*, **10**, 285-289 (1957).
24. Jenkins, R. M., "Reservoir Fish Management—Progress and Challenge," Sport Fishing Inst., Washington, D.C., 1-22, 1961.
25. Jenkins, R. M., and Elkin, R. E., *Okla. Fish Res. Lab. Rept.*, **60**, 1-21 (1957).
26. Jeppson, P., *Prog. Fish-Cult.*, **19**(4), 168-171 (1957).
27. Johnson, M. C., *Prog. Fish-Cult.*, **21**(4), 154-160 (1959).
28. Juday, C., Schloemer, C. L., and Livingston, C., *Prog. Fish-Cult.*, **40**, 24-27 (1938).
29. Langlois, T. H., *Bingham Oceanographic Collection*, **IX**(4), 33-54 (1948).
30. Larimore, R. W., *Ill. Nat. Hist. Surv. Bull.*, **27**(1), 1-83 (1957).
31. Leopold, A., "Game Management," 1-481, N.Y., Chas. Scribner's Sons, 1933.
32. Lucas, C. R., *Am. Fish. Soc. Trans.*, **68**, 67-75 (1939).
33. Markus, H. C., *Am. Fish. Soc. Trans.*, **62**, 202-210 (1932).
34. Meehean, O. L., *Jour. Wildlife Mngt.*, **16**, 233-238 (1952).
35. Moore, E., *Am. Fish. Soc. Trans.*, **61**, 139-142 (1931).
36. Neess, J., *Am. Fish. Soc. Trans.*, **76**, 335-358 (1949).
37. North, R., "Discourse of Fish and Fish Ponds," printed for E. Curll, London, 1713.
38. Shields, J. T., *Am. Fish. Soc. Trans.*, **87**, 356-364 (1958).
39. Stranahan, J. J., *Am. Fish. Soc. Trans.*, **31**, 130-137 (1902).
40. Stroud, R. H., *Jour. Tenn. Acad. Sci.*, **23**(1), 31-99 (1948).
41. Surber, E. W., *Am. Fish. Soc. Trans.*, **61**, 143-148 (1931).
42. Swingle, H. S., and Smith, E. V., *N. A. Wildl Conf. Trans.*, **4**, 332-338 (1939).
43. Tarzwell, C. M., *Am. Fish. Soc. Trans.*, **71**, 201-214 (1942).
44. Thompson, D. H., *Ill. Nat. Hist. Surv. Biol. Notes,* **1**, 1-25 (1933).
45. Thompson, D. H., "A Symposium on Hydrobiology," p. 206-217, Madison, Wis., Univ. Wis. Press, 1941.
46. Thompson, D. H., and Bennett, G. W., *N. A. Wildl. Conf. Trans.*, **4**, 311-317 (1939).
47. Wickliff, E. L., *Am. Fish. Soc. Trans.*, **62**, 275-277 (1933).
48. Wickliff, E. L., and Roach, L. S., *Am. Fish. Soc. Trans.*, **66**, 78-86 (1937).
49. Wiebe, A. H., *Am. Fish. Soc. Trans.*, **59**, 94-106 (1929).
50. Wood, R., *Jour. Tenn. Acad. Sci.*, **26**(3), 214-235 (1951).

2

Artificial Aquatic Habitats

Artificial lakes are of two kinds: (1) *water impoundments* for some definite purpose, such as flood control, water supply, or recreation, and (2) *water-filled depressions* with surface materials or mineral deposits removed. It is interesting to note that these bodies of water show a considerable diversity of aquatic habitat. Thus, artificial lakes (such as lateral-levee lakes along large rivers, navigation pools created by low dams across river channels, or deep main-stream storage reservoirs) are biologically quite similar to natural lakes, whereas, impoundments across small-drainage channels may contain limited biota, species-wise. In fact, when these latter lakes are in densely populated regions, the aquatic animals (primarily birds and mammals) that customarily inhabit remote regions and shun close association with man, are almost entirely absent. The heavy use of a lake by recreation seekers may even drive away animals only moderately man-shy. Neither coots, nor migrating ducks (where protected) are wary of man, but they will leave a lake if boat traffic becomes heavy.

When some of the animals that ideally constitute the natural complex of remote standing waters are absent from artificial lakes, interrelationships of the living organisms that are present will differ from those found in a more primitive environment. Thus when man is disparaging of the kinds and sizes of fish that an artificial lake produces in contrast to a natural one in some remote region, he is not making a proper comparison. The differences in animal populations inhabiting natural and artificial lakes will be considered further in Chapter 5.

Beyond the area of direct human interference is the natural migration of plants and animals. Since most artificial lakes have not been in existence as long as natural ones, certain organisms have not as yet had the time or the opportunity to populate these newly-created waters.

Some organisms get about much more readily than others, many of the smaller forms being carried by the wind as spores, seeds, eggs, or resting stages that are protected from desiccation by waterproof coverings.

15

Aquatic animals and plants might be arranged in a scale of decreasing ability to traverse the gap between one body of water and another, with some moving in almost as soon as a new lake has been created but with others arriving less rapidly. In fact, opportunities for the movement of some aquatic organisms may be so infrequent as to require many years for their arrival, and others, lacking their usual mode of transportation, may never breach the gap. Certain organisms may gain entry as a result of accident or stocking by man. Because of these variations in migration time and the relatively short existence of artificial lakes, populations of their organisms are usually simpler than those of natural ones.

Motivation for the construction of artificial lakes varies with our need for water. Today in the U.S. we inhabit all of our arable lands, and must devise ways to supply water for diverse uses. Although sometimes water problems are related to too much water, usually the amount is inadequate or availability is not synchronized with need.

At the turn of the century, engineers envisioned multiple uses for impoundments. Reservoirs were built on community, state, and federal levels to supply water for cities and industries, to irrigate dry lands, and to generate power. More recently, impoundments have been constructed to supply water for navigation during dry seasons and to control floods during abnormally wet ones. However, it was not until the 1930's that many reservoirs were built for recreational purposes, because aquatic recreation had little or no recognized monetary value prior to this time.

After the drought and depression years of the 1930's, considerable interest centered on farm ponds, largely as a result of the activities of the U.S. Soil Conservation Service which began during that period. Not only were ponds promoted as sources of water for stock but also for their usefulness as a general farm-water supply for orchard spraying, fire protection, limited irrigation in dry years, and for recreation in the form of fishing, swimming and boating. Furthermore, the damming of eroded gullies stopped the movement of soil down hill so that impoundments created by these dams could be combined with contour plowing and strip cropping as an integral part of the soil and water conservation plan.

Other types of artificial water resulted from man's activities in digging at the earth's surface for sand and gravel, limestone and other rocks, coal and other minerals. The empty holes became filled with water and formed ponds and lakes.

These, then, are the artificial waters available for fish management. They are often more manageable than natural lakes because they are man-created and are so engineered that they can be better manipulated: In some, construction was originally planned to give maximum recreational values; in others, recreational uses were planned to follow an original but transitory value (such as the removal of gravel).

THE FARM POND

The most common type of artificial impoundment and the least expensive to create is probably the woods or pasture pond made by building an earthen dam across a small intermittent watercourse (Figure 2.1). Superficially, these ponds seem to be the simplest type of aquatic habitat, and perhaps they are; however, intensive investigation of the physical, chemical, and biological characteristics of ponds indicate that even this type of habitat is so far from simple that an exact duplication of any pond is nearly impossible.

Figure 2.1. Pasture pond formed by damming a small intermittent water course.

No one knows the exact number of farm ponds in the United States, but in a recent report of the U.S. Bureau of Sport Fisheries and Wildlife,[17] Dr. Willis King estimated that since World War II the Bureau has stocked from 30,000 to 40,000 farm ponds annually, which would approximate a total of 450,000 to 600,000 in this 15-year period. Because many ponds had been built prior to World War II, it is quite possible that the total number approaches a million or more.

PURPOSES OF FARM PONDS

When farmers who had built ponds were asked to list their reasons for doing so, 80 per cent gave water for livestock as a reason; 70 per cent wanted to provide fishing; 13 per cent, to provide irrigation water; 9 per cent, for swimming; 5 per cent, for wildlife; and 4 per cent for all other uses.[17] Many farm families are interested in various forms of outdoor recreation, and the farm pond may be the center of these activities: fishing, swimming, picnicking, hunting, boating, and in the north, ice skating.

ENGINEERING CONSIDERATIONS FOR FARM PONDS

Engineering specifications for ponds must vary for parts of the country in accordance with differences in rainfall, runoff, tightness of soils, and types of vegetative cover. Ponds must be deeper in the north than in the south in order that the cold winters and thick ice do not result in loss of fish. Increased depth is also a boon to regions characterized by long periods of dry weather. In planning the shore line of the pond, water areas less than 2 or 3 feet in depth should be eliminated, because shallow waters may become choked with aquatic vegetation such as cattail and bulrush, which may form a continuous band around a pond edge.

A satisfactory pond must have an adequate water supply that is silt-free. This water supply may be runoff from lands managed under a soil conservation program, or from springs, flowing wells, or very small streams.[7] The pond should be impounded behind a well-built dam with a spillway adequate to carry off flood waters. Trees and brush should not be allowed to grow on the dam, or continuously around the shore of the pond. The pond should be supplied with a drain pipe and valve large enough to allow fish to pass through the pipe out of the pond with the outflowing water (Figure 2.2).

Much attention has been given to the regional engineering aspects of pond construction by the United States Soil Conservation Service and the agricultural colleges of many State universities. Information for most localities of the United States is available for those wishing to construct ponds, and no attempt will be made here to consider more than a few of the simpler aspects of farm-pond construction.

Engineering methods for ponds in the southeastern U.S. are much different from those of northeastern, central, southwestern, or northwestern regions.

In the West, certain ponds (for example, in Colorado and Arizona) are used as sources of water for irrigation.[19] These ponds are pumped full and then are partly drained to irrigate crops during a 24-hour period. These irrigation ponds fluctuate as much as 10 feet, and the water is usually cold. Such ponds no not provide satisfactory fish habitats.

However, most ponds are built for uses other than irrigation and are more suitable for fish production, even though their primary function may be supplying water for stock or fire protection. Even if all ponds were built primarily for sport fishing, the engineering considerations for each section of the country would be highly variable.

United States Geological Survey quadrangle maps are very helpful for locating sites suitable for ponds. These maps show 5- or 10-foot contour lines on relatively small areas of land, so that it is possible to select on these maps locations for dams on intermittent water courses, to outline the pond shore line above each selected dam site, and to estimate the approximate acreage of land sloping toward the pond site from which surface water will drain into the pond. Once the prospective builder

Figure 2.2. A partially drained pond. The deep area near the center of the picture was specially constructed to permit fish to congregate there in winter.

has located all possible sites for his dam, then a local engineer experienced in pond construction can look over the actual sites, select the best ones, make test borings to determine soil strata under the dam sites, and plan the dams and spillway structures necessary to handle the estimated runoff.

Many ponds have been built without engineering assistance, and some of them have been successful. However, do-it-yourself pond building is not recommended beyond the preliminary steps described above, because of the close tolerances between the runoff water handled and the type and size of spillway structure required for it. Thus, if the spillway is of the wrong type or is too small, the first flood may wash away the dam. On the other hand, if the watershed is not large enough in relation to the storage capacity of the pond, the pond may be full or nearly full only in wet weather. In dry years such a pond could become useless both for water supply and recreation.

Farm ponds usually range in size from ¼ acre to several acres. Those smaller than about 1 acre are unsatisfactory for fishing. Often when a pond or lake is planned to exceed 10 acres, the builder has in mind some commercial use, rather than farm water supply and recreation.

WHEN IS A POND A LAKE?

The question of when a body of water is a lake and when it is a pond has never been settled to everyone's satisfaction. According to some limnologists,[10] "A lake is thermally stratified, through most of the year, into an epi-, meta-, and hypolimnion.* Only a body of water conforming to this specification will be considered when using the term lake." [asterisk mine] To many this definition is unsatisfactory because most small ponds built by damming steep-sided ravines are thermally stratified "through most of the year," although the stratification is such that the upper edge of the hypolimnion may be indefinite. In contrast, it seems illogical to call a large, shallow body of water a pond; for example, Chautauqua Lake, a natural basin in the floodplain of the Illinois River valley near Havana, Illinois, almost never shows thermal stratification. By definition this lake should be considered a pond, although it has a surface area of nearly 3500 acres.

In Oklahoma, 10 acres represents the point of separation between lakes and ponds; thus bodies of water with less than this surface area are ponds and those above it, lakes.[16] However, Dr. W. C. Starrett suggests that the point of separation be set at 4 acres, and Humphrys and Veatch [13] consider Michigan waters of less than 5 acres as "lakelets and ponds." In any case, if we are not to use the terms interchangeably, the separation should be based on an arbitrary upper size-limit for ponds, and any body of standing water above this limit should automatically be considered a lake, regardless of its limnological characteristics.

ARTIFICIAL LAKES FOR DOMESTIC USES

A great many artificial lakes have been constructed throughout the United States for urban and/or industrial water supplies. These artificial impoundments may vary in size from a few hundred acres to many thousands of acres. On these lakes, recreation is of secondary importance to water-supply uses, although an effort often is made to sell the reservoir to the public on the basis of its recreational attractions.

* Epilimnion (upper lake), metalimnion (middle lake or thermocline), hypolimnion (lower lake).

WATER-SUPPLY RESERVOIRS

Water-supply needs for towns and small cities frequently are met through the construction of artificial impoundments of intermediate sizes. In the East, an attempt has been made to restrict trespass on these water-supply reservoirs and thus to prevent their use for public recreation. Only recently has this policy been reversed. In the Midwest and West, almost no attempt has been made to restrict the recreational uses of water-supply reservoirs, and fishing, swimming, and boating are common. Where recreation is not restricted, a great deal of use may be made of water-supply reservoirs; however, water consumption holds priority, and where or when other uses conflict with the primary use, they must be sacrificed. Recently, the health departments of some states have allowed the use of rotenone in water-supply reservoirs to control the overabundance of small stunted fish, or dominant populations of bottom-feeding fishes responsible for stirring up the bottom mud. Rotenone in dosages great enough to kill fishes is nontoxic to warm-blooded vertebrates. A detailed discussion of the use of rotenone will be given later.

Reservoirs built for city and town water supplies are often created by damming permanent streams or small rivers. The smallest stream capable of filling the reservoir basin and also of supplying the annual needs of the community is the most practical choice. This is true because the silt load carried by a stream is roughly proportional to its size, and the useful life of a reservoir depends upon the rate of silt deposition in its basin.

All permanent streams contain fishes: some species can not maintain their populations in impounded waters, others multiply excessively in reservoirs and create a constant turbidity through bottom-rooting activities. These latter species spoil the fishing by reducing the visibility for fish that feed by sight, and also reduce aesthetic values for swimmers and boaters.

New water-supply reservoirs stocked with bass and pan fish usually go through a regular fishing cycle which requires about 6 or 7 years from the time water is first impounded. At the end of that time active measures must be taken if recreational and aesthetic values are to be maintained. These techniques will be discussed in Chapter 6.

Most water-supply reservoirs for cities in agricultural regions are relatively shallow because of the moderate slope of the land. These reservoirs are almost always thermally stratified in summer and lose their supply of oxygen in the deeper water (eutrophic lakes).

Usually in rough or mountainous regions, water-supply reservoirs are comparatively deep and infertile. Because the deeper sterile waters do not lose their summer oxygen supply, these lakes (oligotrophic) support cold-water fishes such as lake trout and whitefish.

NAVIGATION POOLS

In some of our larger rivers, locks and dams have been installed to maintain water depths for navigation. Examples of such rivers are the Mississippi, Ohio, and Illinois. Although these relatively shallow impoundments retain some current, the river rapids (important in the successful spawning of some fishes such as the blue sucker) have been largely eliminated. Navigation locks and dams are under the jurisdiction of the U.S. Corps of Army Engineers, which builds new dams, maintaining the present installations and also a river channel of a specified depth for the movement of towboats and barges.

Studies of the fishes living in the navigation pools of the upper Mississippi indicate that they support both an extensive sport, and a commercial fishery.[1, 28]

Low dams across a large river will result in the permanent flooding of backwater areas adjacent to the river, except when the level of an upstream pool may be lowered to furnish water for navigation downstream. When this occurs, backwater lakes may be drained quite rapidly, sometimes to the detriment of their fish, particularly in winter when these backwaters are covered by thick ice.

LATERAL-LEVEE RESERVOIRS

Low lands in the flood plains of rivers are sometimes protected from the river by levees; these low lands are pumped dry for agricultural uses. However, when these areas are abandoned or reconverted into lakes with the levees still intact, they become lateral-levee reservoirs. These shallow reservoirs are very productive.

Some of them are supplied with stone or concrete spillways to allow the entrance of water from the adjacent river when it rises above the spillway crest. Then, as the river level recedes, water flows out of the lake until the spillway crest level is again reached. The water in such a lateral-levee reservoir may fluctuate moderately to follow changing levels in the river when the level of the reservoir is below the spillway crest due to slow seepage through the levee.

These lakes are quite turbid, due primarily to the action of wind.[15] They are productive of hook-and-line fish,[9, 27] and at the same time may support a large commercial fishery for such river species as carp, buffalo, freshwater drum, and channel catfish.

MULTI-PURPOSE RESERVOIRS

Large impoundments constructed by the federal government in many parts of the United States have been justified on the basis of a combination of two or more uses, such as flood control, navigation, the generation of electric power, irrigation, and recreation. Not all of these values are assigned to one reservoir; usually irrigation is a western assignment, navigation may be a localized or general assignment, and the generation of power requires a dependable and constant source of water.

Some of these uses appear to conflict with one another. For example, flood control demands an empty reservoir to give maximum flood storage, whereas navigation, irrigation, and the generation of power require a full basin, since they depend upon the release of water from the reservoir. Furthermore, although recreation may ride along with a changing water level, it is gone when the reservoir basin is dry (as in some flood control projects). However, generally speaking, needs are seasonal, so there may not be intensive competition for water at any one time.

These apparent conflicts of purpose are resolved by assigning a range of levels to specific uses. First, the basic purpose is taken care of by setting a conservation-pool level or elevation near the bottom of the reservoir. Until this "absolute minimum" water level has been exceeded, no large amount of water will be released. In a reservoir of 24,000 to 30,000 acres, water at the conservation-pool level might create a lake of 3000 to 6000 acres. Then, other fractions of the reservoir's storage capacity may be assigned to power, navigation, or irrigation. Usually the flood control function belongs to the upper layer of reservoir capacity which is drained off after each flood as rapidly as the river channel below the dam will permit (bank full), so that the upper lake in the reservoir will be available for storing water once again should another flood occur.

In the operation of a multi-purpose reservoir, water in the river channel below the dam is never allowed to exceed the top of the river banks (as long as any storage capacity exists in the reservoir), or to fall below a certain minimum flow in drought periods, even if it means using some water assigned to the conservation pool. This minimum flow is so small in relation to the capacity of the conservation pool that there is little danger of ever draining the latter. The controlled release of water into the river channel below the dam insures a constant supply for agrarian users and towns situated on the river and maintains the fish population that inhabits the river below the dam.

Experience has shown that fish congregate in waters below the outlets of these large reservoirs through upstream migration, and extensive sport fisheries have developed in these tailwaters. The type of fishery that results is dependent upon (1) the temperature of the water released from the dam during summer, (2) what fish are available in the stream below, and (3) which ones may be stocked in it. The temperature of the water, in turn, depends upon the vertical location of the outlet gates on the face of the dam.

PONDS AND LAKES WITH EXCAVATED BASINS

Although lake and pond basins can be completely excavated with earth-moving equipment, this is infrequently done because of the high cost. However, sometimes the clay needed for a pond dam may be removed from the sides of the pond basin, so that the basin can be enlarged and deepened in the process of building the dam. Also, ponds are sometimes dug or enlarged and deepened in real-estate developments or in other special locations where cost is of secondary importance.

On the other hand, there are many kinds of excavations made by man that become filled with ground water and are eventually stocked with fish. These "holes" are excavations for the removal of gravel, limstone, stone, coal, or other near-surface mineral deposits. Some of these water-filled pits are among the most attractive waters to be found south of the lake states, because they are clear and quite infertile. Recent construction of super-highways has resulted in many ponds where clay has been removed to build grades for road overpasses.

GRAVEL-PIT LAKES

Gravel deposits have been left by rivers from melting glaciers. Most of these deposits, although covered with soils, are readily relocated by test borings in regions where excavations (such as well drillings) or other evidence have shown the presence of gravel. Since considerable gravel is needed for road beds and as a component of concrete, this product is in constant local demand. The sale of gravel, therefore, while not so remunerative as that of most other minerals, furnishes more than enough to pay for the cost of pond excavation. With a little planning, the excavations left when operations are over, become attractive recreational waters.

When digging is done primarily to develop recreational ponds (often the case when gravel deposits are located under high-priced farm lands), plans may be made for the arrangement of ponds, the leveling of the spoil banks, and the respreading of the top soil over leveled areas in order to greatly improve the pit area (Figure 2.3). In regions where lakes and ponds are scarce, a well-planned recreational area superimposed on an abandoned gravel works may bring a better price than the original farm land, or, if strategically located and properly managed, produce annual income equal to, or exceeding, the income from farm crops.

A flooded gravel works may consist of a number of small ponds separated by levees of sand or clay. Often when the pit owner decides to develop the area for recreation, his first thought is to connect all of these ponds. Yet, experience shows that several isolated ponds are more easily managed for fishing than a single large one. Moreover, separated ponds allow a greater variety of fishing because species can be stocked in some, that would not survive if placed in one large pond containing other more aggressive fishes. However, no pond should have an area of much less than one acre; otherwise, it will be too small for satisfactory fishing.

The standing crop of fish supported by gravel pits may be lower than that of artificial ponds receiving direct surface runoff from farm lands,

Figure 2.3. Gravel-pit ponds planned for recreational uses after gravel removal. Current gravel-removal operations were confined to the long narrow ponds in the pit area at the upper left. Bodies of water were kept separated and stocked with various combinations of fish, so that each pond could be easily renovated if fishing became poor. The square pond at the upper left is about 4 acres; a bathing beach and diving pier were built at its lower left corner.

but the fish-population size (weight) is related to the fertility of the surrounding land, in spite of the fact that there may be no direct surface runoff into the gravel-pit ponds.

The water level in a gravel-pit pond is that of the water-table level because the sand-bottomed basin will not hold water. This may be demonstrated by transferring water from one pond into another by a large pump. The pond from which water is being pumped may drop several feet and the other pond rise in proportion, but if the pump is stopped, water will seep out of the high pond and into the low one, so that within a very short time both will again be at ground water level.

Since levels in gravel pits fluctuate from one to three feet during most years, this annual fluctuation should be taken into consideration when bottom contours are being planned. The exposure of large areas of the bottom, as a result of normal annual fluctuation, is unsightly and may be avoided if the more shallow areas are deepened.

Where gravel beds are extensive, gravel digging operations can be planned to create areas of open water up to four or five acres, or to create relatively narrow meandering channels. Once the spoil banks have become vegetated with trees, shrubs and herbaceous plants, the channel arrangement is more attractive to anglers than is a large area of open water.

Gravel-pit ponds are thermally stratified in summer because they are surrounded by high lands that reduce the wind action on the water.

STRIPMINE LAKES

Stripmine lakes result from the flooding of surface excavations after the removal of coal deposits. Layers of coal may vary in depth below the surface, and stripmining equipment can operate at a profit on deposits as deep as 50 to 90 feet. Before the coal can be stripped, the top soil and clay overburden must be removed. This operation is done with giant cranes supplied with digging buckets which pile the waste material in long ridges running parallel to the cuts they are making. As the coal in each cut is exhausted, the crane moves over to dig a new cut parallel to the other one, and the material from the new strip is piled into or along the previously exhausted excavation. Thus, strip mining actually turns land upside down (because the topsoil is buried under the clay over-burden) and leaves an area of land as a series of long parallel ridges many feet high. In some stripped areas, water collects in the valleys between these ridges and forms long narrow lakes usually connected to similar lakes between other ridges by channels. The last "cut" or strip that the crane makes before abandoning an area is not filled in and may form a lake several hundred feet wide, as deep as 60 feet, and a mile or more long, depending upon the size of the stripped area, the depth of the coal, and the lengths of the booms of the stripping cranes.

Coal deposits are associated with deposits of sulfur, iron, and other minerals. When the abandoned mines are flooded, these dissolved minerals often make the mine ponds too acid to provide a habitat for aquatic organisms.[22] However, ponds become less acid with age; the sulfuric acid buffered with calcium from limestone deposits and other carbonates, or the runoff water from higher lands may flush out the stripmine lakes, removing some of the acidic material. Occasionally, stripped lands adjacent to small rivers are flooded by the latter, resulting in a great improvement in the sulfate composition of the stripmine water after the flood recedes.

In many respects, stripmine lakes are similar to gravel-pit lakes, but they usually differ markedly from them in the acid and mineral content of the water. Stripmine waters usually contain several hundred parts per million of sulfate; in one instance, fish were found living and reproducing in a mine pond that contained 1500 ppm of sulfate.

Stripmine ponds vary considerably with one another in the weight of fish supported because of their great range of dissolved salts. It is reasonable that fish production might be low in new stripmine waters, since many invertebrate animals and algae in the food chain are more sensitive than fishes to abnormal mineral content. But aging, weathering, flooding, and the annual accumulation of dust and leaves gradually build up the basic fertility and reduce the chemical imbalance of these waters until they become very fertile.[18] The waters of the South Pollywog Association, an 80-year-old stripmine area in Vermilion County, Illinois, support populations of miscellaneous fishes as high as 750 pounds per acre.

QUARRY LAKES

A great deal of limestone is used in agriculture as limestone dust to neutralize acid soils and as crushed rock in road building and other construction. Other deposits of rock of value in building may be quarried from near-surface deposits. Quarrying and strip mining operations are somewhat similar in that often the top soil and overburden are first removed, leaving the strata of limestone or other rock exposed. In quarrying, limestone and other rocks are subsequently loosened by blasting, and loaded in large trucks by cranes. Then, the blasted rock (the limestone portion) is taken to a rock crusher capable of producing particle sizes, from limestone dust to rocks as large as hens' eggs. Since deposits of limestone are often below the level of the water table, quarrying operations depend upon pumps to remove the water as it seeps into the quarry pits.

When all of the valuable rock has been extracted, the pumps are stopped and the pits fill up to the level of ground water (Figure 2.4), forming one or several bodies of water. New limestone quarry waters are usually quite infertile because they contain almost no phosphates, nitrates or organic material. However, minerals causing hard water are present in abundance and organic nutrient materials may be carried into quarries through surface runoff from surrounding lands, so that the production of fish may increase quite rapidly as the water in the abandoned quarry ages.

Quarry ponds are similar to gravel-pit ponds and stripmine ponds in that they are usually dependent on subsurface waters rather than superficial drainage. Also, they are thermally stratified in summer, due to their relatively great depths and to the limited action of winds on the surfaces of these ponds. In depth, quarry ponds may exceed gravel pits and stripmines, depending upon the depths of the deposits, and whether it is economically feasible to quarry them.

Figure 2.4. Ponds resulting from the quarrying of limestone are quite sterile and their waters are usually very clear. They make a satisfactory habitat for smallmouth bass.

LAKES BUILT FOR RECREATION

Within the past decade, many artificial lakes have been built entirely for the purpose of furnishing aquatic recreation (Figure 2.5). There is scarcely any way in which recreation funds can be spent to produce such a large return over so long a period. At first, artificial lakes for recreation appear to be expensive. However, costs of such public lakes can be amortized over the life of the impoundment,[5] providing a long period of usefulness and, consequently, an intangible return great enough to make them highly practical. Furthermore, where lakes are not built primarily for recreation, they still should be planned and constructed to allow easy management of their fish populations, and should have an outlet large enough for quick drainage and a sloping basin that will empty completely. From the standpoint of ease in management, it is more practical to build five 100-acre lakes than one lake of 500 acres.

A satisfactory site for a recreational lake requires a basin with a minimum area of shallow water (less than 4 feet deep). Shallows become problem areas because they frequently become choked with aquatic vegetation. These areas, when filled with dense, rooted aquatic plants, are useless for fishing, boating, and swimming, and may become a breeding location for mosquitoes because the fish are unable to reach the mosquito "wigglers." Extensive shallow areas are unnecessary for the successful reproduction of nest-building fishes as may be demonstrated in stripmine

Figure 2.5. Many lakes are built wholly for recreation. This one on the Fin 'N Feather Club property near Dundee, Illinois is used primarily for large-mouth bass fishing. All trees on the immediate shore line were planted from nursery stock, with even the logs and rocks brought in from outside sources.

and quarry ponds where shallows are very limited. In planning the height of a dam it is sometimes possible to raise or lower the proposed water level a few feet to give a minimum of shallow water.

Lakes built for recreation may be developed to any degree, that is, the grounds may be left in a relatively natural state with only access roads or there may be surfaced roads, boat docks (and boats for rental), bathing beaches, bath house facilities, picnic areas, pavilions, and cabins.

PLANNING AN ARTIFICIAL LAKE OR POND

As was mentioned in connection with the planning of farm ponds, a layman may handle certain preliminary details of impoundment provided he can read a contour map and estimate land areas. In looking for suitable sites, the planner will find the quadrangle maps of the United States Geological Survey very useful. These maps, which are usually available through the federal or state geological surveys, show land elevations through the use of contour lines. This makes it possible to locate on them sites for lake basins and dams, or if a potential site has been found through field observations, to determine several suitable locations for a dam, and to estimate the amount of land that will drain into the pond or lake once the location for the dam has been decided upon.

WATERSHED, RUNOFF, AND WATER MANIPULATION

Rainfall, slope of land, and vegetative cover vary within certain limits, but a definite relationship exists between the volume capacity of a pond basin and the area of the watershed needed to keep that basin filled. Although usually it is impossible for the layman to calculate the volume capacity of a selected pond basin, he may, by the use of a quadrangle map, arrive at the approximate surface area of the basin and then consider this in relation to the area of the watershed. Where soils are relatively tight (for example, in Illinois, Iowa, and Missouri), the approximate limits of range for the watershed are a minimum of 10 acres and a maximum of 50 acres to 1 acre of pond surface assuming a basin of average depth and contour. However, if this index is used and the drainage area is less than 10 acres, insufficient runoff water will be available during dry periods. On the other hand, if the watershed is 50 or more acres, so much water in excess of pond capacity must be passed through the basin that a large and expensive spillway is necessary. Probably the optimum ratio between watershed and pond surface area is in the neighborhood of 20 or 25 to 1. Optimum relationships between the drainage area and the pond size and volume vary greatly among parts of the country with differences in rainfall, slope, soil types, vegetative cover, and evaporation rates.

Small ponds in the north central states having ratios of watershed to pond surface of less than 15 to 1 may be safely constructed with grass waterways to carry off excess water. However, where the watersheds and ponds are larger, spillways are usually constructed of concrete or stone.

It is unnecessary to screen spillways to prevent the departure of fish from a pond or lake, as only a small fraction of the fish population will leave. Screens across spillways have a way of becoming clogged during floods and sometimes are responsible for washouts of dams. It is more important to prevent fish from moving up over a dam from below, and spillways should be planned to provide insurmountable barriers to fish moving upstream.

There are many problems involved in handling water flowing in and out of a pond basin. Some of these are associated with differences in rainfall and evaporation rates. Others involve local situations such as variations in land slope and cover, control of water from a constant source (such as a spring or a flowing well), or the by-passing of excess water where the only suitable site for a pond is adjacent to a water course too large to be impounded. Solutions to most of these special problems will require the services of a competent hydraulic engineer.

THERMAL STRATIFICATION AND LOSS OF OXYGEN

Most artificial ponds and lakes in the United States are thermally stratified during the warmer months. This stratification may develop in early March and extend well into November in the South. In the extreme North, summer thermal stratification may begin in late May or early June and end in late August or early September. Most artificial impoundments, with the exception of the deeper power and water-supply reservoirs, are eutrophic in character, that is, they contain no oxygen in the colder, deeper waters during the greater part of the period of summer stratification. It is true that early in the season, once the lake has become thermally stratified, there may be oxygen in the lower waters. Gradually, however, the oxygen demand from decay and from respiration of bacteria, plankton, and fishes uses up all of the available oxygen in the lower lake level (hypolimnion) so that this water may be completely devoid of oxygen.

Sometimes dewatering structures (spillways) have their lake-side openings near the bottom of the lake, in order to expel oxygen-deficient water from far below the surface. For example, at Ridge Lake, Coles County, Illinois,[4] a tower spillway on the inner face of the dam was designed to release water from the bottom of the full lake each time runoff from rainfall raised its level. Studies of dissolved gases and bottom fauna in this lake indicated that the beneficial effect on it of this disposal of oxygen-deficient water was, at best, very temporary. Even though oxygen was added to the lower levels of the lake each time a substantial rain fell on the watershed, this new oxygen was so rapidly used up that no aerobic bottom organisms had an opportunity to develop.

SEASONAL THERMAL STRATIFICATION

A lake or pond is stratified when layers of water at various depths do not and will not mix with one another. For a detailed explanation of all of the ramifications of thermal stratification see Welch, Ruttner, or Hutchison.[14, 26, 31]

Briefly, stratification has its basis in the fact that water shows maximum density (weight) at 4°C (39.2°F), becoming *less dense* (lighter in weight) both *above* and *below* this temperature. Let us consider the fact that soon after the ice melts in the spring, the temperature of the water in a lake rises to 4°C, bringing the entire lake to a uniform density. Then, winds blowing across the lake surface pile the water up on the windward side, and in order to compensate for this, water passes downward across the bottom of the lake to the upwind side. The entire lake begins to circulate from top to bottom. As spring advances, however, there are days when the wind blows lightly or not at all, and the sun beating down on the lake begins warming the water on the surface, causing it to become less dense (lighter) than the colder water below. After the surface water has warmed a few degrees above the water in the lake depths, thermal stratification has begun and no ordinary wind will cause the two to mix.

The surface water will mix with itself down to a depth of several feet or yards (meters), the depth depending upon the wind velocity and the area of lake surface acted upon. Thus the warm surface layer (epilimnion) tends to be thicker on large lakes than on small ones. The temperature of the epilimnion is about the same from top to bottom, but this may vary a few degrees during days when the surface is warming rapidly and winds are light.

Below the epilimnion is a layer of water (the thermocline or metalimnion) where the temperature of the stratum decreases rapidly as one progresses downward, that is, one degree centigrade per meter (about 1.7°F per yard). The thermocline may vary in thickness in different lakes and at different times during the period of stratification. Although in large lakes the thermocline usually is a thinner layer than the epilimnion, in small ponds it may continue from the lower edge of the epilimnion to the pond bottom.

In large deep lakes the volume of water below the thermocline (hypolimnion) tends to show a fairly uniform temperature. Where there is a significant temperature decrease as one moves downward, that change is less than 1°C per meter. As mentioned previously, lack of dissolved oxygen makes the hypolimnions of some lakes uninhabitable for most aquatic organisms. The rapidity and extent of eutrophication is dependent upon the volume of oxygenated water and the amount of organic decay and respiration placing demands upon the oxygen. For example, after the spring period of complete circulation, very deep and relatively infertile lakes have a very great volume of oxygenated water in the hypolimnion, and the oxygen-consuming organisms and processes are proportionately small. In these lakes, the oxygen is not used up in the hypolimnion during summer stratification, and they are inhabited by all kinds of oxygen-requiring organisms, including such fishes as lake trout, white fish, and walleye. This lake type is called oligotrophic.

VARIATIONS IN THERMAL STRATIFICATION

Bardach [2] describes the progress of summer stratification in Lake West Okoboji, Iowa. In this lake, thermal stratification normally begins between May 15 and June 1 after the water below 30 meters has already reached 10°C (50°F.) Then, during the summer the hypolimnion warms up further, to 12° or 13°C (53.6° or 55.4°F).

However, in 1925, 1926, and 1950, when unusually heavy winds were recorded in late spring, West Okoboji did not form a thermocline until very late in the season or not at all, and, if it did form one, it was situated at a greater depth than usual. In some years this abnormal stratification consisted of an upper warm layer, below which the temperature gradually dropped as one progressed toward the lake bottom, until at 22 meters (72.2 ft.) the temperature was 6 degrees centigrade lower than in the epilimnion [epilimnion, 20.6°C (69.1°F), and bottom, 14.3°C (57.7°F)]. The vertical change in temperature was less than 1°C per meter so that by definition no thermocline was present. Nonetheless, there was no evidence that thermal stratification was ever completely broken up during the summer months. As mentioned previously, a similar type of stratification appears to be characteristic of numerous small artificial impoundments.

FALL OVERTURN

Summer thermal stratification is broken up in the fall by wind action after the epilimnion cools to a temperature approximately that of the hypolimnion. Gradually, the entire lake begins to circulate, as the winds create water currents across the surface and compensating currents develop across the lake bottom. Water that has remained trapped in the lake depths all summer again comes in contact with the surface layers where free and dissolved carbon dioxide has an opportunity to escape and the dissolved oxygen supply is replenished.

As fall progresses into winter, the lake water cools to 4°C (39.2°F) and below, and the colder upper layer becomes less dense: In the north a film of ice seals the surface and the lake is again thermally stratified, with the ice and colder water above the mass of water at 4°C. As long as ice covers the lake, very little circulation takes place. Some convection currents may be set up through the mild warming of water in contact with the bottom, but these warming forces are counteracted by colder water immediately under the ice. Once the lake is sealed from the air, the oxygen supply under the ice is dependent upon the photosynthetic activity of algae which in turn is supported by light transmission through the ice.

ATTEMPTS TO UPSET THERMAL STRATIFICATION

Some attempts have been made to upset the thermal stratification of small lakes.[8, 12] For example, 180 hours of pumping of warm surface water into the bottom of a small German lake increased the temperature of the bottom water by 5°C.[8] Also, this pumping initiated movements of water within the hypolimnion, thus causing an increase in its thickness as well as a shorter temperature gradient within another stratum, the thermocline.

In an experiment in a 3.6-acre Michigan lake, water was pumped from the hypolimnion to the surface.[12] This caused a progressive increase in the depth of the epilimnion, a sinking of the thermocline at a nearly constant rate, and a decrease in the thickness of the hypolimnion as the bottom water was displaced. The upper limit of the thermocline was lowered from 13 feet to 25 feet, and the volume of the epilimnion was increased by 49.9 per cent. An attempt was made to follow the movement of the cold bottom water after its release at the surface. Apparently, the cool water became mixed rather thoroughly with surface water within the upper 4 to 5 feet.

These experiments demonstrate that a large amount of energy is required to modify normal thermal stratification in even a small lake. In lakes of moderate or large size, such a program would be highly impractical.

THERMAL STRATIFICATION AND RESERVOIR OUTLETS

Many large reservoirs are equipped with outlet gates at or near the bottom of the impounding dams, Figure 2.6. Temperatures of water released through these gates range from 4° to 18.3°C (39.2° to 65°F), and may or may not contain sufficient oxygen for fishes. Usually if the water does not have an adequate amount, it become aerated a short distance below the outlet of the dam. In this location, trout are able to survive, and often grow very well, extending their range downstream until the water becomes too warm.[23] Where such a trout fishery has developed, it usually has been necessary to modify the original water-release program designed by the engineers, since to restrict the flow to only a few months of a year is impractical from the standpoint of developing an artificial trout stream. In addition, it is worth noting that the release of cold water alters the bottom faunal pattern from large warm-water species to small cold-water species, such as the insect families, Tendipedidae, Simulidae, and Hydropsychidae, as well as snails and the scud *Gammarus*.[23]

The tailwater discharge below Dale Hollow Reservoir is an example of a man-made trout stream.[22] This tailwater flows for 7.3 miles before it

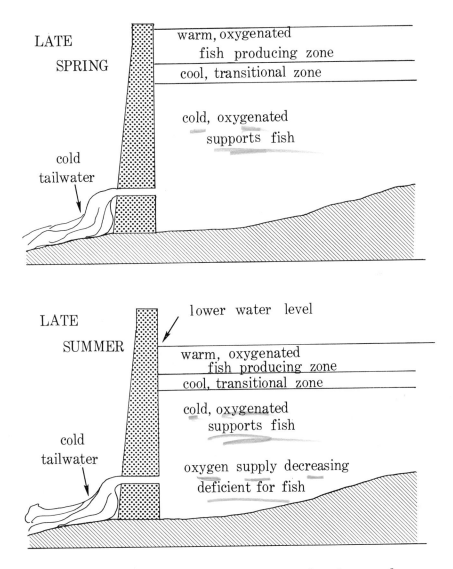

Figure 2.6. Storage reservoirs with deep water outlets. A water-release program that will furnish an adequate quantity of water cold enough for a year-round trout stream often supplies very fine fishing. However, trout must be stocked from hatcheries, as tailwater streams usually are not suitable for natural spawnings. [Redrawn from Stroud, R. H., and Jenkins, R. M., *Sport Fishing Inst. Bull.*, 98 (1960)]

enters the Cumberland River in Clay County, Tennessee. The combined minimum flow when water is operating the three turbines is 5900 cubic feet per second. When the turbines are not in operation, there is a natural cold-water discharge of 19 cubic feet per second. Discharge schedules vary from year to year; shutdown periods of several days are common in the summer and fall, and levels of the tailwaters fluctuate within a 10-foot range.

The water discharge below the Dale Hollow Dam is always clear (turbidity less than 5 ppm), and the water temperature of the discharge ranges between 7.2° and 13.3°C (45° and 56°F). The minimum discharge of 19 cfs has maintained a water temperature cool enough for trout in the upper three miles of the tailwater during extended shutoff periods. However, the best periods for trout fishing are on weekends when the turbines are shut down and water levels are low.

Dale Hollow Reservoir dam is 178 feet high, and the water depth at elevation 651 (spillway level) is 151 feet. The annual water-level fluctuation on this 30,000-acre lake is usually less than 25 feet.

Excellent tailwater fishing for warm-water fish may occur where water is released from a reservoir at surface or near surface levels (Figure 2.7). Fish migrate upstream in the river formed from the overflow, and when they reach the barrier of the dam, they tend to remain in the tailwater pool. These tailwater fisheries never equal the fishing operations in the reservoir above the dam,[29] but this seems to be so because the fishermen are concentrated at the tailwater fisheries.

Stroud and Jenkins [29] favor reservoir outlets located to release cold water (often deficient in oxygen) from reservoir depths because there is "a continuous discharge of oxygen-consuming decomposition materials with the colder, deep waters." This prevents stagnation and makes "maximum reservoir volume available for use by fish life." At the same time, the warm upper water is retained to promote fish production.

OTHER FACTORS AFFECTING THERMAL STRATIFICATION

Sometimes waters that enter lakes from feeder streams influence thermal stratification because such waters seek their appropriate density (weight) level. In south central Nebraska, a small reservoir built across Rock Creek (a stream originating from a large spring) always contained oxygen in the deeper water because the cold water entering from the stream moved along the lake bottom carrying dissolved oxygen with it.

In winter, water from tributary streams may be colder than the lakes into which they flow, forcing lake water from deeper layers upward

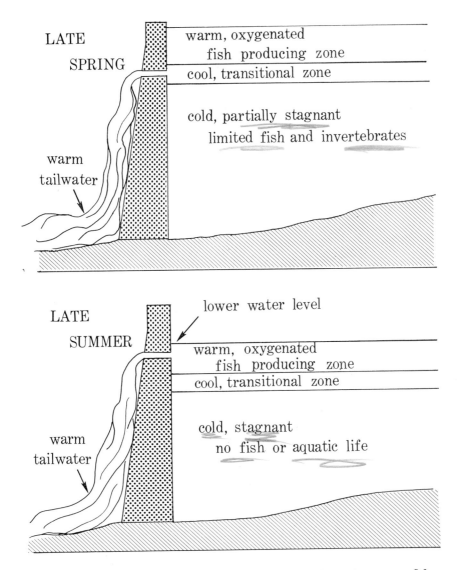

Figure 2.7. Storage reservoirs with shallow water outlets. Warm-water fishes congregate in these tailwaters, having migrated upstream from below. Tailwater fishing is popular, and in a warm tailwater, fishermen may catch a variety of fishes. [Redrawn from Stroud, R. H., and Jenkins, R. M., *S.F.I. Bull.*, 98 (1960)]

toward the surface.[24] Cold, turbid waters entering Norris Reservoir (Tennessee) often formed a wedge of water between surface and bottom.[32, 33] Water above and below this wedge was relatively clear, so that the vertical extent of the wedge could be defined on the basis of turbidity alone.

In small ponds thermal stratification may be affected by blooms of plankton algae which form a near-surface blanket insulating the lower waters from light and the warmth of the sun's rays. For example, a farm pond adjacent to a barn lot near Illiopolis, Illinois, sampled in July 1939, showed an epilimnion 10 inches in thickness, containing a very dense "bloom" of plankton algae. The temperature throughout the epilimnion was 27.2°C (81°F), but at 13 inches below the surface the temperature was 21.6°C (71°F), a drop of 5.6°C (10°F) within 3 inches. Also, the dissolved oxygen was entirely gone at 13 inches below the surface. In spite of these extreme conditions, this pond contained bluegills, some of which were caught in traps set at the surface level.

BIOLOGICAL PRODUCTIVITY OF WATER

The biological productivity of water is a function of the nutrient materials (organic and inorganic salts) dissolved in it and available from other sources.

Although many experiments designed to test the value of inorganic fertilizers in pond fish production will be reviewed in Chapter 6, now it is important to stress that the addition of organic or inorganic plant nutrients to a body of water facilitates an increase in the production of phytoplankton, which, in turn, causes an increase in the production of zooplankton and insect larvae and, somewhat later, of fish. Furthermore, increase in fish production is more pronounced among species that make direct use of the available phyto- and zooplankton organisms and insects than among those species of fishes that are piscivorous or have more specific food requirements.

It can be demonstrated that, in natural waters, the chemistry of soils in the lake basin and its watershed are related to the water of the lake in question.

The amounts of certain chemical compounds dissolved in natural waters are indicators of relative productivity. Several investigators have shown a positive relationship between alkalinity and fish production in lakes grouped as *soft water* (less than 50 ppm Methyl Orange alkalinity), *medium* (50 to 150 ppm) and *hard* (above 150 ppm). However, the greatest interruption of this relationship appears at about 40 ppm,[20] for above 40 ppm there seems to be no concise relationship between carbonate content and fish yield. Also, none could be found between fish yields and varying amounts of ionized hydrogen, carbon dioxide, or chlorides. Further, there was no relationship between sulfates and production until the sulfates exceeded 300 ppm.[20] Table 2.1 shows a productivity classification of natural lakes (Minnesota) on the basis of total alkalinity and sulfate ions.[20]

TABLE 2.1 A CLASSIFICATION OF NATURAL LAKES IN MINNESOTA ON THE BASIS OF TOTAL ALKALINITY AND SULFATE IONS (FROM MOYLE [20]).

Total alkalinity (ppm)	Sulfate ion (ppm)	Classification	Productivity	
			Fish	Plant
0.0-20.0	0.0- 5.0	Very soft	Low	Low
21.0-40.0	0.0- 10.0	Soft	Low to medium	Low to medium
41.0-90.0	0.0- 10.0	Medium hard	Medium to high	Medium to high
91.0 or more	0.0- 50.0	Hard	High	High
100.0 or more	50.0-125.0	Medium alkali	High	High
100.0 or more	126.0-300.0	Alkali	High	High

Minnesota ponds containing amounts of phosphorus below 0.05 ppm had low fish yields.[20] Above a concentration of total phosphorus of 0.05 ppm, there was little difference in either average or maximum yield. Moyle concluded that the optimum concentration of total phosphorus might lie between 0.1 and 0.2 ppm; however, these phosphorus concentrations were usually associated with heavy algal blooms which may create a danger through their ability to cause sudden oxygen depletion.

LAKE SIZE AND PRODUCTIVITY

Prior to 1946, there seemed to be evidence of a straight-line negative logarithmic relationship between size of a lake and fish production, when all data then available were used.[25] These data included complete fish censuses of a number of small ponds, creel censuses as measurements of production on medium-sized waters, and commercial catches of fish on the larger lakes. No consideration was given to the possible effect of the geographical location of these waters and of regional soil fertility on production.

Later, when these data were reworked and consideration was given to location and soil fertility, the apparent relationship between size and productivity disappeared.[6] Information on yields from additional lakes (Minnesota) [20] in the form of average gill net ratios demonstrated that lakes of over 5000 acres in area were more productive than those of smaller sizes, while data from creel censuses indicated that lakes ranging in size between 500 and 1000 acres were more productive than those larger or smaller. One is forced to conclude that lake size alone has little significance as an index of productivity and that the water quality, the conformation of the lake basin, and the length of shoreline are much more important. Shallow lakes are more productive than deeper ones [13, 11] because the most productive zone is that influenced by the sun's rays. Where this layer is in contact with the lake bottom, one may expect to reach a high level of production. Other factors, such as the length of the growing season [30] also influence productivity.

LITERATURE

1. Anon., Ann. Repts. of the Upper Mississippi River Conservation Committee (Mimeo), 1944-1961.
2. Bardach, J. E., *Hydrobiologia*, **7**(4), 309-324 (1955).
3. Bennett, G. W., *Ill. Wildl.*, **1**(2), 8-10 (1946).
4. Bennett, G. W., *Ill. Nat. Hist. Surv. Bull.*, **26**(2), 217-276 (1954).
5. Bennett, G. W., and Durham, L., *Ill. Nat. Hist. Surv. Biol. Notes*, **23**, 1-16 (1951).
6. Carlander, K. D., *Jour. Fish. Res. Bd. Can.*, **12**(4), 543-570 (1955).
7. Davidson, V. E., and Johnson, J. A., *U.S.D.A. Farmer's Bull.*, **1938**, 1-22 (1943).
8. Grim, J., *Allg. Fisch-Ztg.*, *Jahrg.*, **77**(14), 281-283 (1952).
9. Hansen, D. F., *Ill. State Acad. Sci. Trans.*, **35**, 197-204 (1942).
10. Hasler, A. D., and Einsele, W. G., *N. A. Wildl. Conf. Trans.*, **13**, 527-555 (1948).
11. Hayes, F. R., *Jour. Fish. Res. Bd. Can.*, **14**(1), 1-32 (1957).
12. Hooper, F. F., Ball, R. C., and Tanner, H. A., *Am. Fish. Soc. Trans.*, **82**, 222-241 (1953).
13. Humphrys, C. R., and Veatch, J. O., *Mich. Sta. Uni. Ag. Exp. Sta. Water Bull.*, **8**, 1-18 (1961).
14. Hutchison, G. E., "A Treatise on Limnology," Vol. 1, 1015 pp. New York, J. Wiley & Sons, 1957.
15. Jackson, H. O., and Starrett, W. C., *Jour. Wildl. Mgt.*, **23**(2), 157-168 (1959).
16. Jenkins, R. M., *Proc. Okla. Acad. Sci.*, **38**, 157-172 (1958).
17. King, W., *U.S.F.&W. Circ.*, **86**, 1-20 (1960).
18. Maupin, J. K., Wells, J. R., Jr., and Leist, Claude, *Kan. Acad. of Sci. Trans.*, **57**, 164-171 (1954).
19. Meehean, O. L., *Jour. Wildl. Mgt.*, **16**(3), 234-237 (1952).
20. Moyle, J. B., *Am. Fish. Soc. Trans.*, **76**, 322-334 (1949).
21. Parsons, J. D., *Ill. Acad. Sci. Trans.*, **50**, 49-59 (1958).
22. Parsons, J. W., *Am. Fish. Soc. Trans.*, **85**, 75-92 (1957).
23. Pfitzer, D. W., *N. A. Wildl. Conf. Trans.*, **19**, 271-282 (1954).
24. Powers, E. B., Shields, A. R., and Hickman, M. A., *Jour. Tenn. Acad. Sci.*, **14**(2), 239-260 (1939).
25. Rounsefell, G. A., *Copeia*, **1946**(1), 29-40 (1946).
26. Ruttner, F., "Fundamentals of Limnology," Univ. of Toronto Press, Toronto, Ont., Can., 1953.

27. Starrett, W. C., and McNeil, P. L., Jr., *Ill. Nat. Hist. Surv. Biol. Notes,* **30,** 1-31 (1952).
28. Starrett, W. C., and Parr, S. A., *Ill. Nat. Hist. Surv. Biol. Notes,* **25,** 1-35 (1951).
29. Stroud, R. H., and Jenkins, R. M., *Sport Fishing Inst. Bull.,* **98,** 3-6 (1960).
30. Thompson, D. H., "A Symposium on Hydrobiology," pp. 206-217, Univ. of Wis. Press, Madison, Wis., 1941.
31. Welch, P. S., "Limnology," McGraw-Hill Book Co., Inc., New York, 1935.
32. Wiebe, A. H., *Ecology,* **20**(3), 446-450 (1939).
33. Wiebe, A. H., *N. A. Wildl. Conf. Trans.,* **6,** 256-264 (1941).

3 〜〜〜

Interrelationships of Fishes
and Lake Habitats

Several types of artificial aquatic habitats were described in the preceding chapter. Now we will consider some of the components that make up an aquatic habitat, and the relationships of these components with fishes.

Water in a habitat for fish must carry dissolved useful gases, minerals, and other substances of kinds and amounts nontoxic to fish. However, the habitat also consists of physical features, basically the contours of the lake basin, with depths, high ridges, rocks, gravel beds, silt areas, marl deposits, stumps, and fallen trees. Growths of submerged aquatic plants, filamentous algae, and shoreline vegetation are a part of the physical habitat as well as of the biological environment. Other parts of the biological environment include the bacteria, plankton algae, fungi, aquatic invertebrate fauna, and a few kinds of vertebrates other than fish. Some of these organisms are foods, some are enemies, and others change with time—being enemies of small fishes first, and later, as these same fishes grow, becoming their food supply.

As indicated in Chapter 2, artificial lakes, being proximate to man and recent in origin, harbor many abnormal and temporary ecosystems, since plant and animal lake inhabitants may be either slow or rapid invaders, and the stocking of fish by man is limited to the species he wants. In fact, man usually leaves it to other fish to find their own way into the lake he has created. Moreover, some aquatic forms that shun association with man seldom appear, and others that he dislikes are not permitted to enter (or at least to remain).

The status of a fish species in an artificial lake may be directly related to its ability to compensate for the point of greatest maladjustment with its environment. The population density of fish of its own kind or of other kinds may be a factor in maladjustment to a given environment, as there

42

is for all animals, a progressive decrease in the favorability of the environment associated with a progressive increase in population density, until growth and reproduction are inhibited.[25] Hey [15] noted that when the two indigenous species of alga-eating tilapias (*T. mossambica* and *T. sparrmani*) were released in equal numbers in South African sewer ponds, *T. sparrmani* eventually disappeared. If a few *T. mossambica* were placed in a population of T. *sparrmani*, the former disappeared. Neither of these species can be considered as primarily predatory, but both will eat small fishes when they are available.

The biological domination man exerts over most artificial lakes not only upsets interrelationships of aquatic organisms, but enters the picture in other ways, most commonly, perhaps, in water pollution from silt, from organic waste, and from chemicals. These pollutants are damaging to fishes in relation to the capacity of the recipient environment to absorb their effects without itself becoming greatly changed to the detriment of fish populations. Of the three types of pollutants, silt and chemicals are almost uniformly undesirable, while sewage pollution from organic waste may represent a mixed benefit: Organic sewage increases production once certain demands that it makes upon water are met.

SEWAGE POLLUTION AND FERTILITY

Some ponds and lakes receive sewage runoff from septic tanks, overloaded tile disposal fields, and domestic-stock feed lots, or effluent from primary or secondary sewage works. In Europe, the use of municipal sewage as fertilizer for fish ponds [23] is widespread, and cities as large as Munich dispose of most of their effluent in this manner. Rainbow trout and carp from sewage-fed ponds are very acceptable as food in Germany and other countries. Detailed descriptions of the methods used in the propagation of fish in sewage-fed oxidation ponds are given by Kisskalt and Ilzhofer [20] and by Wundsch.[44] In this country some interest has been shown in the development of oxidation ponds for disposing of the sewage of small communities. Also, many stock farmers are building ponds close to cattle barns and hog houses, so that animal waste can be piped directly into them. Although fish cannot be raised in most of these ponds receiving undigested sewage, they can be produced in supplemental ponds connected with the former.

Those interested in unpolluted streams, ponds, and lakes should be made aware of the dangers associated with the predicted increase in human population, even if current practices are followed in sewage disposal. Some of these dangers will soon be apparent.

A part of the fertilizer applied to crop lands is leached from the soil. In some locations as much as 10 per cent of the inorganic phosphorus applied to lands may later appear in streams draining these lands,[36] and the total phosphorus content of the stream water may vary from 10 to nearly 200 ppb.* Without considering the extent that land fertilization may have influenced the phosphorus and nitrogen content of drainage water from southern Wisconsin land, Sawyer [31] estimated the relationship between the nitrogen and phosphorus content of biologically treated human sewage and this drainage water. Treated human sewage supplied about 6 pounds of nitrogen and 1.2 pounds of phosphorus per person per year, and the wastes of 750 persons were equivalent to the agricultural drainage of one square mile of land area in southern Wisconsin on the basis of nitrogen; similarly, treated wastes of 212 persons were equivalent to drainage from the same area on a phosphorus basis.[31]

Phosphorus was proved to be the most important item in the productivity of water.[24, 32] With the greatly increased use of detergents, which are largely complex phosphates, alkyl benzene sulfonates, and other surface active agents, the problems associated with the discharge of effluents from sewage plants, even where processing is complete, have become at least twice as great as they were previous to the beginning of the wide use of these detergents. Because of them, smaller amounts of sewage effluents will cause greater fertilization of aquatic habitats than formerly. It has been suggested that chemical methods may eventually be used to remove a part of the phosphates from sewage effluents.[32]

While alkyl benzene sulfonate is not very toxic to warm-blooded vertebrates,[39] concentrations greater than 1 to 2 ppm are toxic to sensitive fish and aquatic organisms,[14] and excessive phosphates and nitrates may stimulate algal blooms to the extent that much of the esthetic value of a water area may be lost. Moreover, the fish population is subjected to constant danger, due to the fact that a sudden die-off of the algae might result in a severe oxygen deficiency or in the actual poisoning of the fish. These aspects of lake fertilization are discussed further in Chapter 6. Needless to say, pollution may create real nuisance problems and even dangers in the management of fishes in artificial lakes as well as in the navigation pools of large rivers.

pH AND CHEMISTRY OF WATER

No attempt will be made here to describe variations in the mineral content of impounded waters found throughout North America; rather we are interested in waters containing abnormal amounts of certain chemicals picked up from contact with natural deposits of minerals. As is to be expected, the mineral composition of pond or lake water is

* Parts per billion.

dioxide tensions below the surface, to low carbon dioxide tension at the surface. These fish soon became affected by the rapid changes in carbon dioxide tension and died by the millions; larger fish rising to the surface from greater depths also became incapacited by sudden changes in carbon dioxide tension. However, it was significant that throughout the period when fish were dying, there was ample oxygen to support fish at all levels.

Investigating biologists [28] conducted laboratory experiments to determine the cause of death of Norris Lake fish. Rock bass were placed in a hardware-cloth cage and lowered to the bottom of a water-filled 10-gallon carboy. The same number of fish were released in the carboy outside the cage. The carboy was left open so these latter fish could come to the water surface and gulp air. The water in the carboy was supplied with carbon dioxide to produce a CO_2 tension above normal. Fish that were free to come to the surface of the water died before those that were held in the cage, thus indicating that rapid change in carbon dioxide tension from high at the bottom of the carboy to low at the surface affected the fish adversely. However, rock bass in the cage were able, by adjusting the alkalinity of the blood, to counteract the ill effects of high but constant carbon dioxide tension, and thus to extract oxygen as efficiently as if the carbon dioxide tension were low. This situation held as long as the carbon dioxide tension remained fairly constant; but when the fish were forced to alternate between high and low tensions, they soon lost their equilibrium and died.

The combinations of circumstances which produce the biological phenomena described above probably appear rather infrequently. More common are fish deaths occurring under ice in winter and in very weedy lakes during hot summer months.

WINTERKILL AND SUMMERKILL

The terms "winterkill" and "summerkill" are applied to sudden mortalities of fishes which occur in winter and summer, usually as a direct result of suffocation. Conditions that set the stage for a winterkill are, however, very different from those which result in an oxygen deficiency in a lake or pond during the summer.

WINTERKILL

In the north, winter ice forms a seal over lakes and ponds which prevents the exchange of gases between the water-air interface. Moreover, the penetration of light through ice is less than through clear water, and the light may be blanketed out entirely by a layer of snow upon the ice. When all photosynthetic activity is stopped because of insufficient light, the source of additional under-ice oxygen is gone, and in a relatively short time the current supply of oxygen may be completely used up by the respiration of living plants and animals and the demands of organic decay.[8, 11]

In 1945, Greenback [11] published results of a study of the physical, chemical, and biological conditions in ice-covered lakes (Michigan). He measured dissolved oxygen, pH, carbon dioxide, alkalinity, biochemical oxygen demand, and light penetration in these ice-covered lakes, to determine what factors or combinations of factors were responsible for the death of fishes, and to develop more effective methods of preventing winter fish kills. The amount of dissolved oxygen appeared to be the most important single factor in relation to death or survival. This oxygen concentration might change gradually or rather suddenly, depending upon other conditions associated with the body of water in question. For example, at Green Lake (Michigan) Station 5, oxygen at the surface (under ice) changed from 1.8 ppm on February 5, 1943, to 9.8 ppm on February 8, an increase of 8.0 ppm in 3 days, or at the rate of 2.7 ppm per day. The most abrupt decline was noted in Pasinski's Pond (Michigan) Station 27, where the oxygen fell from 12.3 ppm on February 12, 1940, to 2.4 ppm on February 14, at a rate of 5 ppm per day. A delicate balance often exists between the processes which produce oxygen (photosynthesis of plankton algae) and those that use it up.[11] As light is essential to photosynthesis, its transmission through the ice and snow covering a lake or pond is extremely important (Figure 3.1). Measurements of light penetration show that about 85 per cent will pass through 7.5 inches of clear ice, and as much as 11.5 per cent, through 15 inches of ice that is cloudy on top. However, 1 inch of crusted snow limited the light penetration through the snow only to between 10 and 17 per cent of the light that fell on the snow's surface, and 5 inches of dry snow allowed the transmission of only 2.5 per cent of the available light.[11] Clean fresh snow allowed the greatest light penetration, clean wet snow the next greatest, and granular snow the least.

While the rate of photosynthesis is dependent on many factors, it is conceivable that there is a range of light intensity sufficient to stimulate a level of photosynthetic activity during which the oxygen output will exactly equal the oxygen demands of the aquatic environment. This is a dangerous condition because it may depreciate rapidly into a situation of oxygen shortage. There is reason to assume that the amount of light that penetrates 1.5 to 2 feet of moderately clear ice (without snow) is enough to satisfy the requirements for photosynthesis.[11] Further, the evidence is conclusive that a heavy snow cover on ice so greatly reduces the amount of light entering the water, regardless of the clarity of the ice, that photosynthesis of phytoplankton is completely stopped.

Biologists and fish culturists have tried to prevent the winterkill of fishes in various ways, most of which have been ineffectual. Some methods explored for preventing winterkill of fishes are given below:

1. *Aeration of Water under Ice.* Many attempts have been made to blow air immediately under ice with pumps or blowers. This method is largely ineffectual,[11] particularly for waters of any size, because little oxygen becomes dissolved in the water.

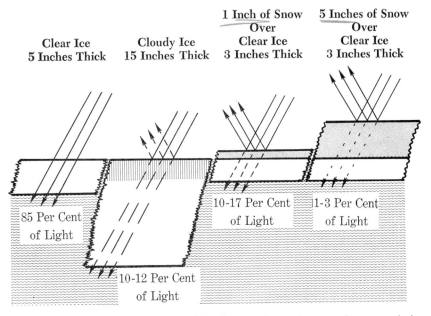

Figure 3.1. Oxygen supply under winter ice depends upon the transmission of sufficient light for photosynthesis of plankton algae and rooted submersed plants. Light passes readily through clear ice and fairly well through cloudy ice. However, an inch of snow blankets out 83 to 90 per cent of the light and 5 inches of snow, 97 to 99 per cent. Winterkill of fishes is more common during winters when the snow on the ice persists for long periods than when it is light or melts between storms.

2. *Aeration of Water above Ice.* In 1935-36, the Michigan Institute for Fisheries Research attempted experimental aeration by pumping water from a lake and spraying it into the air where it fell to the ice and returned through holes cut in the ice.[11] This caused improvement in dissolved oxygen tension, but the effect was very localized, and the oxygen disappeared within 28 hours.

3. *Pumping of Well Water.* Well water at 50°F was run through wire-mesh and over an inclined trough to increase the dissolved oxygen

m about 2 ppm to 4 or 6 ppm. The water was allowed to run into
sinski's Pond (3.75 acres) through holes cut in the ice,[11] and, over a
mber of days, opened a hole in the pond 8 to 10 feet in diameter.
wever, this pumping of aerated well water proved almost useless for
eventing the death of fish, because the dissolution of oxygen was not
cient.

l. **Snow Removal.** Manual removal of snow from hatchery ponds,
hough frequently impractical, has caused improvement in dissolved
'gen under ice. Furthermore, pumps and other equipment may be
ployed. At Green Lake (Michigan) water was pumped onto the surface
the ice, and melted the snow to slush for a one-acre area. There was
increase in the amount of dissolved oxygen in water under the ice,
en though the slush rapidly became frozen.[11]

i. **Lamp Black.** This substance, spread on snow-covered ice from the
melted the snow (through absorption of heat) and thereby allowed
it penetration which resulted in improved oxygen conditions under
ice.[26]

i. **Circulation of Bottom Water.** A perforated plastic hose with small
es at spaced intervals was weighted and laid on the lake bottom to
ow the long axis of the lake. The hose was closed at the distal end
l attached to an air compressor at the proximal end. The compressor
nped air into the hose so that it bubbled out through the small holes
a ng the entire length of the hose. These jets of air passing from the
lake bottom to the surface of the water set up currents of water which
eventually carried bottom water at about 39°F to the surface.[35] This
warmer water eventually melted the ice and kept a strip of open water
above the hose as long as the air compressor was operated, even though
the air temperature was close to 0°F. When this system was operated at
intervals in a lake subject to winterkill of fishes, no loss of fishes occurred.

This method has been used to keep open water for ducks, and to
prevent ice damage to piers, docks, and other installations. It may be the
most successful technique yet devised for preventing winterkill,[6, 29, 33, 34, 35]
but Patriarche[27] demonstrated that in some lakes the circulation of
water having a high biological oxygen demand increased the danger
of winterkill.

An increase in the oxygen supply of water covered by ice can come
about only through photosynthesis. Thus, the maintenance of an adequate
oxygen supply is dependent upon the presence and activity of green plant
life, largely of the plankton algae, and this, in turn, depends upon the
transmission of light for photosynthesis. It is conceivable that most of
these algae might die or go into dormant stages if forced to remain in
darkness (ice covered by snow) for an extended period, so that when
sufficient light for photosynthesis became available again, too few phyto-

strong year classes of white crappies during the summer months where the only evidence of their death was the fact that they suddenly disappeared from wing net catches and never again reappeared.[12, 37] Crappies often are in their poorest condition in the summer, and many apparently fail to recover.

Summerkills comparable in extent to kills occurring under ice in winter sometimes take place in shallow weed-filled lakes during the hot, still nights of July and August. All of the summerkills that I have observed (that did not involve pollution from outside sources) occurred after periods of several days during which skies were cloudy or partly cloudy, temperatures ranged in the 80's and 90's both day and night, and winds were calm or nearly calm. Under these weather conditions, the dissolved oxygen that may be abundant in a weed-choked lake during the daytime may disappear entirely during the calm hot nights with the resulting wholesale death of fishes. Usually, some fishes survive summer oxygen shortages, and these may be seen gasping for air at the lake surface as the first light of the approaching dawn makes them visible. Often a quiet period lasting several days and nights may be broken off by a violent storm which restores the oxygen supply, lowers the water temperature, and stops any further death of fishes. Probably, high water temperatures, darkness, and rapid organic decay in shallow weed-filled lakes combine forces to produce summerkills.

Another type of summerkill of fishes is caused by the decay of "blooms" of toxic algae (usually bluegreens). These toxic algae are concentrated by winds,[16] or they develop from the stimulus of nitrates and phosphates originating from organic pollutants. Death of fishes may be caused by oxygen deficiencies, by toxic substances released from decaying bluegreen algae, or both.[21] The death of domestic stock, forced to drink the alga-filled water, has been attributed to these toxic substances.

High or low oxygen tensions produced by unusual circumstances sometimes will cause the death of fishes. During April, 1940, a loss of fish was observed at the south end of Lake Waubesa (Wisconsin), and in the Yahara River below this lake.[43] At that time an algal bloom of *Chlamydomonas* was concentrated in the south end of the lake and produced oxygen to a level of 30-32 ppm at the lake surface. The death of fishes was attributed to the presence of gas emboli in the gill capillaries which blocked blood circulation. Black crappies, bluegills, northern pike, walleyes, white suckers, and carp were killed.

In October, 1936, a heavy mortality of fish was reported for the Yahara River below Lake Kegonsa (Wisconsin).[21] These fish died from an oxygen deficiency caused by the decay of an almost pure culture of *Aphanizomenon flos-aquae*. The fish were crowding close to shore and were gasping at the surface until they finally expired. The bluegreen alga, *A.*

flos-aquae, is known to release a very toxic substance when it dies and decays; and a secondary cause of death may have been direct poisoning.

Jackson and Starrett [18] described localized kills of fishes (mostly gizzard shad) in Lake Chautauqua on July 9, 1953, that apparently resulted from localized oxygen deficiencies. At 6:20 A.M. the dissolved oxygen content at one point was only 1.6 ppm, and later several fish were observed that presumably had died of asphyxiation. The weather was hot and the lake very quiet.

OTHER DANGERS OF IMPOUNDMENTS

Fishes in small artificial ponds and lakes may be decimated by some "accidents'" that occur because of the physical aspects of these impoundments and the fact that men are careless by nature. These "accidents" are mentioned here so that they may be recognized and avoided.

Loss of Ponds Because of Burrowing Animals

Small ponds are sometimes subjected to washouts through the activities of burrowing crayfish, muskrats, rats, and other burrowing mammals. These animals usually work in the dam, digging tunnels above the normal water level of the pond. No damage appears until a heavy sudden rain raises the pond level well above normal, and the tunnels become water channels through which water escapes to the downstream side of the dam usually taking with it a section of the earth fill and all of the water and fish in the pond.

It is usually impractical to bury wire mesh or metal sheeting in small dams to prevent damage from burrowing animals. The best solution is to maintain a constant vigilance and trap or poison the rodents when they appear to be damaging the pond dam. Burrowing crayfish are sometimes killed by dropping one or more crystals of crude copper sulfate in their holes or "chimneys," or by adding either one teaspoonful of carbide powder or two ounces of stock dip solution to each burrow and then tamping the burrow shut.[1] On ponds larger than 3 or 4 acres, the dams are so wide at the top that there is little danger from burrowing animals.

Wind Action

When artificial lakes and dams are too large to be subject to damage from burrowing animals, prevailing winds acting on such a wide surface can create another danger by blowing parallel to the long axes of the lakes, thus causing waves and currents that cut earth from the fills at the water line. Unless a fill is protected by rip-rapping of concrete, rocks, or by a floating boom, the action of the waves may gradually cut away the dam. Wind and wave action can occur in any part of the lake, often cutting away at one shore and filling up a nearby bay or channel. Where rip-rapping is impractical, booms or deflector structures can be used to stop severe wind and water erosions. Wind-driven ice causes considerable damage in northern lakes.

DANGERS FROM INSECTICIDES

Since the discovery of DDT during World War II, new dangers for fishes and other aquatic organisms have come with the many new insecticides. The toxicity to fishes of some of these insecticides commonly used on agricultural crops is very high (see Table 6.3), and carelessness in application, particularly in crop dusting or spraying by plane, can cause localized damage to fish.

The passage of the Miller Act in 1954 (Public Law 518) established tolerances for residues of insecticides, fungicides, and herbicides in those agricultural commodities involved in interstate commerce. These regulations have reduced carelessness in the application of, or in the use of excessive amounts of insecticides. This, in turn, will reduce to some extent the danger of fish kills.

LITERATURE

1. Beall, H. B., *W. Va. Cons.*, Apr., p. 32 (1959).
2. Beckman, W. C., *Am. Fish. Soc. Trans.*, **78**, 82-90 (1950).
3. Bennett, G. W., *Ill. Nat. Hist. Surv. Biol. Notes*, **19**, 1-9 (1948).
4. Black, E. C., Fry, F. E. J., and Black, V. S., *Can. Jour. Zool.*, **32(6)**, 408-420 (1954).
5. Buck, D. H., *Okla. Fish. Res. Lab. Rept.*, **56**, 1-62 (1956).
6. Burdick, M. E., *Wisc. Cons. Bull.* **24**, 21-23 (1959).
7. Carlander, K. D., *Jour. Wildl. Mgt.*, **16(3)**, 258-261 (1952).
8. Cooper, G. P., and Washburn, G. N., *Am. Fish. Soc. Trans.*, **76**, 23-33 (1946).
9. Ellis, M. M., Westfall, B. A., and Ellis, M. D., *U.S. Fish and Wildl. Ser. Res. Rept.*, **9**, 1-122 (1946).
10. Fry, F. E. J., *Proc. N. E. Atlantic Fish Conf.*, Mimeo., 1-29 (1951).
11. Greenbank, J., *Ecological Mono.*, **15**, 343-392 (1945).
12. Hansen, D. F., *Ill. Nat. Hist. Surv. Bull.*, **25(4)**, 211-265 (1951).
13. Hemphill, J., *Ariz. Game & Fish Dept.*, 8 pp. (1954).
14. Henderson, C., Pickering, Q. H., and Cohen, J. M., *Sewage Ind. Wastes*, **31**, 295-306 (1959).
15. Hey, D., *Proc. Int. Assoc. Theor. & Appd. Limnology*, **12**, 737-742 (1955).
16. Ingram, W. M., and Prescott, G. W., *Am. Midland Nat.*, **52(1)**, 75-87 (1954).
17. Irwin, W. H., *Okla. Agri. and Mech. Coll. Bull.*, **42(11)**, 1-16 (1945).
18. Jackson, H. O., and Starrett, W. C., *Jour. Wildl. Mgt.*, **23(2)**, 157-168 (1959).
19. James, M. C., Meehean, O. L., and Douglas, E. J., *U.S.F.W.S. Cons. Bull.*, **35**, 1-22 (1944).

20. Kesskalt, K., and Ilzhofer, H., *Arch. Hyg. und Bakt.*, **118**, 1-66 (1937).
21. Mackenthun, K. M., and Herman, E. F., *Am. Fish. Soc. Trans.*, **75**, 175-180 (1948).
22. Moen, T., *Iowa Conserv.* **19**(5), 37.
23. Neess, J. C., *Am. Fish. Soc. Trans.*, **76**, 335-358 (1949).
24. Neil, J. H., *Purdue Univ. Engng. Extn. Serv.*, **94**, 301-316 (1957).
25. Nicholson, A. J., *Australian Jour. Zool.*, **2**(1), 9-65 (1954).
26. O'Donnell, D. J., *Midwest Wildl. Conf.*, Mimeo., 9 pp. (1947).
27. Patriarche, M. H., *Jour. Wild. Mgt.* **25**(3), 282-289 (1961).
28. Powers, E. B., Shields, A. R., and Hickman, M. E., *Jour. Tenn. Acad. Sci.*, **14**(2), 239-260 (1939).
29. Rasmussen, D. H., *Prog. Fish-Cult.*, **22**, 185-187 (1960).
30. Rose, E. T., and Moen, T., *Am. Fish. Soc. Trans.*, **80**, 50-55 (1951).
31. Sawyer, C. N., *New Eng. Water Wks. Assoc. Jour.*, **61**(2), 109-127 (1947).
32. Sawyer, C. N., *Sewage and Indust. Wastes*, **24**(6), 768-775 (1952).
33. Scidmore, W. J., *Prog. Fish-Cult.*, **19**, 124-127 (1957).
34. Schmitz, W. R., *Wisc. Cons. Bull.*, **24**, 19-21 (1959).
35. Schmitz, W. R., and Hasler, A. D., *Science*, **128** (3331), 1088-1089 (1958).
36. Smith, M. W., *Jour. Fish. Res. Bd. Canada*, **16**(6), 887-895 (1959).
37. Starrett, W. C., and McNeil, P. L., Jr., *Ill. Nat. Hist. Surv. Biol. Notes*, **30**, 1-31 (1952).
38. Swartley, A. M., *Ore. Dept. Geol. and Min. Indust. Bull.*, **10**, 26-27 (1938).
39. Tusing, T. W., Poynter, O. E., and Opdyke, D. L., *Toxicology and Applied Pharmacology*, **2**(4), 464-473 (1960).
40. Wallen, I. E., *Okla. Agr. and Mech. Coll. Bull.*, **48**(2), 1-24 (1951).
41. Ward, H. B., *Ore. Dept. Geol. & Min. Indust. Bull.*, **10**, 4-25 (1938).
42. Whitmore, C. M., Warren, C. E., and Doudoroff, P., *Am. Fish. Soc. Trans.*, **89**, 17-26 (1960).
43. Woodbury, L. A., *Am. Fish. Soc. Trans.*, **71**, 112-117 (1942).
44. Wundsch, H. H., *Handb. der Binnenfischerei Mitteleuropas Bd.*, **6**, 139-262 (1926).

4 〜〜〜

Carrying Capacity,
Productivity, and Growth

The *carrying capacity* of a container (a pail or basket) is limited by the height of its sides and its diameter. Not so well defined, however, is the ability of an environment to support life. The term "carrying capacity" was probably first used in game management to express the *maximum* population of game animals supported by a limited range during a period covering at least the four seasons of one year.[30] Before we define carrying capacity further, it is important to distinguish between this term and saturation. An adult animal population that tends to be uniform over a wide area may reach a saturation point. Saturation point is defined as a uniform *maximum density of grown individuals* attained by a species, even in the most favorable local environments. However, saturation also implies a degree of intolerance of animals to "piling up," an interaction between individuals that may have little connection with other environmental conditions. Thus, saturation should not be confused with carrying capacity, which always implies a tendency toward uniformity over a wide area.

Carrying capacity when applied to fishes in aquatic habitats may be defined as *the maximum poundage of a given species or complex of species of fishes that a limited and specific aquatic habitat may support during a stated interval of time.* Since adverse environmental factors during certain seasons might actually control the maximum poundage of fish, seasonal adversity could establish the carrying capacity. However, as fishes rarely can be seen readily, or estimated by direct observation, little is known of the effects of seasonal adversity on fish populations. We believe that food is often limiting to population size in fishes, but other factors may be of equal importance. Therefore, at present the concept of carrying capacity is largely theoretical.

CARRYING CAPACITY AND STANDING CROP

In contrast to carrying capacity, which emphasizes *maximum poundage* and a *stated interval of time,* the term *standing crop,* is applied to something very definite, namely, *the poundage of a given species or complex of species of fishes present in a body of water at a given time.* When one

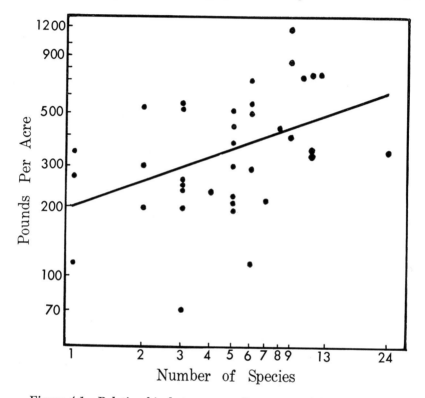

Figure 4.1. Relationship between standing crops of fishes and numbers of species in midwestern reservoirs. [From Carlander, K.D., *J. Fish Res. Bd. Canada,* 12 (4) (1955)]

drains a pond and makes a census of the fish, the census total is the *standing crop* of that pond at the time it was drained. The same fish in the same pond may be censused at a later date to give a different standing crop figure, influenced, perhaps, by a change in the relative abundance of various kinds of fishes present. Still, both census figures represent standing crops of this pond. In theory, the standing crop might be lower than, equal to or in excess of the carrying capacity of the pond.

The relationship of numbers of fishes to carrying capacity and standing crop is not well understood (although, in general, large numbers of fishes are usually associated with small individual sizes of those fishes and vice versa). In theory, a body of water in which the fishes represented the greatest range of species and sizes would offer the maximum in efficient utilization of available food (Figure 4.1), although it is conceivable that the kinds and relative numbers of fishes within any given size range might not be paralleled by an equal abundance of acceptable food for this size range. Thus, a part of a population representing a certain size range of one or more species might be stunted, while in the same species, other sizes might be growing rapidly.

SURFACE AREA

The carrying capacity (in pounds) of a body of water for a specific fish population seems to be largely a function of surface area rather than depth or volume; probably the zone of light penetration at the surface produces the bulk of the food supply (directly or indirectly) for fishes. There seems to be much evidence that carrying capacity is directly related to fish food production, which, in turn, is related to the basic fertility of the water, and conditions allowing the capture of this fertility by the food chain.

EXPERIMENTAL TESTING

Little is known regarding the carrying capacity of any water for individual species of game or pan fish, although European fish farmers engaged in raising commercial fishes for market have recognized that there are production limits of ponds for carp and other commercial species. It is common practice in fish farming to stock ponds with only a sufficient number of fish to produce a marketable product at the end of one or two growing seasons. Boccius [13] wrote: "It has been fully proved that a given space of earth can produce only a certain quantity; so only can a given space or quantity of water produce a certain quantity, either of vegetable matter or animalcules; and curious as it may appear, yet it is as true as curious, that by storing only the proper number of fish adapted to the water, the weight in 3 years will prove equal to what would have been had twice the number been placed therein, so that the smaller number produces the same weight as the larger, from a given quantity of water. By overstocking the water, the fish become sickly, lean and bony."

Swingle and Smith [35] described an experiment in which two ponds were stocked with 6500 newly hatched bluegill fry per acre in late spring, and when the ponds were drained in November, the fish had grown to an average weight of slightly less than one ounce and the total populations in each of the two ponds amounted to approximately 300 pounds per acre. The fish were returned to the refilled ponds and when the ponds were drained two years later, these fish still averaged about an ounce each and the ponds' populations still weighed about 300 pounds per acre.

In another series of experiments,[35] three ponds were stocked with 1300, 3200, and 6500 bluegill fry per acre. When these ponds were drained in November of the same year, the fish in the first pond averaged 4 ounces, those in the second slightly less than 2 ounces, and those in the third approximately one ounce. The total weight produced was approximately 300 pounds per acre in each of the three ponds.

In 1939 these same authors (Swingle and Smith [36]) published the results of other experiments having to do with the carrying capacity of waters:

"In May 1936, one pond was stocked with bluegill bream fry at the rate of 26,000 per acre, weighing 2 pounds 5 ounces. Another pond was stocked with year-old fingerlings at the rate of 13,000 per acre, weighing 180 pounds. . . . When drained the following November, the former pond produced at the rate of 105 pounds of fish per acre and the latter at the rate of 92 pounds per acre. One pond gained 103 pounds per acre, while the other lost 88 pounds per acre due to overstocking."

In a second experiment, Swingle and Smith used a pond of 1.8 acres over a period of 2 years. In the spring of the first year (1935), they stocked 4485 fish of eight common pond species, weighing 40 pounds, 9 ounces. At the end of that year they collected 22,069 fish weighing 293 pounds, and 4 ounces. Early in the spring of 1936 they stocked 236 fish of the same species in this pond, weighing 24 pounds, and 7 ounces. At the end of 1936 they collected 30,405 fish weighing 296 pounds, and 2 ounces.

In these experiments the variation in total numbers and weights of fish stocked seemed to have little effect upon the total weights of fish found in the ponds at the end of one growing season. Rather the total weights of these populations were adjusted upward or downward until they approached a rather uniform level for individual ponds, probably associated with the food production capacities of these ponds.

FACTORS AFFECTING POUNDAGE

We have seen that the poundage of fish supported by a pond or lake of constant size may remain fairly constant, in spite of the numbers of fish stocked. This is true only within limits; and the carrying capacity of a lake or pond for fish may vary (1) with variations in the fertility of water, (2) with age of water if age represents change in chemical composition, (3) with fertility of watershed soil if a change brought about through erosion or artificial fertilization is carried to the pond in runoff water, (4) with changes in the kinds of fishes, or in the relative abundance of certain kinds and sizes of fishes.

Fertilization. Fisheries literature contains listings of many censuses of fish populations made through the draining of ponds and lakes or through the use of rotenone. Many of these censuses have been republished by Carlander [15] in his compilations of growth and population statistics. A great deal has been published on the increase in the standing crops of fishes resulting from the use of various fertilizers.[5, 14, 24, 33, 34, 37] These studies furnish evidence that various inorganic and organic fertilizers introduced into ponds will temporarily increase the standing crop of most fishes, although there is evidence that one species may be benefited through the use of fertilizer to a much greater extent than another inhabiting the same water.[24]

A pond fertilized for a period and then left without the addition of fertilizer will show a reduced standing crop of fishes 3 or more years after fertilization is stopped.[38] This indicates that some of the fertilizer is no longer available, either because it has been washed out of the pond or has become bound up in insoluble compounds in the pond bottom. However, if the standing crop of fishes, even though reduced, is still not as low as it was prior to the beginning of fertilization, this indicates that fertilizer in an available form has accumulated in the pond bottom. This accumulation of fertilizing materials may go on as a natural process (even if a pond or lake owner adds no organic or inorganic fertilizers) through the death of plants and animals in the pond, through the accumulation of dust and leaves blown in from outside sources, and through the addition of nutrients leached from the soils of the pond watershed.

Chemical Basis for Fertility. Moyle [32] demonstrated a positive relationship between the presence of varying amounts of certain chemicals (total phosphorus, total nitrogen, and total alkalinity) in the surface waters of Minnesota lakes and the poundage of fishes supported by those lakes, although this could be expressed as a direct relationship only in the case of total phosphorus.

Kinds of Fishes. Standing crops of fishes vary greatly on the basis of the kinds of fishes making up a population and the relative abundance of each of several kinds (Figure 4.2). Standing crops of fishes in Illinois ponds varied from 75 pounds per acre in soft-water-Ozark-hills ponds of southern Illinois where the population was largemouth bass and green sunfish, to 1100 pounds per acre in a black-soil-flood-plain pond in central Illinois where the population was composed of crappies and bigmouth buffalo. In Iowa the standing crops of fishes ranged from 28 to 1235 pounds per acre.[17] Where the standing crop exceeded 300 pounds, usually bullheads or buffalo were present. Populations of bluegills usually exceeded 100 pounds per acre. In Kentucky poundages ranged from 200 to 1000 pounds per acre in unfertilized ponds.[19]

A number of ponds have been censused one or more times, and these

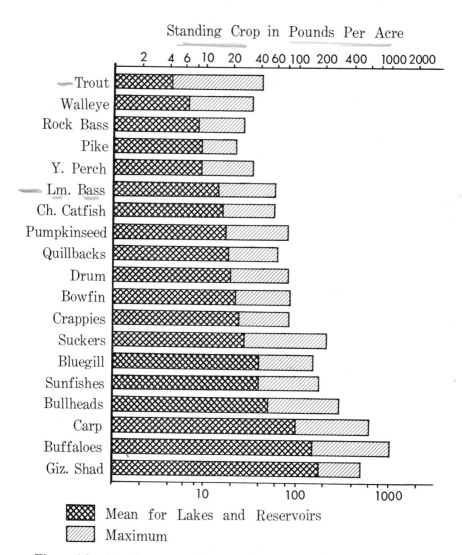

Figure 4.2. **Standing crops of named fishes in North American lakes and reservoirs. Usually these fish were in combination with other species. This figure furnishes a rough approximation of the relative efficiency of the species listed. [From Carlander, K.D., *J. Fish Res. Bd. Canada*, 12(4) (1955)]**

show the influence of kinds of fish upon the standing crop. Ball,[4] re-poisoning Ford Lake (Michigan) for a second time, found 2.4 times the weight of fish which had been recovered when the lake was poisoned 10 years previously. In the earlier census, the yellow perch was dominant in the population while in the latter census, the bluegill was dominant. Ball concluded that the difference in the poundages of fish in the two censuses was due to the fact that the perch is largely piscivorous in its feeding habits, whereas the bluegill is largely dependent on invertebrates for food and thus is closer to the primary food chain.

Fork Lake, a pond of 1.38 acres in central Illinois, was censused at the beginning of a cropping experiment when an undesirable population of fish was poisoned, and again 4 years later when the pond dam was washed out.[9] At the time of the first census, Fork Lake contained 5350 fish weighing 774 pounds or 539 pounds of fish per acre. By weight, carp and bigmouth buffalo made up 47.5 per cent, bullheads (plus 4 channel catfish) 41.2 per cent, and largemouth bass and panfish, 6.3 per cent. At the time of the dam failure, an estimate of the population was 10,300 fish weighing 260.9 pounds or 189.1 pounds per acre. By weight, 64.7 per cent of the population was largemouth bass and 35.3 per cent blue-gills. This population had been subjected to heavy wing net-fishing for bluegills. The earlier population containing carp, buffalo, and bullheads was 2.85 times as heavy as that composed of bass and bluegills.

Duck Pond (3.05 acres), an isolated part of an old flooded stripmine in Vermilion County (Illinois), was censused at two widely separated times. At the time of the first census in 1940, the pond contained 11,269 fishes of 30 species weighing 2051 pounds or 672.5 pounds per acre. The population was composed of 3.0 per cent bass, 12.2 per cent pan fish, 0.6 per cent catfish, 23.5 per cent rough fish (largely quillbacks and carp), and 60.7 per cent forage fish (gizzard shad). In a second census made in 1945, the population consisted of 3450 fishes of 18 species weighing 689.1 pounds or 229.7 pounds per acre. This population was composed of 2.6 per cent largemouth bass, 33.1 per cent pan fish, 1.3 per cent catfish, 41.0 per cent rough fish, and 22.0 per cent forage fish (gizzard shad). The wide discrepancy in the total poundages of fishes in the two censuses is difficult to explain. There were more pounds of bass in the first census (62.4 pounds as compared with 18.2 pounds) and more pounds of pan fish (251.2 pounds to 205.2 pounds). However, the large differences were in the poundages of rough fish (479.8 pounds in the first census, 282.2 pounds in the second) and forage fish (1245.0 pounds of gizzard shad in the first census, 150.0 pounds in the second). Apparently at the time of the second census, the populations of rough fish and gizzard shad were considerably below the carrying capacity of the pond for these species.

Arrowhead Lake, an artificial pond of 2.6 acres on the grounds of the Illinois State 4-H Club Camp, University of Illinois Allerton Estate near Monticello, Illinois, was stocked in 1948 with 22 fingerling bass, 26 adult bluegills, 7 adult warmouths, and 103 black bullheads. This pond was censused by drainage in the springs of 1950, 1952, 1953, and during

TABLE 4.1 NUMBERS AND WEIGHTS OF LARGEMOUTH BASS, BLUEGILLS, WARMOUTHS, AND BLACK BULLHEADS TAKEN IN FOUR CENSUSES OF ARROWHEAD POND, ILLINOIS STATE 4-H CLUB CAMP, MONTICELLO, ILLINOIS.

	1950 Census		1952 Census		1953 Census		1955 Census [3]	
	Number	Weight, Pounds	Number	Weight, Pounds	Number	Weight, Pounds	Number	Weight, Pounds
Largemouth bass	81	52.2	1057	102.1	210	60.0	1019	46.6
					728	133.8 [1]		
Bluegills	6392	395.1	2584	251.3	2108	171.6	389	38.3
Warmouths	28	3.1	417	24.7	436	42.1	546	24.6
Black bullheads	1672	211.2	63	51.2	30	14.8	2260	344.9
					7	4.8 [2]		
Totals	8173	661.6	4121	429.3	3519	427.1	4214	454.4
Per Acre	3143	254.5	1585	165.1	1353	164.3	1621	174.8

[1] Smallmouth bass moved into Arrowhead Pond for wintering October, 1952, to March, 1953.
[2] Six green sunfish weighing 1.0 pound and 1 carp weighing 3.8 pounds.
[3] Outlet valve of pond inadvertently opened at night by parties unknown; fish collected from stream channel throughout several hundred yards below outlet. Probably some large bass and large bluegills taken by poachers.

October in 1955. With the exception of about 700 smallmouth bass that were stored in the pond from October, 1952, to March, 1953, the fish population has consisted of the four species listed above. In the 1950 census (Table 4.1), the bluegills and the bullheads dominated the population; and when fish were restocked following the first census, only 1093 bluegills and 1069 bullheads were returned. In the 1950-1952 period, the bass made the greatest gains (80 fish expanded to 1057), the bluegills increased about 2.5 times, and the bullheads dropped from 1069 to 63 individuals. This reduction in bullheads reflected poor reproductive success and a heavy hook-and-line yield. Following the March, 1952 census, fish replaced in the pond were 541 bass weighing 72.1 pounds, 569 bluegills weighing 140.6 pounds, 16 warmouth weighing 4.2 pounds, and 36 black bullheads weighing 25.6 pounds. The fishing in Arrowhead Pond in 1953 was rather light until October when fishermen discovered that smallmouth bass taken in draining another lake were being stored in Arrowhead. Then, it appeared that considerable poaching occurred.

Following the 1953 census, 104 largemouth bass weighing 56.1 pounds, 834 bluegills weighing 91.6 pounds, 427 warmouth weighing 41.3 pounds, and 30 bullheads weighing 14.8 pounds were returned to the pond.

During the process of draining the pond in March of 1955, the outlet valve was opened wide at night by someone unknown. The next morning, the fish were scattered along the outlet channel for several hundred yards, and footprints indicated that some pre-dawn collection of fish may have taken place. Thus, the 1955 census may be short some large bass and large bluegills.

The four censuses of Arrowhead Pond showed a range of standing crops from 164.3 to 254.5 pounds per acre. The total poundage was lowest when the bass were the most numerous and highest when bluegills and bullheads were abundant. All of these fish except the warmouths appeared to be in competition, each species ready to "take over" the pond if an opportunity should arise.

The fish population of Ridge Lake (central Illinois) has been censused by draining 8 times in the past 20 years (Bennett [10] and unpublished data). Numbers and weights of fish per acre taken in these censuses are listed in Table 4.2. The time interval between each of the first 5 censuses was two years; between the fifth and sixth and the sixth and seventh censuses, three years, and between the seventh and eighth censuses, three and one-half years. Each September, 1951 through 1955 inclusive, the water level of Ridge Lake was lowered to reduce the surface area during the fall months so that the fish populations exposed in the 1953 and 1956 censuses were hardly comparable to the others. Table 4.2 shows that after 1945 the population was composed largely of bass and bluegills. No bluegills were stocked until 1944, a year after the 1943 census. Warmouths were stocked in 1949 and channel catfish, in small numbers in 1951 and 1955. Neither were numerically very abundant because of low success in reproduction; in fact, only a few young catfish were ever observed in the last three censuses. Other fish entered from the small feeder stream or came upstream over the spillway during floods.

TABLE 4.2   NUMBERS AND WEIGHTS OF FISH PER ACRE TAKEN IN 8 DRAINING CENSUSES OF RIDGE LAKE, COLES COUNTY, ILLINOIS. BY 1951 AN ACCUMULATION OF SILT IN THE UPPER LAKE BASIN HAD REDUCED THE LAKE SURFACE AREA FROM 18 TO 17 ACRES.

Censuses	Largemouth Bass		Bluegill		Warmouth		Channel Cats	
	Number	Weight, Pounds	Number	Weight, Pounds	Number	Weight, Pounds	Number	Weight, Pounds
Spring, 1943	265	48.2						
Spring, 1945	91	39.6	559	7.0 ‡				
Spring, 1947	139	31.5	3702	193.3				
Spring, 1949	113	50.4	1095	86.9				
Spring, 1951	84	49.9	2887	105.2	51	4.0		
Spring, 1953 *	116	26.6	440	58.3	15	3.8	38	27.8
Spring, 1956 *	132	37.5	1011	119.9	37	4.6	14	36.4
Fall, 1959	137	30.5	5451	161.7	122	13.2	10	20.2
Av.†	138	41.7	2739	136.8	80	8.9	12	28.3

Censuses	Bullheads		Carp		Miscellaneous		Total	
	Number	Weight, Pounds	Number	Weight, Pounds	Number	Weight, Pounds	Number	Weight, Pounds
Spring, 1943	1	0.4			1	0.2	267	48.8
Spring, 1945	30	23.8			12	1.9	692	72.3
Spring, 1947	27	9.0	3	22.1	7	0.4	3878	256.3
Spring, 1949	3	2.2			3	0.7	1214	140.2
Spring, 1951	9	3.7	tr	0.9			3031	163.7
Spring, 1953 *	tr	0.3			2	0.1	611	116.9
Spring, 1956 *	1	0.8			tr	0.3	1195	199.5
Fall, 1959	tr	0.1	3	20.8	tr	tr	5726	246.4
Av.†	12	6.5					2468	154.6

* Population influenced by September drawdowns.
† Data for 1953 and 1956 not included in average.
‡ Not included because bluegill population newly introduced.

Table 4.2 shows that no two censuses were very similar, either in numbers, or pounds of fish per acre. The poundage of bass in 1943 when almost no other fish were present was exceeded by only two subsequent censuses. Exclusive of the drawdown period, the lowest poundages of bass appeared in the 1947 and 1959 censuses when the bluegills were most abundant, both in numbers and in pounds per acre. Bluegills larger than about 2.5 inches ranged in number from 440 to 5400 per acre and in weight from 58 to 193 pounds per acre.

The standing crops of fish recorded in the 1947, 1949, 1951, and 1959 censuses (which are most nearly comparable to one another, with both bass and bluegills present and no drawdowns) ranged from 140 to 256 pounds per acre. The highest poundage (256) represented more than an 80 per cent increase over the lowest poundage (140).

After each census, *all of the catchable bass were returned to the lake,* and the bluegill populations were drastically reduced, usually to less than 200 per acre of the larger fish. The population after two, three, or four growing seasons (1959 census) reflected the struggle for dominance between the bass and bluegills. From Table 4.2 one is led to believe that fall drawdowns of the lake affect both species: the bass through a poundage decrease with little change in numbers, the bluegills through a decrease in both numbers and poundages, but with a more severe effect on numbers. Thus, the drawdowns were more favorable to bass than to bluegills.

The eight censuses of Ridge Lake parallel the four censuses of Arrowhead Pond in exposing what appears to be competition, primarily between largemouth bass and bluegills in which the bass would rather quickly lose out except for the culling of bluegills on each census. Ridge Lake is a highly favorable habitat for bluegill reproduction and survival, but poor in nutritional resources for bluegills of desirable sizes.

Growing Season. Swingle and Smith[37] state: "After the fish used in stocking have spawned once, more small fish are present than can be adequately supported by the food that the pond is producing. Hence a pond rapidly reaches its maximum carrying capacity, usually within one year."

The length of the fish growing season in the southern part of the United States may be more than 10 months long, whereas in the northern states the fish growing season may be less than 4 months (Figure 4.3), and northern lakes and ponds may be covered with ice from 3 to 5 months. The length of the growing season affects the time of population growth required for it to approach the carrying capacity of an unpopulated body of water. Ball[5] found that the total weight of fish recorded at the end of the third year did not vary greatly from that of the second year. This indicates that two growing seasons are usually sufficient for a population to approach the carrying capacity of a body of water in the northern part of the United States.

Other Factors Related to Standing-Crop Size. The relationships between the standing crops of fishes and certain environmental and fish population characteristics have troubled fishery biologists for years. Recently, using regression methods, Carlander[16] attempted to determine whether certain environmental factors may affect standing crops of fishes. He found no relationship between standing crop and lake area; an increase in standing crops with decreasing average depths (may not be entirely significant), and a significant increase with increasing hardness of the waters. There was also an increase in standing crop with an increase in number of species present (Figure 4.1).

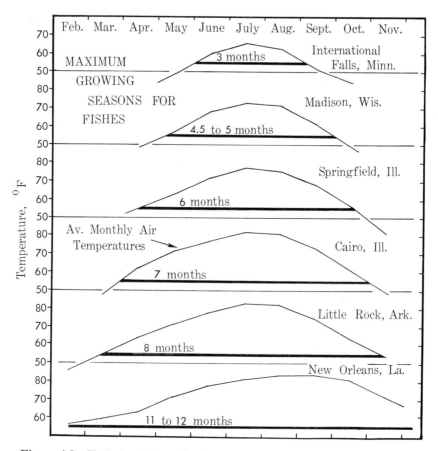

Figure 4.3. Variation in length of the fish growing season, based upon the observation that growth in warm-water fishes is very slow at temperatures below 55°F. (Records from U.S. Weather Bureau, 5-year average.)

As stated previously, Moyle [32] was able to show that the standing crops of fishes in Minnesota increased with increases of phosphorus, nitrogen, and total alkalinity.

Fish of Useful Sizes. In passing judgment on the value of a fish population for sport angling, it becomes necessary to set up arbitrary standards for fish of useful sizes as opposed to those too small to interest anglers. Immediately, we enter an area of controversy among fishery biologists as well as among fishermen. In 1939, Illinois biologists [12] set up arbitrary standards for useful sizes for some common panfish and catfish: 6 inches or larger for bluegills, and other sunfish, 8 inches or larger for black and white crappies, 7 inches or larger for bullheads, and 12 inches or larger for channel catfish. At that time, the length limit of 10 inches for largemouth bass was still in force in Illinois; however, a bass should be 9 inches or longer before it is large enough for table use. In some states bluegills of over 5 inches [5, 34] and bass over 7.2 inches were considered of edible sizes, and bullheads were considered to be of an edible (or salable) size in Michigan at approximately 7 inches total length.[6]

Walleyes and northern pike are too small to be useful unless the walleyes are about 12 or 13 inches long and the northern pike, 16 to 18 inches.

The decision as to what constitutes a fish of useful size may best be made by the fishery biologist rather than the fishing public. Just because the fishing public will take 5-inch bluegills does not mean that they would still do so if enough bluegills of 6 inches or larger were available to satisfy their desire for fish. In taking 5-inch bluegills, fishermen are demonstrating that the 5-inch length is the minimum size for which they can find use. This should not be the goal of the fishery biologist.

Fish management should be able to produce fish of such sizes that the sporting aspects of fishing are satisfied and the end product (in this case the fish) is large enough for table preparation. When the head, fins, and tail are removed from a 6-inch bluegill, the part remaining is barely large enough to make an attractive morsel. A 5-inch fish would scarcely be of interest, unless bones were cooked sufficiently to be eaten without separation from the flesh. Even then the work of cleaning and scaling is large for such a small return. The only reason for recommending a minimum crappie size of 8 inches is that these fish have small bones that are almost impossible to separate from the meat in fish smaller than 8 inches.

As mentioned above, the potential angling value of a fish population may be defined on the basis of numbers of fish of useful sizes, that are present in a population. A large standing crop of fishes may mean nothing from the aspect of potential angling if these fishes are too small to be usable.

FISH PRODUCTION

DEFINITION OF PRODUCTION

The term *production* is generally applied to *the increase in number of individuals and/or the weight of fish flesh added during a limited period.* For example, if a new pond containing no fish were stocked in March with 1500 bluegill fry weighing a total of 1.0 pound and in November when the pond was drained 200 pounds of bluegills were collected, the fish production for that season would be 199 pounds plus as additional poundage of fish that had been lost through natural causes during the season. In addition, flesh added to fish that later died and decayed or were eaten by predators, must be included in a total production estimate. Thus, if this same pond were restocked in March of the next season with 203 pounds of bluegills and drained in November, with a population weighing 204 pounds, the production the second year would be 1 pound plus a poundage lost as above.

The term "production," therefore, is more definitely associated with yield than with standing crop, although it is never entirely synonymous with yield unless one is willing to assume that, for a given period, there has been a complete replacement of fish flesh equal to that removed through predation and "natural" deaths as well as through human predation (fishing, netting, spearing [21]). According to Carlander,[16] "Since the annual rate of turnover probably varies less from one fish population to another than does the standing crop, standing-crop data are probably fairly good estimates of fish production." However, Clark [18] states that, "the magnitude of the standing crop at any moment does not give a measure of the rate at which production is going on since it (standing crop) is determined by the difference between the rates of production and destruction over the whole previous history of the population up to the time considered." (material in parentheses mine)

FOOD CONVERSION

Various kinds of fish are able to convert foods (of several kinds palatable to them) into flesh at various rates. Maximum efficiency in food conversion is attained when food is available for consumption at a rate between maintenance requirements and the maximum a fish is able to eat in a specified period. When food is scarce, a fish may expend too much energy in finding the food and, therefore, be unable to approach maximum efficiency. Where food is super-abundant, the fish may consume more than it can digest and assimilate so that a loss of efficiency results.

Thompson [39] stated that at 70°F 2.5 pounds of minnows are required to produce one pound of bass. When larger amounts were fed to the bass, the food was used less efficiently and conversion values were 3.8 for largemouth bass and 4.5 for smallmouth bass.[43]

Markus [31] has shown that the rate of digestion in largemouth bass is very slow at temperatures below 65°F, but that it increases rapidly between 65° and 90°F. Thompson [39] used Markus' temperature-digestion rate curve along with mean monthly temperatures at each of seven different localities within the range of largemouth bass in the United States to compute the total quantity of minnows which a 10-inch bass could digest in a year at each of these locations. Since the maximum yield is probably proportional to the total of potential digestion, it may be possible to show the relationship between carrying capacity and potential yield at different latitudes. Carrying this idea further, Thompson published a table showing the theoretical effect of latitude on potential annual sustained yield (Table 4.3).

TABLE 4.3 EFFECT OF LATITUDE ON ANNUAL YIELD AS ESTI-
MATED FROM MEAN MONTHLY TEMPERATURES OF
DIFFERENT LOCALITIES.[39] (From Needham, J. G.,
"A Symposium on Hydrobiology," the University
of Wisconsin Press, Madison, Wisconsin, 1941.)

Locality	Latitude	Maximum Annual Yield as Percentage of Carrying Capacity
Vilas County, Wisconsin	46° North	21
Madison, Wisconsin	43° North	39
Urbana, Illinois	40° North	50
Cairo, Illinois	37° North	74
Memphis, Tennessee	35° North	86
Jackson, Mississippi	32° North	102
New Orleans, Louisiana	30° North	118

RELATION TO STANDING CROP

Actual data on the relationship between production (as expressed by fish yields) and the standing crops of fishes are as yet inadequate to test Thompson's theory as expressed in Table 4.3. Where data on yields and standing crops are available for comparison, there are other factors that obscure a clear relationship, such as fishing pressure, apparent uncooperativeness on the part of fish, known differences in food chains, etc. For example, the yields of bass at Ridge Lake were influenced more by the presence or absence of available foods than by fishing pressure [10]; but even in years when the highest yields were taken (about 65 or 70 per cent of the available weight of bass in the lake), there was no indication that these yields reduced potential yields for following seasons.

A recent study of a smallmouth bass population in a gravel-pit pond [11] that produced hook-and-line yields of more than 100 pounds per acre for two successive years and then in the third year produced a yield of 80 pounds per acre, suggests that the maximum annual yield of fish in the region of central Illinois may be nearer 100 per cent of the carrying capacity than 50 per cent as given by Thompson (Table 4.3). The smallmouth bass yield from this pond for any one season was almost wholly dependent upon fish spawned during the two preceding years. When the population was censused after 4 years of high yields, the standing crop at the beginning of the fifth year (fish caught by fishermen in April, May, and early June plus the fish taken in a June census of all remaining fish) was approximately 100 pounds per acre which is considered relatively high for this kind of fish in this type of water (gravel pit) in central Illinois.

Largemouth bass are less predictable than are smallmouth bass. Certainly, the fishing pressure was heavy enough at Onized Lake (Illinois)[8] in 1939 and 1940 to insure a crop of fish by hook-and-line methods, large enough to tax the production capacity of that body of water. The yield of largemouth bass here was 53.0 pounds per acre in 1939 and 19.8 pounds per acre in 1940. The weight of bass caught in April, May, and June of 1941, when added to the weight of bass taken in the total fish census of June 24, 1941, suggested that the standing crop of bass at the beginning of 1941 may have been between 50 and 60 pounds per acre or about 2.5 times the weight of bass taken in 1940 when the total fishing pressure exerted on the lake was 1647 man-hours per acre. On the basis of the 1939 yield of 53.0 pounds per acre, the carrying capacity of Onized Lake for bass could be estimated to lie between 50 and 100 pounds per acre, which is anything but specific. However, the fact that yields of largemouth bass are influenced largely by factors other than angling pressure makes it unsafe to estimate its turnover, production, or carrying capacity in a mixed population of fishes.

Bluegill yields from Onized Lake for 1939 and 1940 were 174 and 66 pounds per acre, respectively. The estimated standing crop at the beginning of 1941 was around 153 pounds per acre, which must have been considerably under the carrying capacity of Onized Lake for bluegills. More than 6500 bluegills were taken in the final census, June 24, 1941, which was more than 3200 per acre, a sufficient number of active digestive tracts to convert food to flesh quickly if an excess of food (over maintenance needs) was available.

These feeble attempts to unravel the basic relationships between standing crops, observed yields, and productive capacity in populations composed of several species of fishes emphasize the need for more data on fish populations composed entirely of one species. Current information demonstrates the validity of these concepts and their importance in understanding fish-population dynamics.

ESTIMATING PRODUCTION

A fairly close estimate of total production of fish flesh may be obtained for one or two growing seasons provided the fish are tagged or marked when released at the beginning of the period, and are collected by draining for a census at the end. In the final census, marked fish are counted to determine natural mortality, and of course fishing mortality within the period must be measured through a creel census. Marked fish in the "draining" census are weighed individually to calculate the gain in flesh made during the period. Unmarked fish are weighed, as they also represent production.

Total production equals:
   (1) flesh gained by recaptured marked fish,
plus (2) flesh produced by new recruits entering the population
plus (3) flesh gained by fish lost through natural mortality
plus (4) flesh gained by fish captured by anglers.

An estimation of flesh gained by marked fish eventually lost through natural causes may be made if one assumes that these fish remained alive for half the period in question. Under this assumption their gain per individual would equal one-half that of marked fish of a comparable size range. Loss of production through natural deaths among new recruits is an unknown quantity, although it might not represent a very large poundage of fish flesh. Estimated production in long-lived species is probably more accurate than that in short-lived species because the annual turn-over (recruitment and death rate) is smaller. Using the method outlined above for bass in Ridge Lake (Illinois) with a period limit of two years, the gains are as follows: in the the 1941-1943 period, 58.5 pounds per acre; in the 1943-1945 period, 34.2 pounds per acre; in the 1945-1947 period, 37.2 pounds per acre; in the 1947-1949 period, 59.8 pounds per acre; and in the 1949-1951 period, 53.5 pounds per acre.[10] However, these estimates of production for two-year periods cannot be used to estimate the maximum production for a single year.

RELATIVE PLUMPNESS OF FISH

Everyone who has an opportunity to handle large numbers of fish soon becomes aware of the variation in the plumpness of individual fish in any species. Usually, this variation in the relative condition of each of several species of fish inhabiting a body of water is greater than that among individuals of one species; for example, bass in a lake may be in good flesh while sunfish may be thin. While there is some variation in the plumpness of individuals of a single species at any one time, larger changes in relative plumpness for that species may follow annual cycles or even longer periods, in the latter instance perhaps reflecting variations in feeding conditions or population densities. All of these variations may be expressed numerically when weights and lengths of individual fish are used for calculating some form of condition factor.

METHODS OF MEASURING CONDITION

In order to describe the relative plumpness of a fish as a numerical value, a formula involving the relationship of surface (length) to volume (weight) is applied to the fish. The solution of this formula gives a number known as a *condition factor*, that stands for *a measurement of relative plumpness:* A fat fish of a given species and length will show a higher condition factor than a thin fish of the same species and length. By calculating these condition factors for an adequate number of fish of one species and of a limited range in length, taken from a single body of water during a limited period of time, and averaging them, one may arrive at an *average condition factor* for the species under the experimental conditions adhered to above. In this way, the range of relative plumpness for a species may be defined, and cycles of relative plumpness associated with seasonal feeding or other kinds of behavior may come to light.

Coefficient of Condition. One of the first formulas developed by fisheries workers [25] for figuring relative plumpness required the use of the weight of a fish in grams, and its standard length in centimeters (the standard length of a fish is the distance from the tip of the snout to the base of, but not including, the tail fin). In this formula K, the "Coefficient of Condition," is equal to the weight of the fish in grams times 100, divided by the cube of the standard length in centimeters, thus:

$$K = \frac{100\,W}{L^3}$$

When this formula was used for figuring the coefficient of condition for fish with laterally compressed but deep bodies, such as the white crappie, or the bluegill, the numerical value of K usually ranged from 2.00 to 4.00. Fishes with bodies of lesser depth, such as the largemouth bass, usually had K values ranging from 1.00 to 3.00. The numerical values for K meant nothing in themselves but allowed comparisons between individuals or groups of fishes.

Index of Condition. The use of the Coefficient of Condition K had one great drawback, namely that the average fisherman and even most fisheries biologists were unable to "think" of fish in terms either of weight in grams or of body lengths (without tails) in centimeters.[26] Fishermen were used to measuring the maximum length of a fish with its mouth closed and the tail pinched so that the longest rays of the tail were parallel to the body axis. Lengths of fish were measured in inches and fractions of inches and weights in pounds and fractions of pounds. As the numerical values derived from condition formulas are useful for comparisons only, Thompson and Bennett [40] developed a new condition formula in which the total length of a fish was taken in inches and tenths of inches and the weight in pounds and hundredths of pounds. This formula required neither conversions of centimeters to inches nor grams to pounds, and the entire fish was measured rather than some fraction of the total length. Tenths of inches and hundredths of pounds were used instead of quarters of inches or ounces in order to facilitate rapid calculations. The formula was as follows:

$$\text{Index of Condition, } C = \frac{10,000 \ W}{L^3}$$

where W represents weight of the fish to the nearest hundredth of a pound, and L represents total length to the nearest tenth of an inch. When calculations are made using the lengths and weights of largemouth bass between 5 and 15 inches of total length, an Index of Condition of 3.5 to 4.5 denotes a fish in poor flesh, 4.6 to 5.5 one of average plumpness, and 5.6 to 6.5 a very fat fish.

In fish such as the bluegill, which is deep in proportion to length and laterally compressed, the figures for condition are higher. In bluegills from 5 to 8 inches of total length, an Index of Condition figure of 7.0 or below denotes a fish in poor flesh, 7.1 to 8.0 one of normal plumpness, and above 8.0 one of unusual plumpness.

Condition Factor of E. M. Corbett. A system used by the English for figuring condition was the "Condition Factor" invented by E. M. Corbett and issued by the Salmon and Trout Association, Fishmongers Hall, E.C. 4, London (date unknown). Corbett used total length in inches and weight in pounds and ounces, but actually converted fractions of inches into tenths and ounces into hundredths of pounds. Using essentially the same formula as that proposed by Thompson and Bennett, Corbett multiplied his numerator by 100,000 instead of 10,000 to get rid of the decimal point. His formula is as follows:

$$\text{Condition Factor, } C.F. = \frac{100,000 \ W}{L^3}$$

where W = weight in pounds and L = length in inches. This formula gave a condition factor as a whole number. For example, a bluegill having an Index of Condition of 7.22 with the Thompson and Bennett method of calculation was equal to $C.F. = 72$ with the Corbett system.

Applying the Corbett system to bass and bluegills in South Africa, A. Cecil Harrison arrived at the same range of condition figures (times ten) for thin, average, and fat fish that Thompson and Bennett found for Illinois fish of these species.

Condition Factor of Cooper and Benson. Still another method of figuring condition is that of Cooper and Benson [20]:

$$\text{Coefficient of Condition, } R = \frac{10\,W}{L^3}$$

Where W = weight in *grams*, and
L = total length in *inches*.

This mixed method of figuring condition was used on small trout conveniently weighed in grams, whereas measuring boards were calibrated in inches and tenths.

Conversion was as follows: to the English system (*C.F.*), $R \times 22.038$ = *C.F.*; to the Thompson and Bennett system, $R \times 2.2038 = C$.

CONDITION CYCLES

Some fish species follow cycles of condition associated with seasons. For example, the bluegills in a pond in central Illinois [9] showed high condition during May and early June at the beginning of the spawning season, followed by a gradual drop in condition throughout the summer and fall until a low point was reached in October or November. Over the winter, the condition gradually rose, but the most rapid rise took place in early spring, during the months of March, April, and May, when bluegills were feeding heavily on dipterous larvae and cladocera. Some of the loss in condition of bluegills, beginning in late May and extending throughout the summer was undoubtedly associated with the long spawning season of this fish, which began in May and extended into early September.

A seasonal condition cycle for white crappies in a lake in the same region [23] was quite different from the bluegill cycle of condition. Lake Decatur (Illinois) crappies of 6 to 8.5 inches usually showed their highest condition in the fall and winter, and the condition of these fish dropped sharply from early spring to June or July. Following a low point, usually in July, the condition of the crappies began to rise in August and continued to rise until winter.

Several studies on condition in largemouth bass suggest that these fish show no seasonal cycle of plumpness. There is evidence, however, that the average condition of a bass population may change rather suddenly with changing feeding conditions. For example, in 1941 at the time of an extensive natural die-off of the pond weed, *P. foliosus*, in a pond,[9] the bass had an average condition of 5.00. After the plant die-off began, they became very fat and their average condition rose to 6.15,

CONDITION AND GROWTH RATE

High condition of fishes is usually associated with rapid growth, but this is not always so, particularly where fish are living in very soft water in which there may be such a shortage of calcium as to curtail the growth of the fishes' skeleton. In some other locations, relatively rapid growth seems to be associated with moderately low condition, at least during a part of a year.

USE OF CONDITION IN MANAGEMENT

An important value of condition factors is in their use in determining the well-being of a fish population in which one has a special interest, either as a sport fisherman or as a lake owner. Often, when fish are in poor condition (exclusive of lows of normal cycles), it may mean over-population or disease. A high condition may mean a sparse population or a high temporary food supply. When either of the extremes of condition may appear, the situation may bear investigation.

The condition of any component of a population of fishes is related to the relative abundance of food for that group, and this relative abundance of food may be related to high natural food production of the aquatic habitat; but more especially to the number of individuals among which a specific quantity of food must be divided. Thus, rapid growth, high condition, and large average size of a species may be essentially a function of natural or artificial cropping, because the type and intensity of cropping that occurs may determine the amount of food an individual fish is able to gather in a given period of time.

Average condition figures have been calculated for most species of fresh-water fishes of interest to anglers.[15] These condition figures may be used by lake and pond owners as well as fishery biologists as a basis for comparison with the condition of fish that are members of a local population.

GROWTH

Although a new-born Great Dane or Chihuahua pup may be expected to grow to a rather definite size within a period of about a year and then remain the same size throughout the rest of its life, no amount of wholesome food would cause a Chihuahua to approach the size of a Great Dane, nor would a severe shortage of food prevent a Great Dane pup from greatly exceeding the size of a mature Chihuahua in the one-year period.

However, growth in fishes is unlike growth in most warm-blooded animals in that it is relatively indeterminate and follows no exact pattern of attaining a maximum size in relation to a specific length of time. Thus,

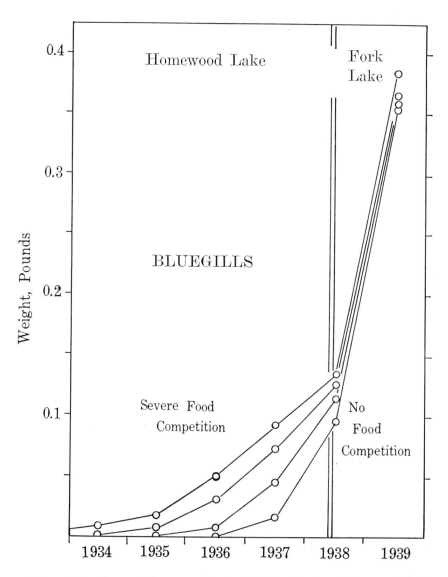

Figure 4.4. Three- to five-year-old stunted bluegills from Homewood Lake (Illinois) more than tripled their weight in one season after release in Fork Lake where adequate food was available. [From Bennett, G. W., Thompson, D. H., and Parr, S., *Ill. Nat. Hist. Surv. Biol. Notes*, 14 (1940)]

although every species of fish probably is characterized by a maximum size (length and weight), this size is so much greater than the *average* maximum attained by any given individual of any selected species in most waters that fishing contests with prizes for the largest examples of each kind of fish have flourished and will continue to flourish as long as man is interested in angling.

Growth stoppage in fishes is not associated with sexual maturity as it is in most warm-blooded animals, and fishes continue to grow throughout life, although growth is relatively slower in larger and older fishes than in smaller and younger ones.

Effects of Starvation

Under conditions of near-starvation, fishes may remain the same size for an indefinite period, and after months or years of life on a maintenance diet, they still retain the capacity to grow rapidly to large average sizes should an abundance of food suddenly become available.[9, 41] This was demonstrated with bluegills when fish 3 to 5 years old and averaging 0.08 pound each were moved into a renovated pond where food competition was probably absent (Figure 4.4). The fish grew to average about 0.40 pound each in one growing season, although they had been badly stunted in past years.

Growth of Fish in New Waters

Fish often grow rapidly and reach exceptionally large sizes when first introduced into new waters. This superior growth is largely due to an abundance of food and space and possibly an absence of parasites and other biological forces which may slow down the rate of growth in waters where these fish have been present for some years.

One of the most interesting of introductions was that of the importation of certain game and food fishes from Europe and North America into the waters of South Africa.[1, 2, 3] The importation of trouts into South Africa came early with the brown trout in 1892 and the rainbow in 1897. Introductions of exotic fishes were carp from England in 1896, European perch in 1915, and largemouth bass from an English hatchery in 1927. Fish importations to South Africa from the United States were smallmouth bass from Maryland in 1937, bluegills from Maryland in 1938, and spotted bass from Ohio in 1939. The live-bearing top minnow gambusia appeared in South Africa in 1936 from an unknown source. Following are some records of catches of warm-water fishes of known ages, that had been stocked in South African waters:

A largemouth bass caught on January 19, 1949, by Mr. D. S. Stewart and reported by Mr. H. Manson, Hon. Secretary of the White River Angling Society, was 23 inches long, girth 17 inches and weight 7 pounds

10 ounces. Growth calculations from scale measurements indicated a growth to 9 inches the first year, then 15 inches, 18, 20, 21, 22 and 23 inches; its age was 7 years plus part of an additional summer. Official record largemouth bass from Paarde Vlei Lake, Sommerset West, in July, 1936, weighed 5 pounds 1 ounce, was 19 inches long and was stocked in 1930 as a fingerling. These bass growth records are similar to examples of maximum growth for largemouth in northern United States (increment of about one pound per year), but no example of largemouths of 8 to 10 pounds which are fairly common in the United States has been recorded for South Africa. This may be related to the genetics of the original stock, the source of which (in the U. S.) is unknown.

A bluegill was caught on March 17, 1947, by Mr. H. F. Palmer that weighed 3 pounds 1 ounce in a dam (pond) at Butha Buthe in Basutoland. "The fish could not swim upright in 9 inches of water." It could not have been more than 8 years old because the first bluegills were imported in 1938 and the first fingerlings were distributed in 1939. At least one bluegill exceeding three pounds is recorded for the United States, so here again maximum sizes may be comparable in South Africa and North America.

FACTORS AFFECTING RATE OF GROWTH

In comparing growth rates of fishes in various parts of the United States, fisheries biologists have emphasized the importance of (1) the genetic growth potential of a given species, (2) a large available food supply per individual fish, (3) and the length of the growing season, *e.g.*, length of the period when the water is warm enough to allow rapid digestion and assimilation of food. All of these growth-controlling factors are important, but *in the production of fishes of above average size, a large source of available food per individual fish seems to exceed in importance the length of the growing season* (Figure 4.5). Often a large supply of available food is present for the few fish that are restocked in renovated lakes, and they grow phenomenally during the first season before population expansion has reduced the food supply per individual fish.[22]

In studying the growth of largemouth and smallmouth bass in Norris Reservoir, Jones[28] concluded that although the agricultural growing season at Knoxville, Tennessee, was almost 7 months, the bass growing season was only 4 months. He assumed that because the bass stopped growing they could not grow after late September or early October, even though the water was still warm. Jones apparently misinterpreted the effects of what presumably was a temporary fall shortage of bass foods in Norris Reservoir, and he assumed that these effects represented a definite bass growing season which was much shorter than the agricultural growing season. Others have shown that bass may grow rapidly during

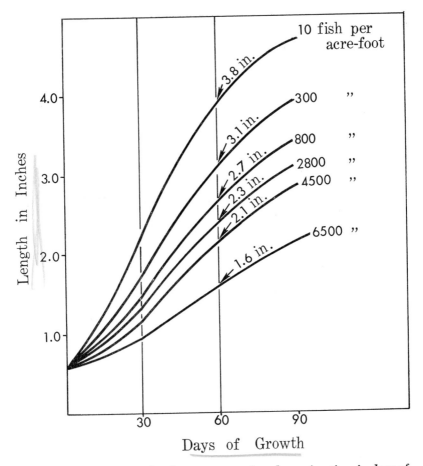

Figure 4.5. Relationship between growth and growing time in days of small walleyes in ponds, showing population density in fish per acre-foot. These growth curves are actually a measure of relative abundance of food. [From Dobie, J., *Prog. Fish-Cult.*, 18(2) (1956)]

April, September, and October in waters several hundred miles north of Norris, Tennessee, provided the water is above 60°F and an abundance of food is available.[9] The length of the growing season for fishes which rather closely parallels the agricultural growing season, but is somewhat shorter, limits the annual growth cycle to a definite period of weeks or months (Figure 4.3). The amount of growth actually taking place during this time depends (within limits) upon available food resources. At one extreme, a fish might approach the maximum rate of gain for a given species in a location where food was abundant and the growing season was less than 3 months; at the other extreme, a fish might remain at a constant weight throughout a growing season of 8 or 9 months if it were living under conditions that furnished no more than a maintenance diet. There are aspects of a short growing season that may have an important bearing on management practices. In some Michigan waters where the length of the growing season does not exceed 5 months and ice and snow cover the lakes for 4 or 5 months, bluegills seldom mature sexually until the third summer of life.[7] This means that all phases of management that bear any relationship to time of sexual maturity of the fishes must be adjusted accordingly.

Viosca [42] described the growth of warm-water fishes—largemouth bass, spotted bass, and crappies—in the International Paper Company reservoir at Springhill, Louisiana, where the growth period for these fishes is limited by draining and refilling operations rather than the length of the natural growing season. The lake basin (270 acres) is pumped full in April and May, and newly-hatched fry are brought in with the water. The lake is drained in September or October to make room for waste water from the paper mill so the growing season for fry of various fishes ranges from 5.5 to 6.5 months. Fish that enter the reservoir through the pumps as fry in April and May produce a "field day" for anglers by late summer. In 1949, largemouth bass (age group 0) ranged from 11.1 to 13.8 inches and 11.4 to 24.5 ounces; spotted bass (10 times as numerous as largemouth) ranged from 6.1 to 10.6 inches and 1.4 to 11.6 ounces. In 1950, crappies reached sizes as large as 9.8 inches and weights of 12 ounces in 6.5 months. These crappies averaged a weight increment of 1.8 ounces per month, which is very near their maximum rate of growth. The accumulation of nutrients from the decayed paper waste added to the productivity of this reservoir.

There is evidence, both from laboratory feeding experiments and field studies,[12] that fish supplied with quantities of one or several live foods alternate between periods (weeks) of heavy feeding with rapid growth and periods of little or no food consumption with subsequent growth stoppage. Fish, like other animals, find a heavy diet without variety unattractive.

In the laboratory experiments cited above, bluegills that stopped feeding were being fed earthworms at the rate of 7 to 8 per cent of their body weight per day. However, other bluegills receiving earthworms in smaller quantity (3 to 5 per cent of body weight per day) did not stop feeding.

A continuous study of the ecology and growth of one or several species making up a small fish population will show that there are times when certain types of food are abnormally abundant and that this abundance is often reflected in unusual growth. For example, in August, 1941, a sudden die-off of heavy growths of submerged aquatic plants in a pond in central Illinois [9] was followed during August, September, and October of 1941 by a rapid growth of largemouth bass. These plants were protecting a large population of small fish which suddenly became easily available. Bass that were between 10.5 and 11.0 inches before the plant die-off, averaged 13.0 inches in October; those about 7.0 to 8.0 inches before the die-off averaged 10.5 inches in October; and the surviving members of the current year class averaged nearly 6.5 inches by October. No comparable growth rate increase was shown among bluegills, even though the pond developed a bloom of plankton algae following the death of the higher aquatic plants. In this instance, a large supply of food suddenly became available to the bass with no comparable increase in foods for bluegills. The cause of death of the rooted aquatic plants was unknown, but its effect was highly favorable to a species of fish having little direct ecological relationship to aquatic plants.

INTERPRETATION OF GROWTH FROM FISH SCALES

Variations in growth rates and the occurrence of growth stoppage are recorded on the scales of the fishes. When a fish is growing rapidly, the circuli (fine lines of new material) laid down on the edges of the scales are relatively coarse and spaced far apart; on the other hand, when growth is slow, the circuli are fine and close together. A fish subjected to a period of starvation not only loses body flesh, but erosion with resorption of material on the edges of the scales may also take place. However, on a maintenance diet where the condition of a fish remains constant, there appears to be neither increment nor erosion of the scales. Thus, the correct interpretation of the marks on the scale surface will give an accurate growth history of a fish.

The years of a fish's life are recorded as a series of annuli or distinct rings laid down around the focus or center of the scale, each one representing a year. The circuli are between the focus of the scale and the first annulus and are also between the other annuli. A newly-hatched fish may be scaleless, but if it is of a scaled species, the scales soon form. Once the fish becomes covered with scales, the number remains constant throughout life, and to form a covering for the fish, the scales must grow as the body grows. Any natural or artificial phenomenon that will stop feeding and growth of a fish for about 14 days or longer will be followed, once growth is resumed, by the appearance of an "annulus," on the margin of the scales. The so-called "true annulus" was first called a winter ring because it was not visible until new circuli were laid down in the spring when the fish had resumed growth. Further studies of annulus formation showed that some fishes in some locations did not begin to grow until the middle of summer [23] so that the winter ring became a summer ring. Hubbs and Cooper [27] recorded a double annulus in green and long-eared sun-

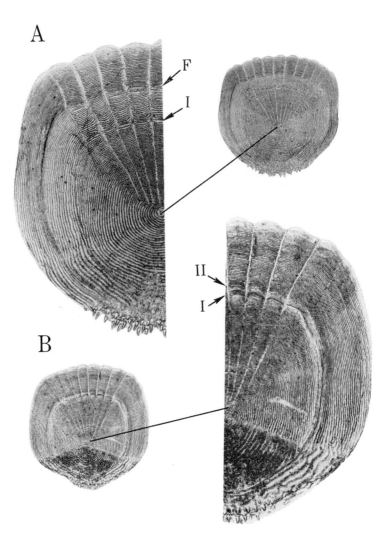

Figure 4.6. Abnormal growth rings on fish scales. A. Yearling bluegill from Fork Lake, 1938 year-class, taken September 22, 1939, age 16 months, showing well-defined annulus (I) and false annulus (F). The false annulus was formed on this scale about July. B. Largemouth bass, 10.1 inches, weight 0.49 pound, female taken April 20, 1941, before the 1941 annulus had formed. This is a 1938 year-class fish in which the 1939 annulus (I) and the 1940 annulus (II) are separated only in the anterior field of the scale.

fishes in Michigan. They believed that the outside member of the double ring was the true annulus, whereas this outer ring in actuality probably was a mark laid down during the first early peak of spawning.

The 1938-brood bluegills at Fork Lake (Illinois) [9] were growing very rapidly in 1939 and during the summer growing period of that year, many members of this brood laid down two or three distinct "annuli" on their scales (Figure 4.6a): formation of the true annulus was completed by the last of May; the second annulus (false) first became visible during the latter part of June and the third annulus (false) appeared on the scales of a small per cent of the population in July and August. There was no satisfactory method of separating false from true annuli.[12] It is my belief that the false annuli appeared on the scales of the Fork Lake bluegills because they went "off their feed" for short periods.

Some abnormalities of growth, which are reflected on the scales of a fish and cause difficulty in the correct interpretation of age and growth, are:

(1) *False annuli*—false rings having all of the characteristics of true annuli, but which form during the middle of the growing period and after the true annulus has formed for the current year (Figure 4.6a).

(2) *Skipped annuli*—where the position of the annulus for one year coincides with that of the preceding year, *e.g.* the fish does not grow during one growing season (Figure 4.7b).

(3) *Overlapping annuli*—where growth in length through one growing season is very small with no corresponding increase in plumpness. The annulus for one year coincides in part with that of the next, but in part (usually in the anterior field) is separated by 4 or 5 circuli (Figure 4.6b). Without detailed growth information, a scale reader is likely to consider the second component of the double ring as a false annulus.

(4) *Close spacing of annuli*—where growth for one season is small and two annuli are separated entirely, but by only a few circuli. Without growth information, a scale reader is liable to consider the outer annulus as false.

Scales, spines, bones, and otoliths of fishes have been used successfully in age determinations. Studies of these parts from fishes of known ages prove that most species usually lay down a single growth ring each year. However, there are some exceptions, such as European carp, which frequently form extra "annuli." But even the scales of carp may be interpreted on the basis of "growth patterns" for successive growing seasons, provided a specific population is being studied intensively over a period of several years.

In the wake of the many excellent studies on the age and growth of fishes, the methodology for using scales (and other structures such as ear stones, vertebrae, spines, and opercular bones that show annual rings)

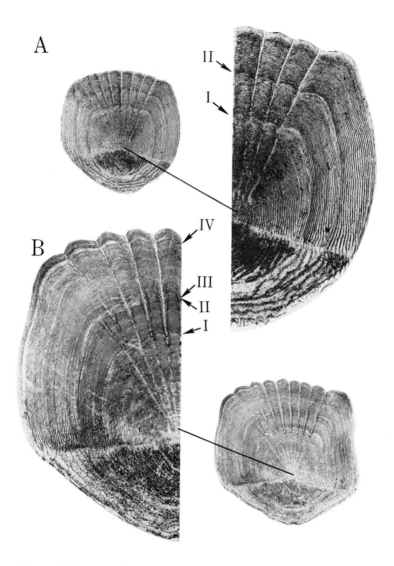

Figure 4.7. Normal and abnormal growth rings on largemouth bass scales. A. Normal scale pattern for 1938 year-class largemouth bass in Fork Lake (Illinois) after 2+ years of growth. This bass was 9.6 inches, weighed 0.45 pound, a male taken August 30, 1940. B. A 1938 year-class bass in which the second (II) and third (III) annuli coincide. This fish was 15 inches, weighed 2 pounds, a female taken July 8, 1942 from Fork Lake. This could not have been a 1939 year-class fish because there was no 1939 year-class in this pond (1938 year-class original fry were sexually immature in 1939).

in an interpretation of growth, has become standardized.[15] In this chapter, *the abnormalities of growth have been stressed because the more one knows about a population of fishes the more accurate one's interpretation of growth.* For example, Dr. R. W. Larimore found a mark on the scales of Vernard Lake warmouths [29] that corresponded in time to a period when a drag line was dredging the shallows of the pond from which these warmouths were taken. Without a series of fish collections before and after the drag line operation, it would have been impossible to explain the "false annulus" that appeared on the scales of many warmouths, apparently caused by the "feeding disturbance" resulting from the operation of the drag line.

There is more to reading scales than counting rings. One must become familiar with the usual variations in the marks and ridges on scales of specific species, as well as the potential for abnormalities on these scales and causes for the abnormalities.

LITERATURE

1. Anon., *Inland Fisheries Dept., Union of So. Africa, Cape Town,* **1**, 1-47 (1945).
2. Anon., *Jour. Cape Pisc. Soc.,* **1**(2), 14 (1947).
3. Anon., *Jour. Cape Pisc. Soc.,* **3**(9), 12-14 (1949).
4. Ball, R. C., *Am. Fish. Soc. Trans.,* **75**, 36-42 (1948).
5. Ball, R. C., *Jour. Wildl. Mgt.,* **16**(3), 267-269 (1952).
6. Ball, R. C., and Ford, J. R., *Agri. Exp. Sta. Mich. St. Coll. Bull.,* **35**(3), 384-391 (1953).
7. Ball, R. C., and Tait, H. D., *Mich. St. Coll. Agr. Exp. Sta., Tech. Bull.,* **231**, 1-25 (1952).
8. Bennett, G. W., *Ill. Nat. Hist. Surv. Bull.,* **23**(3), 373-406 (1945).
9. Bennett, G. W., *Ill. Nat. Hist. Surv. Bull.,* **24**(3), 377-412 (1948).
10. Bennett, G. W., *Ill. Nat. Hist. Surv. Bull.,* **26**(2), 217-276 (1954).
11. Bennett, G. W., and Childers, W. F., *Jour. Wildl. Mgt.,* **21**(4), 414-424 (1957).
12. Bennett, G. W., Thompson, D. H., and Parr, S. A., *Ill. Nat. Hist. Surv. Biol. Notes,* **14**, 1-24 (1940).
13. Boccius, G., "A Treatise on the Management of Fresh-Water Fish," J. Van Voorst, London, 1841.
14. Brown, W. H., *Tex. Game, Fish and Oyster Comm.,* 1-21 (1951).
15. Carlander, K. D., "Handbook of Freshwater Fishery Biology with the First Supplement," pp. 1-429, Dubuque, Iowa, Wm. C. Brown, Inc., 1953.
16. Carlander, K. D., *Jour. Fish. Res. Bd. of Can.,* **12**(4), 543-570 (1955).
17. Carlander, K. D., and Moorman, R. B., *Proc. of the Iowa Acad. of Sci.,* **63**, 659-668 (1956).
18. Clark, G. L., *Ecol. Mono.,* **16**, 321-335 (1946).
19. Clark, M., *Jour. Wildl. Mgt.,* **16**(3), 262-266 (1952).
20. Cooper, E. L., and Benson, N. G., *Prog. Fish-Cult.,* **13**(4), 181-192 (1951).

21. Cooper, G. P., and Latta, W. C., *Pap. Mich. Acad. Sci., Arts & Letts.*, **39**, 209-223 (1954).

22. Grice, F., *Am. Fish Soc. Trans.*, **88**(4), 332-335 (1959).

23. Hansen, D. F., *Ill. Nat. Hist. Surv. Bull.*, **25**(4), 211-265 (1951).

24. Hansen, D. F., Bennett, G. W., Webb, R. J., and Lewis, J. M., *Ill. Nat. Hist. Surv. Bull.*, **27**(5), 345-390 (1960).

25. Hile, R., *U.S. Bur. Fish. Bull.*, **48**(19), 211-317 (1936).

26. Hile, R., *Am. Fish. Soc. Trans.*, **75**, 157-164 (1948).

27. Hubbs, C. L., and Cooper, G. P., *Pap. Mich. Acad. Sci., Arts & Letts.*, **20**, 669-696 (1935).

28. Jones, A. M., *Am. Fish. Soc. Trans.*, **70**, 183-187 (1941).

29. Larimore, R. W., *Ill. Nat. Hist. Surv. Bull.*, **27**, 1-83 (1957).

30. Leopold, A., "Game Management," pp. 1-481, Chas. Scribner's Sons, New York, 1933.

31. Markus, H. C., *Am. Fish. Soc. Trans.*, **62**, 202-210 (1932).

32. Moyle, J. B., *Jour. Wildl. Mgt.*, **20**(3), 303-320 (1956).

33. Swingle, H. S., *Ag. Exp. Sta. Ala. Poly. Inst. Bull.*, **264**, 1-34 (1947).

34. Swingle, H. S., *Jour. Wildl. Mgmt.*, **16**(3), 243-249 (1952).

35. Swingle, H. S., and Smith, E. V., *Ala. Poly. Inst. Ag. Exp. Sta., Mimeo*, 1-6 (1938).

36. Swingle, H. S., and Smith, E. V., *N. A. Wildl. Conf. Trans.*, **4**, 332-338 (1939).

37. Swingle, H. S., and Smith, E. V., *Ag. Exp. Sta. Ala. Poly. Inst. Bull.*, **254**, 1-30 (1947).

38. Tanner, H. A., *Am. Fish. Soc. Trans.*, **89**(2), 198-205 (1960).

39. Thompson, D. H., "A Symposium on Hydrobiology," pp. 206-217, Univ. of Wis. Press, Madison, Wis., 1941.

40. Thompson, D. H., and Bennett, G. W., *Ill. Nat. Hist. Surv. Biol. Notes*, **11**, 1-24 (1939).

41. Tiemeier, O. W., *Kan. Acad. Sci. Trans.*, **60**(3), 294-296 (1957).

42. Viosca, P., Jr., *Am. Fish. Soc. Trans.*, **82**, 255-264 (1953).

43. Williams, W. E., *Am. Fish. Soc. Trans.*, **88**(2), 125-127 (1959).

5 ~~~~~
Reproduction, Competition, and Predation

If the habitat is suitable for fish, the success of various components of a fish population may depend upon the interrelationships of three forces, namely, reproduction, competition, and predation. Reproduction produces new individuals, not only to replace losses of mature animals but also to enter the trophic cycle—the young fishes feeding on lesser animals and themselves becoming food for other larger ones. Thus, the products of *reproduction* push the population *toward expansion.* In opposition, the forces of *competition* (inter-specific and intra-specific) and *predation* tend to *counteract population expansion.* This interrelationship of reproduction, competition, and predation is normal and necessary to the well being of the population, although considerable variations exist. Thus, some populations, that appear engaged in a constant struggle for existence, may show comparatively little fluctuation from year to year in actual number of surviving individuals. However, other populations may require a cycle of two or more years to achieve maximum abundance, while still others may fluctuate irregularly between maximum and minimum limits.

Geological evidence has shown that fishes have existed on the earth's surface for many millions of years. Yet in spite of the fact that they have furnished food for many forms of vertebrates—fishes, amphibians, reptiles, birds, and mammals including man—and some kinds of invertebrates, they must be considered as one of the more successful groups of vertebrates. A number of species of fishes alive today are scarcely changed in form from those found as fossils in deposits representing the Devonian Period, 360 million years ago.

REPRODUCTION

Most of the vertebrates that prey upon fishes are more recent (geologically speaking) than their victims. Thus, it is conceivable that as predators of fishes evolved and accumulated, the reproductive potential of fishes expanded to compensate for greater and greater losses through predation, until the reproductive potential became very high. Less than 100 years ago in the United States man began to dominate other vertebrates, and he purposely or inadvertently upset the normal relationships between fish predators and their prey. The high reproductive potential of a fish without an accompanying high predation rate became a detriment to the well-being of a fish species in that too many individuals survived for the available food supply. This high reproductive potential of fishes has remained unchanged, and its significance must be appreciated in any plan for the management of a species.

REPRODUCTIVE POTENTIAL OF FISHES

Common warm-water fishes produce numbers of eggs in an inverse relationship to the amount of protection that they give the sex products after they are released. In species such as the European carp which offer no protection to its sex products, a single female may produce several hundred thousand eggs. In contrast, the stickleback, which builds a complicated nest of plant material and then actively guards it, may lay a few hundred eggs. Between these extremes are the sunfishes depositing their eggs in depressions which they have made in the river or lake bottom and then attempting to guard against the predatory activities of their own kind, and other kinds of aquatic predators. Here the number of eggs is intermediate, ranging from 5000 to 10,000 in largemouth and smallmouth basses to 20,000 to 50,000 in the crappies and larger sunfishes. Jenkins [40] cited an example in which 50 adult crappies with a reproduction potential of 590,000 produced a population of one-year-old fish of 200,500.

Actual counts of eggs produced by various kinds of warm-water fishes have demonstrated that the reproductive potential of every species is more than adequate to replace the losses of the adults that produced them. For example, one pair of bluegills may easily produce 50,000 to 75,000 fertile eggs in a life time. The survival of only two of these embryos, through development, hatching, and growth to sexual maturity, is necessary to replace the loss of the parents.

In order to investigate the success of natural reproduction of some common nest-building fishes, Carbine [18] siphoned off the fry from the nests of largemouth bass, rock bass, common sunfish, and bluegills in Deep Lake, Oakland County, Michigan, and made counts of the number of fry collected from each nest. He found that numbers of largemouth bass fry varied between 751 and 11,457, with an average of 4375 per nest (5 nests); rock bass from 344 to 1756 with an average of 796 per nest (9 nests); common sunfish 1509 and 14,639 per nest (2 nests); and bluegills from 4670 to 61,815 per nest with an average of 17,914 (17 nests). On the basis of the number of nests being used by these centrarchids during the 1938 season, the minimum number of fry produced in Deep Lake (surface area 14.9 acres) was estimated as follows: bluegill 6,610,-000; common sunfish 1,518,000; rock bass 46,000; and largemouth bass 164,000. As this lake probably would not support a fish population of more than 8000 to 10,000 individuals of useful sizes, it is obvious that any one of the 4 species listed above produced enough young fish in 1938 to overpopulate the lake.

Other pan and sport fishes produce large numbers of eggs. Female warmouths ranging in size from 3.5 to 7.0 inches contained from 4500 to more than 50,000 eggs per fish.[52] The female walleyes in Lake Gogebic (Michigan) [29] ranging from 16.0 to 22.7 inches yielded from 37,000 to nearly 155,000 eggs per fish. On the average, 34 walleye females from Gogebic yielded 28,112 eggs per pound of body weight. Wisconsin muskellunge from 25 to 53 inches in length were reported to produce 22,000 to 180,000 eggs per fish at each spawning, and northern pike are known to produce about the same numbers.[60]

As mentioned above, only a small fraction of the young produced by any fish species survives. For example, in the spring of 1941, Ridge Lake, Coles County, Illinois (18 acres), was stocked with 100 sexually mature largemouth bass.[11] Thirty-eight schools of young were observed in early June, each containing at least 2000 individual free-swimming fry; a conservative estimate of the total was 76,000. When the lake was drained in March, 1943, almost 2 years later, slightly more than 4000 of these young bass were still present and even with this number, Ridge Lake was overpopulated with bass.

Heaviest predation probably takes place during the first few weeks of life when the fish are very small and relatively helpless. This was substantiated by studies on the spawning of northern pike in Houghton Lake (Michigan) in 1939 and 1940.[19] Weirs were installed to catch fish in the spawning migration of northern pike into the ditches tributary to the north bay of Houghton Lake and to trap the returning young pike from the ditches. In 1939, 125 female and 280 male adult pike migrated into the ditches, and 7239 young pike were caught migrating toward the lake. In 1940, 65 females and 81 males migrated into the ditches, and only 1495 young migrated out. In both years, newly-hatched pike fry were about equally abundant in the ditches, but in 1939, minnows and perch were allowed to migrate into the ditches on only one day, while in 1940, minnows and perch could enter the ditches during the entire period of the investigation. In 1939, 58 young per spawning female returned, while in 1940 this dropped to 23.

Predation on young fish begins in the embryo stages and continues through one or two growing seasons for the slow-growing or small species. Predators large enough to use fast-growing large species for prey may be relatively rare after the first few months of growth.

Spawn Production and Number of Spawners

If natural reproduction of fishes is so successful, why have populations of many important game and food fishes continued to dwindle? The answer seems to be that although many more young of these fishes are produced than a body of water may support, the survival rate of these young between the time that they first begin to develop and the time when they grow too large for easy predation is inadequate to balance the natural and accidental death rates of adults. Fish embryos and newly-hatched fry are vulnerable to many decimating forces: sudden temperature changes, disease, absence of adequate food, turbidity, aquatic fungi, and fluctuating water levels, and a host of aquatic animals that would use them for food. There are many "accidents" that may eliminate very small fish.

Carbine's study of predation by perch on the young of northern pike, described above, is a concrete example of interspecific predation which may have been the most important cause for a reduction of northern pike in Houghton Lake. In many situations where the survival of spawn of an important species of fish is inadequate to maintain a population of these fish, no amount of stocking will help because (1) hatchery-reared fish small enough to be supplied in quantity are more vulnerable to predation than naturally spawned fish of the same sizes, and (2) fish too large to be preyed upon by most kinds of predators can be reared in such small numbers in hatchery ponds that they are insignificant when they are released in large natural waters (Houghton Lake has an area of 20,044 acres).

Predation rates may vary from very high to very low, while reproductive potentials remain uniformly high. The end result of these counter forces is to obscure the relationship between number (or poundage) of spawning adults and the number of young produced (Figure 5.1). For example, suppose that in a given spawning season the survival rate of bass fry (to a length of one inch) from 10 spawning pairs was 90 per cent and the average number of eggs produced was 2000 per female. Thus,

$$10 \times .90 \times 2000 = 18,000 \text{ fry produced.}$$

In another year, the spawn of 100 pairs of bass producing an average of 2000 eggs per female was subject to such heavy predation that the survival rate was only 5 per cent. Thus,

$$100 \times .05 \times 2000 = 10{,}000 \text{ fry produced.}$$

In these illustrations, twenty spawners in the first spawning season would produce more 1-inch fry than would 200 spawners in the following season.

Figure 5.1. Production of carp in small ponds at Lake Mills, Wisconsin. These experiments demonstrate that there is no consistent relationship between the number of adult fish stocked (pounds) and poundage of young carp produced. The poundage of young brought forth by the smallest poundage of adults usually equals or exceeds the poundage of young produced by larger numbers of adults (pounds). Also, the total poundage of all carp produced in individual ponds is not consistent from year to year. [From Mraz, D., and Cooper, E. L., *Jour. Wildlife Mangt.*, 21(1) (1957)]

In comparing annual estimates of schooling bass fry with the numbers of sexually mature bass known to be present in Ridge Lake in each of 10 years (1941-1951), I was unable to show any correlation between number of spawners and the fry produced other than an indication of a negative relationship, e.g., in several years when the numbers of spawners were smaller than average, the numbers of fry produced were larger than average.[11] Mraz and Cooper [58] also found little correlation between the number of brood fish stocked in ponds and the strength of the resulting year classes (Figure 5.1).

AGE AND SEXUAL MATURITY

The age of a fish at the time of sexual maturity varies with its size and the latitude of its habitat. According to Swingle and Smith,[77] bluegills as small as one-half ounce have been known to spawn when 1 year old (in Alabama) and where food was extremely plentiful, young bluegills weighing 2 ounces spawned when only 5 months old. Largemouth bass as small as 6 ounces and crappies as small as 2 ounces have been known to spawn when 1 year old (Alabama).

Eschmeyer [28] stated that some of the largemouth taken from the Clinch River below Norris Dam (Tennessee) would probably have spawned at 1 year of age.

Farther north in central Illinois, James [38] making a histological study of the gonads of largemouth bass and bluegills concluded that while a few male bass produced small numbers of sperm at 1 year, none of the females produced mature eggs. Many of the yearling bass that James studied were more than 10 inches in length and weighed 0.50 to 0.60 pound each. The larger and medium-sized 1-year-old bluegills produced mature eggs or sperm, but those less than 2 inches contained only small oocytes, indicating that they were sexually immature.

North American centrarchids imported to South Africa have had their seasons reversed and some showed rapid attainment of sexual maturity.[33] Smallmouth bass reproduced at 17 months and bluegills at 7 months when their seasons were reversed south of the equator. These fish originated in Maryland and Ohio.

In the north central states, most of the common game and pan fish require one year (bluegill, rock bass), two years (crappie, largemouth, smallmouth), or three years (northern pike, walleye) to reach sexual maturity. The age of a fish at sexual maturity is important in planning stocking rates for new or renovated lakes or ponds.

SEX RATIOS

Most studies of sex ratios of the individuals composing isolated populations of fresh-water fishes have shown that more males than females are to be found among the young of the year, but among older fish the dominance of females was so great as to leave little doubt that the males die off much faster than females. This is not only true in the pike and perch families but also in some of the nest-building centrarchids.[31]

EXTERNAL SEX CHARACTERISTICS

In many kinds of fresh-water fish, secondary sex characteristics develop as the adult fishes approach the spawning season. These characteristics make it possible to separate the sexes, either through differences in coloration (Figure 5.2), or through structural differences (such as tubercules on the heads of some male cyprinids or a complete change in body appearance in some male channel catfish and salmonids). In many species, male secondary sex characteristics are so definite as to make

Figure 5.2. Sexual dimorphism in hybrid crappies. During the spawning season the male crappie (lower) becomes very dark, particularly on the head, ventral side, and fins.

accurate sexing of males easy; in others only long experience can develop proficiency in sex determination. An ability to separate the sexes may be useful and important when stocking new or renovated waters because it allows one to set up balanced or unbalanced sex ratios of selected kinds of fish; also, one may be relatively certain of the sex of individuals released in ponds for the production of hybrids between two closely related species.

SPAWNING

Nearly all of the warm-water fish begin spawning during the first 6 months of the year; some have short spawning periods lasting only a few days; others may spawn for 1 or 2 weeks, while still others may spawn intermittently over a period as long as 3 or 4 months.

Among the earliest spawners is the northern pike which spawns at water temperatures of 40° to 46°F. Walleyes spawn at 45° to 50°F, yellow perch a little after walleyes and muskellunge at 48° to 56°F.[44] The pikes, walleyes, and perch begin spawning soon after the ice goes out in the early spring. Eschmeyer[29] described the spawning of walleyes at Lake Gogebic (Michigan): "At Lake Gogebic walleyes arrived on the spawning shoals immediately after the break-up of the ice in the spring. Usually they occurred in small numbers at first, followed by rapidly increasing numbers as the water warmed. . . .

"Almost all spawning activity which has been observed at Lake Gogebic has occurred within the shallow-water strip along the shoreline —exposed by the lowered water level. . . . The entire shoreline along which spawning occurs is densely wooded and is washed almost continuously by waves as a result of its exposure to the prevailing northwest winds. . . . Since spawning occurred almost exclusively at night, much of the activity of fish on the shoals was observed with an automobile spotlight powered by a storage battery carried in the rowboat from which the observations were made. The eyes of walleyes reflect light, to appear as bright orange-red globes, thus greatly facilitating the location of fish on the shoals.

"Walleye spawning seasons reported by other workers in various localities extend from late March to early June, but always include a portion of April or May."

The nesting habits of the sunfishes (including largemouth and smallmouth basses and black and white crappies) are among the most interesting of warm-water fishes. Breder[14] described the nesting behaviour of many members of this family. Some nest in groups, such as bluegills which select areas of shallow water 1 to 4 feet in depth and exposed to the direct rays of the sun for at least a part of the day. Here they scoop out their shallow nests often located so close together that only a narrow ridge of earth separates one nest from others surrounding it. Bluegills have a long nesting season; Fork Lake (Illinois) bluegills became ripe in late May and some ripe fish were collected every month thereafter until mid-September. Bluegills usually show two peaks of spawning activity, the first and largest at the beginning of the spawning season and a second peak a month or so later, usually in early July in the north. However, some bluegill reproduction continued throughout most of their long spawning period. Some warmouths were found to be in spawning condition from about May 15 until August 15 in central Illinois[52] although no fish were completely spent until September 1.

Both largemouth bass and crappies have short spawning seasons compared to bluegills and other sunfish, although the spawning period of crappies is somewhat longer than that of the largemouth.[31] Crappies and largemouth begin spawning in late May or June in the north, but some-what earlier in the south. The water temperature seems to have an im-portant effect in initiating spawning activity of all the centrarchids. Also, sudden drops in water temperature associated with periods of cold spring weather may stop all spawning activity and sometimes kill the embryos already in the nests.

Bullheads and catfish also sweep out nests and offer protection to embryos and young fish. Channel catfish spawn during the period from late May to mid-July in Missouri,[55] with a peak occurring in early June and one in late June. Bullheads usually spawn during late May and early June as far north as central Iowa and Illinois.

HYBRIDIZATION

Hybridization within certain families of warm-water fishes is not un-common. Hybrids have been observed in many groups of fishes including the Cyprinidae (minnows) and Esocidae (pikes), and they are relatively common in the Centrarchidae (sunfishes). The artificial production of hybrids in the laboratory is not difficult if one is able to obtain ripe or nearly-ripe individuals of species capable of hybridization. In nature, hy-brids may be produced accidentally, and they are much more common among fresh-water fishes than among salt-water species.[36] However, as the stimulus of a ripe male appears to be necessary in some species to induce the females to release eggs, the possibility seems remote that sperms from an outside source might fertilize the eggs thus released. There are recorded instances, however, of female carp releasing ripe eggs without the stimulus of a male fish. No similar behavior has been reported for members of the sunfish family, although it is difficult to see how ripe females could retain all of their eggs, due to the pressure within the fishes' abdomen. Probably most of the unspawned eggs are resorbed.

Among closely related genera "mating behavior patterns" and "con-sciousness of species" may fail to prevent a certain amount of promiscuity, particularly in crowded populations where there is competition for spawning ground space. Under these conditions, hybrids may be as common as one in 10 of the young produced in a spawning season, al-though the production of hybrids rarely exceeds 1 or 2 per cent.

Some use has been made of hybridization in fish management, e.g., hybridization of the northern pike, with the muskellunge, to produce the "silver musky" (which is highly regarded by some fishermen), or the use of hybrid sunfish to produce larger individuals with a low reproductive potential.

Several studies of natural and artificial hybrids (Figure 5.3) of various species of sunfishes have been made.[24, 37, 48, 54, 63, 78] Sunfish hybrids have been reported between species in the following list: green sunfish, blue-

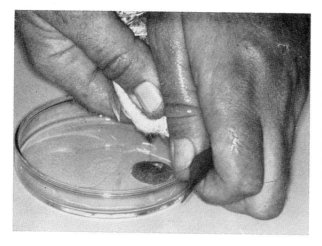

Figure 5.3. Hybrid sunfish are produced in the laboratory.

A. Ripe eggs from a female of one species are gently squeezed into a petri dish.

B. Immediately milt from a ripe male of another species is sprayed over the eggs. Eggs and milt are gently mixed and then left for two minutes.

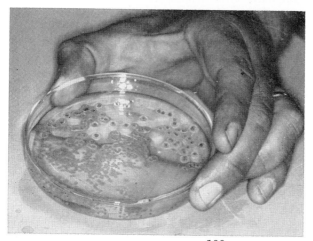

C. Fertilized eggs are then placed in other petri dishes— a few hundred in each—and washed with aged tap water. When eggs are washed, they adhere to the bottom of the dish. [From Childers, W. F., and Bennett, G. W., *Ill. Nat. Hist. Surv. Biol. Notes*, 46 (1961)]

gill, pumpkinseed, orange-spotted sunfish, longear sunfish, red-ear sunfish, and warmouth.

Hubbs and Hubbs [37] using hybrids of bluegill × green sunfish and pumpkinseed × green sunfish determined that under nearly identical conditions the hybrids grew faster and attained larger sizes than either parent species. Ricker [63] stocked new ponds with hybrid sunfishes from male bluegill and female red-ear parents. He reported that in the absence of competition from other species these hybrids weighed between 3 and 4 ounces at the end of their first growing season and a pound after three growing seasons. Krumholz [48] working with the same hybrid (bluegill male × red-ear female) found that the hybrid was heavier in relation to its length than either of the parent species.

Most of the F_1 hybrid sunfish that have been studied have demonstrated unbalanced sex ratios, usually in the direction of 70 to 95 per cent males. [24] Some authors have reported no offspring from F_1 hybrid parents. [37] When crossing members of the F_1 generation, numbers of F_2 young are reported as varying from a few to as many as occur in natural spawning of pure species. [24, 48] Back crosses of hybrid sunfish to parent types have been accomplished in the laboratory, [24, 54] and intergradations of hybrid sunfish types found in nature suggest that backcrosses as well as F_1 hybrids are relatively common. [78]

Recently, all possible crosses and reciprocal crosses between bluegill, red-ear sunfish, and green sunfish (Figure 5.4) were produced artifically by fertilizing the ripe eggs of one species with sperm from another (Figure 5.3). [24] After development in the laboratory, newly-hatched fry were placed in isolated ponds and allowed to grow for one or more years. A number of backcrosses and outcrosses were made and in one instance eggs from an F_1 hybrid of red-ear male × green sunfish female were fertilized with sperms from a bluegill, producing an outcross that was one-half bluegill, one-fourth red-ear, and one-fourth green sunfish. As yearlings, these fish could be separated into four rather distinct types.

From these observations and experiments, it is conceivable that the hybrid sunfish may show some of the advantages in pond management that hybrid corn and hybrid domestic stock have shown in agriculture. It may be possible to develop a hybrid sunfish with characteristics better suited to the needs of modern angling than any sunfish species now in existence. A start in this direction was made by Ricker and Krumholz when they used bluegill × red-ear hybrids for stocking farm ponds in Indiana.

SELECTIVE BREEDING

Changes through selective breeding have been accomplished in carp, goldfish, and some other species of "domestic" fish raised in fish-farming operations. Most of this work has been done in Asia and Europe, where fish are raised for food or display. These fish are usually not exposed to "wild" conditions; when they escape to compete with wild fish, they either die or revert to their original wild type as the European carp has done in this country.

Fish that have been raised in hatcheries for many years have probably been subjected to unintentional as well as intentional selection. Hatchery

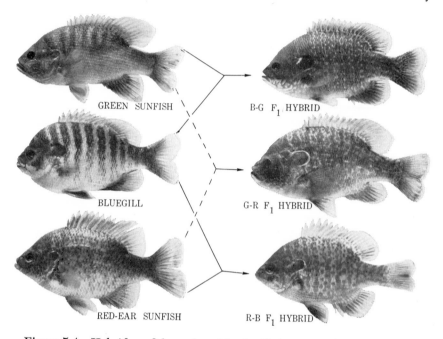

Figure 5.4. Hybrid sunfish produced by fertilizing eggs of one species with milt from a different one. In this experiment, fish were limited to green sunfish, bluegills, and red-ear sunfish. Hybrids showed characteristics intermediate between those of parents but were usually heavier-bodied. Males were more abundant than females in most hybrid combinations. [From Childers, W. F., and Bennett, G. W., *INHS Biol. Notes*, 46 (1961)]

personnel may consciously choose the heaviest-bodied and fastest-growing fish for egg production; at the same time they may unconsciously select the fish that are most easily handled, e.g., those that have lost most of their "wildness." This type of selection has made hatchery trout somewhat less desirable than wild fish [80] for sport fishing and has reduced their ability to survive under "wild" conditions.

Attempts at selection for improving species of warm-water fishes apparently have accomplished little. However, artificial selection may be operative in heavily-fished, isolated small lakes and ponds that receive no stock from outside sources. Fish in waters that receive 500 or more hours of fishing pressure per acre per season and that escape being caught are probably more wary than those that are caught. If wariness is associated with an inherited behavior pattern, it might in time become incorporated in all of the fish in this population. No one has devised a means for testing this theory, but it is conceivable that an isolated large-mouth bass population exposed to this type of selection for many generations might furnish low annual production to anglers.

UNSUCCESSFUL REPRODUCTION

Control of overproduction of young fish often is one of the major problems in fish management. In this respect, low production or non-production of certain hybrids may be an asset. Although most fishes have a high reproductive potential, as described on page 92, this potential may not be realized, either because of unfavorable environmental conditions, actual predation, or intense intraspecific competition of young. Eschmeyer [29] described unusual concentrations of dead walleye eggs observed in 1948 in Lake Gogebic. He was unable to determine causes for the low viability of these eggs. In Fork Lake (Illinois) the production of 40 bluegill nests was almost completely wiped out by predation from stunted yearling bass.[13] Channel catfish and flathead cat usually fail to reproduce in ponds.[77] Under certain conditions this inability to reproduce might be an asset, in that one could control the numbers of these catfishes in ponds through stocking, which is impossible when using any of the species of bullheads.

Observations of the limiting or curtailing of fish reproduction that can be traced to identifiable causes are extremely important because methods may be suggested for curtailing the survival of the young of a less desirable species while improving that of a more desirable one.

STOCKING

Many tests of stocking procedures have been made since 1935. However, the recommendations of the states and provinces throughout the United States and Canada do not reveal much agreement among fisheries biologists upon the kinds and numbers of fish useful for stocking new waters or renovated old ones. This is due in part to dissimilarities among the fish habitats of North America, to differences in the biology of certain game and pan fishes in widely-separated parts of their present ranges, as well as to regional variations in the popularity of certain fishes. Also, some of the divergences in recommendations may be related to differences in the objectives of stocking. For example, some biologists stock to produce excellent but short-term angling as quickly as is possible; others to produce satisfactory angling over a longer period of time; others, to favor one species; others, to give equal status to two or more species. These variations in objectives can be accommodated only by differences in stocking methods.

Fishes Used

As early as 1944, evidence was available to show conclusively that warm-water fishes raised in hatcheries were valuable only for stocking new or renovated waters, or for stocking "waters seriously depleted as a result of overfishing, pollution, or other special circumstances."[39]

The Bass-Bluegill Combination. The bass-bluegill combination was re-born in the 1930's, although it had been used in ponds by Dyche before 1914 and by Barney and Canfield before 1922.[6, 26] In theory this combination seemed excellent: both largemouth bass and bluegills would be available for sport fishing; the bluegills would convert small invertebrate animals in the pond into bluegill flesh and the small bluegills would serve as food for the bass, the latter controlling excessive numbers of bluegills, so that the few that survived would grow to large average sizes.

As with most theories involving specific behavior patterns for animals, the bass-bluegill combination did not always follow the original theory. The bass often were unable to control the expansion of bluegill numbers, and as Dyche[26] observed, the number of bass were more often controlled by bluegills than vice versa.

Shortly, however, biologists discovered that this combination furnished satisfactory fishing for both bass and bluegills as long as neither species was allowed to become overabundant. Interest was immediately directed toward stocking specific ratios of these fish because these ratios had an influence upon the length of time required for a newly-stocked pond to reach overabundance, either of bluegills or bass.

In the southeast, the bluegill was more easily controlled by bass than elsewhere, and both species reproduced when one year old.[72] Thus, stocking ratios were 1 to 15 in favor of bluegills. According to Swingle and Smith,[77] fertilized ponds should be stocked with 100 bass fingerlings and 1500 bluegill fingerlings per acre, unfertilized ponds with 30 bass fingerlings and 400 bluegill fingerlings per acre. These ratios apparently were not considered satisfactory for the Southwest as Brown[15] recommended either 200 to 400 largemouth bass per acre alone or in conjunction with about the same number of bluegills or other pond fish.

In the north central states, the bass were usually unable to attain sexual maturity at the age of one year, although Clark[22] reported that they did so in Kentucky. Bluegills were sexually mature the next season after hatching. Thus, when fingerling bass and fingerling bluegills were stocked together in the same pond, the bluegills reproduced during the first spawning season, while the bass did not, and by the time the bass had reached sexual maturity after a second growing season, so many yearling and two-year-old bluegills were present that they limited the survival of bass embryos and fry. To prevent this early shift toward an overpopulation of bluegills, mid-continent fishery biologists stocked ratios to give bass a better chance to survive and reproduce: 100 largemouth bass fingerlings to an equal number of bluegill fingerlings. During the first season, the bass fingerlings would prey upon the bluegill fingerlings reducing their number to a low figure but still not so low as to preclude the survival of a small number of bluegills to spawn the following season. Furthermore, the pond was not too crowded with bluegills by the second season to prevent a successful spawn of bass when they became sexually mature. Fishing for bluegills is ponds stocked originally with 100 bass fingerlings and 100 bluegill fingerlings might not be satisfactory until after individuals of the first bluegill brood spawned in the pond, had reached a length of 6 inches, usually late in the third summer. This process could be speeded up one full season by stocking fingerling or fry-size bass at the rate of 100 per acre along with adult bluegills (that would spawn the same season as stocked) at the rate of 10 to 30 per acre. Clark [22] stated that this was the only satisfactory ratio for stocking bass and bluegills in Kentucky; more recent findings do not support Clark's specific statement for a satisfactory ratio. [30, 66]

In southern Illinois, six ponds on the lands of the University of Illinois, College of Agriculture Dixon Springs Experiment Station were stocked with stunted largemouth bass, 6 to 10 inches long and with bluegill fingerlings averaging 1 inch in length. [32] Then their progress was followed closely for six years. Three of the ponds scheduled to receive fertilizer were stocked with 89, 91, and 109 bass and 1127, 1250, and 1630 bluegills per acre, respectively. Three unfertilized ponds were stocked with 21, 30, and 36 bass and 310, 396, and 412 bluegills per acre, respectively. A nearly complete creel census throughout the 6-year period showed that bass fishing was best during the first year. By the second season bluegills were of worthwhile sizes (6 inches) and the bluegill fishing (rate of catch) improved for the next few fishing seasons, reaching a peak in about 5 years.

Often it is impractical or impossible to obtain enough fry or fingerling bass for stocking new artificial impoundments of 100 to 1000 acres at rates of 100 small bass per acre. In these instances, stocking might be done at rates of 1 adult bass per 3 to 20 acres of water along with bluegills at a somewhat higher rate. Usually, after the first spawning season, young bass can be collected in numbers in all parts of the lake, and it is nearly impossible to find any bluegills. Two seasons later the lake might furnish excellent fishing for both bass and bluegills.

For artificial impoundments of intermediate sizes between farm ponds and large reservoirs, a stocking of 2 to 10 adult bass per acre, followed by a stocking of 100 small bluegills per acre after the bass had produced young, usually gave satisfactory fishing one or two seasons later.

In the northernmost states and southern Canada, the bass-bluegill combination was nearly useless because waters were infertile and growing seasons were short; thus, both species of fish required three growing seasons to reach sexual maturity. Also, the bluegills showed a strong tendency to overpopulate and become stunted. Rawson and Ruttan [62] stated that yellow perch grew better than bluegills in Saskatchewan and recommend stocking ponds with yellow perch and bass or northern pike. Ball [2] suggested stocking ponds in Michigan with 100 fingerling bass and 10 adult bluegills per acre. By so doing, the bass would have forage immediately instead of two or three seasons later. Later Ball and Ford [3] stated that the largemouth bass-golden shiner combination was more satisfactory for the production of bass fishing in Michigan than was the bass-bluegill combination. Neither Brown and Thoreson [17] in the northwest (Montana) nor Saila [65] in the northeast (New York) would recommend the bass-bluegill combination for ponds in these regions because results were unpredictable.

A perusal of published material on the bass-bluebill combination will show that it apparently is most successful in the southeast. Farther north, results may be good but good results are not necessarily a certainty, although records of one bass-bluegill pond in Illinois showed a high yield of both bass and bluegills for 12 years after stocking.[25] This pond of 2.5 acres was stocked originally with 100 bass fingerlings and 100 bluegill fingerlings.

In Illinois, the bass-bluegill combination usually moved in the direction of an overpopulation of bluegills. If ponds were stocked with equal numbers of bass and bluegill fingerlings per acre, this condition of overpopulation of bluegills might not arrive for 5 to 12 years. However, bluegills were very efficient in controlling populations of largemouth bass after bluegill numbers reach 1000 or more per acre,[11] particularly if these bluegills were small. Control was exerted through predation of small bluegills on bass eggs and fry in the nests. Stunted bluegills would gather around a bass nest guarded by a male and sooner or later a bluegill would venture close enough to cause the male bass to give chase. While the male was away from the nest, other bluegills entered and fed upon bass embryos or fry. The bluegills scattered when the male bass returned, but soon the process was repeated and before long the eggs or young bass would be greatly reduced or eliminated. This was the only period in the life cycle of largemouth bass when these fish were highly vulnerable to bluegill predation, but if bluegill predation on bass embryos and fry were consistent and efficient for several years in succession, the bass population of a lake might dwindle to a few old fish which lived well but were unable to produce a new year-class of young bass, because of an ever-increasing population pressure by stunted bluegills.

Small bass are also vulnerable to crappie predation where the latter are abundant. Young crappies are much more inclined to hide in aquatic vegetation than are young largemouths, and for that reason the latter are usually more vulnerable to adult crappie predation than are small crappies.

An overpopulation of stunted crappies (or bluegills) plus a few large bass unable to reproduce successfully was self perpetuating and continued until the bass were caught or died of old age. Only drastic thinning of the stunted fishes allowed the bass to bring off a successful spawn.

In contrast, an overpopulation of small bass might be controlled in a single season of fishing, provided the fishermen were educated to the necessity of taking these fish in spite of their small size.[11]

If bass could be expected to prey upon bluegills exclusively, either through "normal" feeding habits or through a special taste for them, the bass-bluegill combination would be considerably more dependable than at present. However, bass actually select a variety of foods (including the larger aquatic insects, crustaceans, and fishes), and the evidence is that they will feed upon crayfish and their own young in preference to bluegills. Therefore, in order to control bluegills indefinitely, bass need assistance, several types of which will be described later.

Other Combinations of Fishes. There is reason to assume that other combinations might be more satisfactory from the standpoint of angling and easier to manage than the bass-bluegill combination. Since largemouth, smallmouth, and spotted bass are fairly omnivorous in their feeding and can get along well on crayfish, large aquatic insects, and their own young, any one of the three bass species stocked in a pond by itself should produce bass fishing without the complications of controlling bluegills or other fish stocked with bass. Experiments testing the ability of each bass species to survive in its own pond have proved very satisfactory, particularly if the population is set up originally by stocking several year-classes to prevent the development of a dominant year-class, which might become stunted. This was quite easily done by stocking and assortment of bass larger than 10 inches *in addition* to 100 fingerling bass per acre. At the first spawning season after stocking, the adult bass produced young; however, the fingerlings already present prevented the development of a dominant brood. Experiments have shown that populations of bass by themselves are as large, or larger in pounds per acre than are bass populations in combination with other species of fish.

Several fisheries biologists have tested largemouth or smallmouth bass in combination with one or several species of minnows. Ball and Ford [3] tried a combination of largemouth bass and golden shiners which proved to be very successful. After 5 years, there were still plenty of shiners present as well as bass. Bluntnose minnows were able to maintain a population over at least a three-year period when confined in a very clear pond (gravel-pit) with smallmouth bass. This pond contained some rooted aquatic vegetation. Smallmouths taken from this pond showed a higher average condition than others taken from a nearby pond which contained only smallmouths.

The largemouth-bass-red-ear-sunfish combination has been tested extensively in Indiana [47, 49] and Illinois.[10] In no case where only largemouth bass and red-ears were present has there been any evidence of overpopulation of red-ears. However, the red-ear sunfish is somewhat less desirable as a sport fish than is the bluegill because the former prefers live bait fished deep and will seldom hit artificial flies or poppers at the water's surface.

Larimore [52] combined largemouth bass with warmouths in stocking more than 15 ponds in central Illinois. This combination was very satisfactory. The warmouths showed little tendency to overpopulate and both warmouths and bass grew rapidly to useful sizes.

Jenkins [41] concluded from his observations in Oklahoma that largemouth bass, channel catfish, warmouth, and red-ear sunfish produced more harvestable-sized fish in comparison with their total standing crops than any other warm-water fishes.

In north-central Nebraska several ponds of 5 acres or larger have been stocked with a northern pike-bluegill combination. The pike were released as fingerlings and bluegills as adults so that the latter furnished young bluegills for pike forage during the first season.[57] Recently, some experiments have been started to test the usefulness of muskellunge (Figure 5.5) in the control of overpopulation of sunfishes.

Smallmouth bass do well in warm-water ponds if they do not have to compete with some of the more prolific warm-water fishes, such as bluegills, green sunfish, and black bullheads.[12] For example, smallmouths maintained a large population in a 14-acre central Illinois lake until excessive numbers of green sunfish prevented their successful reproduction. This lake was made by damming a pasture ravine and contained no sand or gravel in the shoal areas.

Several studies have been made of combinations involving three, four, and five species of fishes, such as the bass, bowfin, and bluegill combination of Krumholz [47] or the bass, bluegill, warmouth, and channel catfish combination used in Ridge Lake.[11] The study of Thompson [79] of an unfertilized fishing club lake in Macoupin County, Illinois, illustrates that the bass, crappie, bluegill, and bullhead combination in a lake with limited shallows may be productive of substantial annual yields, if the lake is fished intensively when the fish are biting (annual yield was about 100 pounds of fish per acre of lake).

Every practicing fishery biologist will discover, sooner or later, at least, one pond or lake that, although unmanaged or "mismanaged," still produces as good or better fishing than any lake or pond toward which he may be directing his management efforts at that time. I have found several. In some, the high production was transitory, and they eventually became poor fishing waters, usually because of overpopulation. There

Figure 5.5. Muskellunge are sometimes stocked in small numbers in artificial lakes as a "bonus" fish and as an aid in the control of sunfish populations.

were and are, however, a few others in which there seems to be a delicate relationship between reproductive success of the fishes and the natural food supply, perhaps through the action of predators of which I am unaware. In these waters, bluegills may range between two and three to the pound, with scarcely any of smaller sizes, or green sunfish may grow to 8 or 9 inches and may be represented by a few hundred fish instead of tens of thousands of 3- to 5-inch fish. These lakes always seem to contain many small bass, usually from 6 to 9 inches. There may be some unrecognized relationship between the physical environment and the fish and aquatic organisms that inhabit it. In later chapters, we will discuss this possibility.

It is the author's opinion that one would be naïve to expect any combination of fishes stocked in a man-made lake or pond to be productive of good fishing for an indefinite period of time. Too many of the integrated forces and counter-forces that are active for promoting the well-being of a fish population in a primitive environment are absent from a man-made and man-dominated lake.

CHANGES IN FISHING

There are many records of lakes and ponds that once produced excellent fishing but which lost their productiveness after a few years because of the introduction and expansion of undesirable fish or the overpopulation and stunting of desirable ones.

Krumholz [48] working on hybrid sunfish in ponds in Indiana found that 39 of 78 ponds stocked originally with hybrids and largemouth bass contained, after two years, other species of fish than were originally stocked. After questioning the owners of 29 of these ponds, 26 admitted that they had introduced other kinds of fish. Among the fish that were introduced were largemouth bass, bluegills, black and white crappies, green sunfish, orange-spotted sunfish, longear sunfish, and warmouth, and in two instances, smallmouth buffalo. Most of the pond owners explained their actions with the statement that they wanted to catch a greater variety of fish.

Ball and Tait [4] state: "The knowledge and effort necessary to maintain, over a period of time, a pond producing fast-growing bass and bluegills are beyond the scope of the average pond owner. Consequently, it is recommended that (1) small ponds be stocked in such a way as to produce the species desired in the greatest edible weight in the shortest time, (2) these fish to be harvested, and (3) restocking be done instead of attempting to maintain a 'balanced' pond over a period of years." This may be a practical solution if ponds are supplied with a drain outlet and fish for restocking are readily available.

In recording the history of Fork Lake, a farm pond in central Illinois,[8] it was discovered that fishing had been considered good from 1926 to 1930 but had become poor through the development of large populations of black bullheads, carp, and buffalo fishes. At the time that Fork Lake was censused in 1938, it contained 5350 fish weighing 774 pounds (539 pounds per acre) and consisting of 16 species. Only 145 fish of the 5350 were of such species and sizes as to interest anglers.

STOCKING FOR IMPROVEMENT OF A POPULATION

Biologists are not in complete agreement on the value of adding fish stocks for the improvement of a population that, from the standpoint of fishing, is somewhat less than optimum. Viosca,[81] after censusing ponds in Louisiana, concluded that the stocking of ponds which already contain fish may cause almost no change in a population of fish. He cited an example of a pond stocked with 1500 largemouth bass fingerlings which after a year or so yielded only 6 stunted individuals weighing a total of 1.85 pounds as against 12,505 bluegills and green sunfish weighing 201 pounds. A deeper pond nearby was stocked with 4500 largemouth bass fingerlings. Here a mixed crappie population which was already present dominated bass and other fish. Later, when the pond was censused the proportions were 8.4 pounds of crappies and 1.4 pounds of sunfish to each pound of bass. According to Viosca: "—this type of evidence completely discredits the idea that artificial restocking will restore the largemouth bass population of a pond dominated by other species." In contrast, Swingle, Prather, and Lawrence [76] state that "Since partial poisoning is normally required in populations containing too few bass and all small bass in the pond edges are killed, marginal or sectional poisoning in the spring or summer is detrimental unless followed by restocking of bass." However, stocking of fish after a partial poisoning operation is not comparable to a situation such as Viosca described, because partial poisoning makes living space available for the stocked bass.

Lagler and DeRoth [51] came to the same conclusion as Viosca, after stocking fin-clipped bass fingerlings in the Loch Alpine ponds (Michigan); none of the 4000 bass fingerlings stocked in 4 years were seen again. These ponds had uncontrolled outlets, and the small bass were free to move out.

Cooper [23] on the fish stocking policy for Michigan says that this state has largely dispensed with plantings of warm-water fishes such as bass, bluegills, perch, walleyes, and northern pike. In the past, plantings of these warm-water game species were distributed among hundreds of lakes on a rather orderly schedule. While the state-wide totals of fish stocked were large, the yearly plants to individual waters were small: bluegills were stocked at the average rate of 35 fingerlings per acre; largemouth bass at the rate of 2.4 fingerlings per acre and smallmouth bass at the rate of 1.9 fingerlings per acre. At the same time (1947) large numbers of fingerlings of these species could be seined in most of these lakes. In 12 of these lakes selected on the basis of public interest, intensive seining operations on shoal areas indicated populations of young fish ranging from 103 to 1760 per acre with an average of 742 per acre for the 12 lakes. This so far overshadows the maximum stocking efforts of state personnel as to make their efforts of little consequence.

By stocking 300 adult bluegills per acre in Kentucky farm ponds overpopulated with largemouth bass, Clark [22] produced satisfactory fishing for both bass and bluegills. Swingle and Smith [77] state that for ponds containing stunted bluegill populations a stocking of 100 bass fry or fingerlings per acre plus "proper fertilization" and heavy fishing for bluegills to reduce their numbers will correct this condition in a few months. This statement appears to be counter to the findings of Viosca [81] and Lagler and DeRoth,[51] except that "proper fertilization" may increase the available food for bluegills or at least produce enough additional plankton to allow some survival of bass.

Even with a high rate of survival of stocked fish, corrective stocking will not effectively improve a fish population unless the number of fish stocked per acre is large enough to approach that found in "superior" populations of these same fish.[21] However, this is not always easy to achieve. Thus, if bass fry were stocked at the rate of 100 per acre into a population of stunted bluegills and the survival rate of the bass was 75 per cent (a very unlikely assumption), they soon might grow large enough to feed upon the smaller bluegills, reducing food competition among the bluegills and thus facilitating the growth of the larger ones to useful sizes. However, in most instances of bass-fry stocking, the evidence indicates a low survival of the bass fry. Thus, the larger the young fish are allowed to grow before they are stocked from a hatchery, the better are their chances of survival. The problem here is that hatchery production of large fingerlings as compared to fry might be 1 to 1000, so that the fingerling production of the hatcheries of an entire state might be able to stock only a relatively small number of ponds at the rate of 100 large fingerlings per acre.

The kinds of warm-water fishes that are prone to overpopulate and stunt in certain waters often may be introduced successfully into existing fish populations with the release of only a few adults. Under severe competition, these adults are incapable of producing a substantial population in one or two years, but after three or more years, these fish may appear in large numbers. Bluegills, red-ear sunfish, green sunfish, white crappies, and black bullheads have all been observed to increase in this manner after a small number of individuals were introduced into a dominant population of other fishes.

Corrective stocking is always more dependable where a part of the population has been removed by poisoning or through mechanical means (seining, etc.). This procedure reduces the standing crop of fish to a point below the carrying capacity of the water and leaves food and space for the fish that are introduced.

Corrective stocking should not be attempted unless a source of fish is available for introducing a large enough number of a given species to approach the carrying capacity of the water for that species, e.g., 100 bass per acre, 300 to 1000 bluegills per acre, etc.

STOCKING TO IMPROVE A FOOD CHAIN

This type of stocking is done in an attempt to improve the production of game fish in an existing fish population by increasing the forage for these game fish. The introduction of the threadfin shad into large southern reservoirs was an example of this type of stocking.[42] McCaig, Mullan, and Dodge [56] recorded that the introduction of smelt into Quabbin Reservoir (Massachusetts) furnished an improved food supply for lake trout so that the latter reached a length of 18 inches in their fourth year instead of the fifth as they had done before the smelt were abundant.

This type of stocking should be considered very carefully before it is done because: (1) food chains of fishes are very complex and the introduced species may not serve the purpose intended; moreover, (2) forage fishes that are capable of expanding their populations in the face of existing populations of predatory species already present may constitute a danger from overpopulation as the gizzard shad has done in some waters.

Invertebrates such as crayfish, scuds, and insect larvae are sometimes stocked in new ponds and small lakes, and these stocking attempts are frequently successful.

FAILURES IN STOCKING FISH

Biologists in various parts of the country have developed stocking numbers and ratios of fishes intended to give satisfactory results in fishing returns. However, these stocking recommendations sometimes result in poor fishing or no fishing. There may be one or several reasons for these unsatisfactory results:

(1) Poor fishing in new impoundments may result from unauthorized stocking prior to or after the lake or pond has been stocked with tested ratios of kinds and numbers of desirable fish. Krumholz [48] mentions the problem of maintaining uncontaminated hybrid ponds in southern Indiana. In Illinois, and probably in most states, there are fishermen who spend a part of their time as amateur fish managers; one of their main activities is the promiscuous stocking of small numbers of most of the kinds of warm-water fishes to be caught on hook-and-line. If one finds bluegills where red-ears were stocked or largemouth bass where there should be smallmouth bass only, one may be observing the work of an amateur fish manager. Many fishermen release left-over live minnows into streams or lakes; the contamination from the minnows may be of minor importance if none of them are goldfish, carp fingerlings, or suckers.

(2) Some contamination takes place, usually in lakes or ponds near large urban centers of population, through the release of aquarium fishes when the owners tire of caring for them. Goldfish usually survive but guppies and other tropical fishes cannot winter over except in the deep south.

New waters that have been contaminated with local warm-water fishes soon become useless for fishing unless through accident a reasonable number of bass are also present. As discussed previously, corrective stocking of a water area that already contains fish is largely useless; it is better to kill all the fish and start again with correct numbers of selected fish.

(3) Poor results may be obtained because the fish stocked in new or renovated ponds died after they were released "in good condition." Even though the fish released were active and swam into deep water in a normal manner, they may have sustained injuries through handling prior to release that later resulted in their death.

For example, Brown [16] found the survival rate of bass fingerlings in bass-bluegill stocking experiments ranged from 47.1 to 83.3 per cent. Other investigators have obtained 69.2 to 100 per cent survival [71] and a 75 per cent survival for one pond. [67]

A striking example of this type of injury was observed by the author while tracing the final dispensation of the original adult and yearling bass released in Ridge Lake (Illinois) in 1941. [11] These bass consisted of 58 adults from Crab Orchard Lake near Carbondale, 42 adults from Lake Chautauqua near Havana, and 335 yearlings from Lake Glendale near Robbs.

The 58 Crab-Orchard-Lake bass were caught and held in wing nets, April 27-29 inclusive, moved into a tank truck supplied with an air compressor, and transported to Ridge Lake, a distance of 150 miles by road. The weather was unseasonably warm for April. Although the fish appeared in good condition when released, 44 of these fish (75.8 per cent) were believed to have died, soon after release, from injuries sustained in capture and transportation. These 44 bass were not caught by anglers in 1941 and 1942 and were not present when the lake was drained in 1943.

The 42 adult bass from Chautauqua Lake (also caught in wing nets) were the survivors of a much larger number taken in March and April and held indoors for several weeks in aerated holding tanks. Fish injured in netting operations were removed and discarded. On May 1, bass remaining in the tanks were transported in the early morning to Ridge Lake, a distance of 145 miles. Sixteen of the 42 bass disappeared without a trace and probably died from injuries (38.1 per cent).

The 335 Lake Glendale yearlings (5.0 to 7.0 inches) were seined on June 17, held overnight in a holding net staked out in the lake, and then were hauled in aerated tanks to Ridge Lake—a road distance of 180 miles. The weather was hot, and a few of the fish died in transit, but those released appeared to be in good shape. In this group, 317 of the 335 bass (94.6 per cent) disappeared. Some may have been eaten by the larger bass, but with only 100 of the larger bass released in 18 acres of water, the fish were not crowded and predation probably was not heavy. The assumption that these fish died from improper handling was further substantiated by the high survival rates of marked bass which were recorded in later years when the lake was drained in March, the fish censused, and the marked fish returned immediately to the refilling lake basin. One of the Chautauqua Lake fish that survived the original road trip and stocking in 1941 later survived 4 lake drainings and fish censuses and was caught by a fisherman in 1949.

Stroud [70] tagged fish released in Massachusetts ponds in order to measure the recovery from angling of largemouth and smallmouth bass, pickerel, bullheads, white perch, and yellow perch. He recorded several instances of high mortality shortly after stocking, presumably from injury during handling prior to release.

Fingerlings or fry may be more or less sensitive to rough handling and poor water conditions during transportation and stocking than yearling or adult fish. However, stocking ratios of bass and other fish mean little if the stocking mortality is abnormally high. A 10 per cent loss of bass or bluegills in a specific stocking ratio might mean little, but a 75 per cent loss of the bass (or bluegills) through unsuspected injury during transportation and stocking would certainly influence the future dynamics of a bass-bluegill population.

Most hatchery men and biologists recognize the need for extreme care in the handling of fish to be stocked. The problem is largely related to the shortness of the season for moving fish (late fall and to a lesser extent early spring) and the magnitude of the operation. Often, inexperienced help must be used in the handling and moving of fish which consequently become overheated or exposed to other unfavorable conditions before their final release in new locations.

Some hatchery ponds are too badly silted for fish to be removed without having to hold them in silt-filled water for comparatively long periods. The danger here lies in the high-oxygen demand and the products of anaerobic decay in this silt. Thus, unless an outside source of clear water is directed into the pond to reach the fish concentrated in the seines, high mortality is almost certain to follow.

PREDATION

The Role of Predation in Fish Management

At the beginning of this chapter we noted that the fishes have inhabited the earth for more than 350 million years and during this period have been relatively successful. Part of their success was due to the development of a high reproductive potential that allowed them to out-strip the predators that evolved to feed upon them. As each higher class of vertebrates appeared, certain members became predators of fishes, so that in a modern fresh-water environment, fish predators are represented by a variety of vertebrates each modified for predation activity in or on the water. With a little thought anyone can name at least 10 common fish predators such as:

garfishes	loons
pikes and muskellunge	ospreys
bullfrogs	cormorants
snapping turtles	gulls
alligators	terns
watersnakes	pelicans
mergansers	eagles
kingfishers	mink
ducks and geese	otter
herons	men

These predators, with the exception of man, are opportunists, willing to catch and feed upon whatever fish are available. Although most of them prefer taking fish as large as they can capture and hold, the predators of small fishes are much more numerous than those of the larger ones. In fact, among fishes of the largest sizes (such as the muskellunge, lake sturgeon, and salmon) only bears and men are predators.

Most numerous of all are the animals that prey upon fish eggs and newly-hatched fry, because not only are many small fishes of all kinds included in this grouping, but also several kinds of invertebrates, especially well represented by the predaceous aquatic insects, such as beetle larvae and dragonfly nymphs. With all of these aquatic animals actively foraging upon small fish, most of the losses from predation occur while the fish are very small. These losses represent tremendous numbers of individuals but relatively small amounts of fish flesh.

In the primitive environment where man was sparsely represented, predators of fishes were much more numerous than they are now, except perhaps in the more remote parts of North America. Some idea of the extent of predation in remote regions may be gathered through estimating the food requirements of small temporary concentrations of mergansers or cormorants. For example, about 1000 cormorants were observed to be feeding on Chautauqua Lake, a U. S. Fish and Wildlife Refuge near Havana, Illinois, during the fall of 1954. These birds were present throughout a period of 3 weeks. Studies of cormorants in captivity have demonstrated their voracity; an adult cormorant requires a maintenance diet of about 1 pound of fish per day, and it can eat more than 2 pounds per day if the opportunity arises. Using a food consumption estimate of 1.5 pounds of fish per bird per day, the Chautauqua Lake flock must have been consuming 1500 pounds of fish per day or for the 3-week period, a total of 31,500 pounds or 15.75 tons of fish. Although these fish may have been mostly gizzard shad if available, it is well to remember that if largemouth bass or crappies were more accessible than the shad, the cormorants would have been eating bass or crappies instead. This behavior pattern of most predatory animals of taking the available prey that can be conquered at a given time and place has the partly or wholly beneficial effect of reducing excessive numbers of concentrations of prey animals, which, in itself, is an important function.[34]

We see the direct effects of curtailed fish predation among the fishes stocked by man in artificial impoundments. These fish still reproduce as though they were subjected to the usual complex of decimating factors; but because many types of natural predators are relatively scarce where man controls the environment, there is insufficient culling of the fish population, and overpopulation, excessive food competition, and stunting are commonplace. These conditions eventually eliminate certain kinds of game fish from a fish population and stunt other kinds so badly that scarcely any grow to sizes large enough to interest anglers.

For a long time anglers looked upon fish predators as direct competitors with themselves for the fishes of our streams and lakes, and they destroyed garfish, watersnakes, turtles, mergansers, herons, pelicans, and other known fish-eaters whenever the opportunity appeared. There is little doubt that some of these fish-eaters, particularly fish-eating birds, may make serious inroads on abnormal concentrations of fish such as are found in hatchery ponds or in cold-water streams where numbers of hatchery-reared trout have been stocked. In most other waters their impact upon fish populations is beneficial.

Man's own activities and attitudes regarding fishes have in part been responsible for the poor fishing that has plagued him. This situation stems from his substitution of a new type of predation for that which occurs in nature. Man preyed upon large fish, but protected and pampered small ones. This new type of predation and protection coupled with the fact that no change occurred in the fishes' reproductive potential resulted in excessive survival and competition among the young. In this competition bass and other game fish lost out to hoards of stunted crappies, sunfish, and yellow perch.

Thus, many of the techniques of fish management that will be discussed in Chapter 6 are simply methods of population control or environmental manipulation used to prevent the development of dominant populations of some kinds of fishes and to stimulate the dominance of other kinds. Many observations have been made to show that where predators of fish (other than the fish themselves) are reduced, a prey species of fish may actively control the survival of its normal (fish) predator. I have produced evidence that young bluegills may control the survival of young bass.[9] Carbine [19] demonstrated that perch and minnows may control the survival of aelvins and juvenile northern pike; and Eschmeyer [29] cites several recorded instances of yellow perch, minnows, sturgeon, catfish, and suckers eating walleye eggs and fry.

COMPETITION

Several types of competition occur among the fishes in an aquatic habitat. Although the most common rivalry is probably for food, competition for space in specific habitats, as when sunfish vie for nesting areas, may be somewhat more obvious. Not much is known of the extent and importance of any specific type of competition in a specific habitat, but we can demonstrate the end results by the changes that take place in crowded populations where several types of competition are severe.

COMPETITION FOR FOOD

Most fishes depend upon a wide variety of food, rather than upon a restricted diet. Thus, if a seasonal or localized shortage of one food occurs, a species may shift to another type.[50, 52] Anyone who has had occasion to study the stomach contents of individuals of any single species of fish collected over a period of several months or seasons, has no doubt marveled at the changes in the kinds of foods as well as in the quantities of a single aquatic organism sometimes found in a single stomach. One is almost led to believe that the taking of some foods becomes habit during certain seasons. It is often very difficult to recognize competition between two kinds of fishes for a specific food organism as was described by Johannes and Larkin [43] for rainbow trout and red-side shiners. In this case, competition was recognized only because a study had been made of the feeding of the trout before the red-side shiner had become abundant.

To what extent is an available food utilized? Patriarche and Ball [61] emphasize the importance of the "forage ratio" of Hess and Swartz [35] which is the ratio of the percentage of occurrence of an organism in an aquatic population to its percentage of occurrence in the stomach of a fish species. If this ratio varies significantly from 1:1, it should be due to either a difference in availability or a difference in preference. Allen [1] offered an "availability factor" for forage ratio and Leonard [53] suggested that the forage ratio be used as a measure of availability only.

In many cases where a specific food organism is abundant there is little question as to its availability to fish; in others it is impossible to measure the difficulty involved in the capture and ingestion of an abundant organism.

Most aquatic biologists agree that the bacteria and algae are at the base of the food chain. The bacteria use complex waste materials in the water, and the algae are able to utilize inorganic salts, carbon dioxide, and water in sunlight, to make carbohydrates and proteins, which are used as a source of food by other organisms. However, the food chain from bacteria or algae to the larger fishes does not consist of a single series of links, but many. A few of these food chains may be dominant during one season or under certain environmental conditions while others may replace them at another time or season. Thus, at certain times, foods more suitable for one species of fish may be more abundant than at other times. This may be reflected in changes in condition, growth rate, and in standing crop of the fish.

Larimore [52] could not show definite food competition between largemouth bass and warmouths inhabiting the same lakes, although these two species often fed on similar types of organisms. Warmouths tended to feed on organisms on soft bottoms in shallow waters and along banks while largemouths fed more on the surface organisms and free swimming forms in deeper or more open parts of the lakes.

Studies of the food habits of closely related fishes may show similarities, yet with certain important differences. Ball and Tanner [5] in studying the foods of bluegills and pumpkinseed sunfish from the same waters, discovered that the pumpkinseeds selected a larger proportion of molluscs and hard-bodied insects than did the bluegills; while the bluegills ate larger amounts of aquatic vegetation than did the pumpkinseeds. The selection of these types of foods by bluegill × pumpkinseed hybrids was intermediate between the two parent species. Both parent types were feeding upon about the same range of foods, but distinct preferences for certain types were clearly evident.

In fishes of widely different food habits, such as largemouth bass and bluegills, there may be some evidence of food competition at times and under certain conditions. For example, bass and bluegills in one pond competed for insects when fish or crayfish were not available for the bass.[13] Under these conditions, however, bass ate more flying insects and bluegills more larval aquatic forms. In this particular situation, it was impossible to evaluate the degree of competition between these two species.

COMPETITION FOR SPACE

When fish are forced to compete for living space, there is evidence that in some species (and perhaps all species) growth rate and reproduction are affected adversely. Anyone who has kept goldfish or tropical fish in aquaria indoors and then has placed these fish in an outdoor pool during a summer period, has had a demonstration of the change in growth rate brought about by increased space. Usually, a part of the increased growth rate is due to an improved diet, but even where aquarium fishes are receiving a completely balanced diet, their growth appears to be affected by the amount of space for each fish.

Experiments designed to expose the causes of reduced growth and reproduction in crowded fishes have furnished evidence that where adequate food was available, inhibited growth and reproduction was due to ammonia and other material excreted into the water by the fishes themselves.[46, 64, 75, 82] In most of the experiments in which conclusive results were obtained, the fish were tropical aquarium fish, goldfish, European carp, or one of the species of buffalo—fish that have a reputation for intermittent production of year classes.

Goldfish stocked in small ponds at the beginning of the growing season at the rate of 200 4-ounce fish per acre produced large numbers of young, while those stocked at the rate of 2000 or more of 4 ounces or larger produced few or no young.[75] Originally, it was thought that the goldfish ate their own eggs and young in the ponds stocked with the larger numbers of adults; however, examination of adult females showed that eggs were well formed but never laid. Later, it was discovered that each time during the summer that adult goldfish were moved from their regular ponds into new ponds freshly filled with water, that the fish spawned within 48 hours.

On the basis of these and other experiments, Swingle[75] postulated the presence of a repressive factor composed of a secretion or excretion produced by the goldfish themselves that inhibited final development and deposition of eggs, although these eggs were already practically mature.

Additional experiments showed that the inhibitory material was excreted into the water by the goldfish and that when this water was moved into new ponds it retained its ability to inhibit reproduction, even when it was diluted 2:1 with fresh water. Similar tests using carp and bigmouth buffalo gave results comparable to those from goldfish experiments.

Swingle believed that largemouth bass were affected by an inhibitory factor. Certainly there is evidence that the production of young in this species is never directly related to number of spawners; usually there appears to be an inverse relationship between bass fry and number of adults available for spawning.[11]

It was also assumed that overcrowded bluegills depressed the production of largemouth bass through the secretion of a repressive factor. If this were so, why were bluegills able to build up overcrowded populations and depress bass reproduction without curtailing their own reproduction? More experimental work must be done before exact evidence is available to prove or disprove this hypothesis, particularly when crowded bluegills have been observed repeatedly to feed upon bass eggs and fry.

Yashouv[82] placed two small carp in each of a number of aquaria containing 26-27 liters of water. These fish were fed 10 per cent of their body weight per day and held at water temperatures warm enough for growth. Water was changed in all aquaria at two-day intervals throughout experiments extending from 43 to 80 days. Controls received no other treatments, but experimental aquaria received varying amounts of metabolic water obtained by stocking a small container with a large number of fish for 30 to 40 minutes or until they had difficulty in breathing. Fish in aquaria receiving metabolic water gained slightly or lost weight while control fish gained 150 to 275 per cent of original weight.

As yet, there is no exact agreement among investigators as to the causative agent responsible for this inhibition of growth and reproduction. One believes it is a hormone-like substance, another a substance that created a vitamin deficiency. When fish-conditioned water was given to rats for drinking they lost weight and died after 45 to 50 days.[82] These rats displayed characteristic symptoms of Vitamin B_1 deficiency.

In the Far East where fish are grown in boxes in streams there is no growth inhibition, although the density of fish in the boxes amounts to as much as 50 per cubic meter. Here the metabolic waste is carried away by the current. Yashouv [82] thinks that this action of metabolic waste may represent a defense mechanism (for slowing population growth) of the existing population.

Mraz and Cooper [58] found little relationship between population density of adult carp (within the range of 75 and 450 pounds per acre) and the weight of young carp present with them at the end of the first summer (3 months), Figure 5.1. Adult carp were stocked in May just prior to the spawning season, and the ponds were drained in August or early September. These adult fish always produced a spawn; when less than 100 pounds of adult carp per acre were stocked, the fish usually gained in weight; a loss in weight followed, when adults were stocked, at rates of 150 to 450 pounds per acre. Average size of these young carp ranged from 2.7 to 5.0 inches after 3 months, and the weight per acre of young carp ranged from 98.4 to 308.7 pounds. As the carp were stocked just prior to the spawning season, there was no inhibition in spawning, but growth of adults and young may have been affected later.

Among game and pan fishes in hatchery ponds no clear effect of crowding upon growth (where adequate food was available) and reproduction has been demonstrated, although one may assume that accumulation of waste may function as a growth inhibitor.

Larimore [52] demonstrated a very significant difference in the numbers of ova carried by female warmouth living under different conditions. For example, a female warmouth of 5.3 inches from Venard Lake (Illinois) contained 40,400 ova in various stages of development, while a female of the same length from Park Pond contained only 12,500 ova. Venard

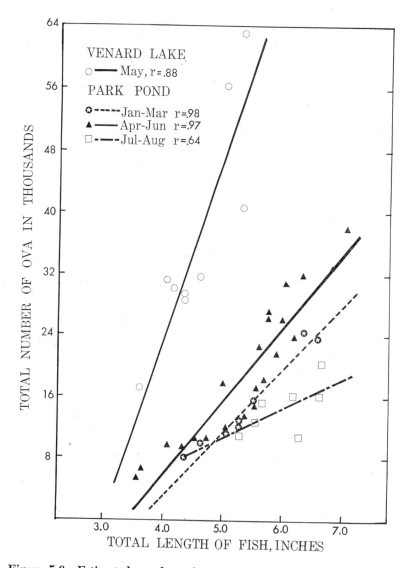

Figure 5.6. Estimated number of ova from warmouths of various total lengths in collections from Venard Lake and Park Pond (Illinois) in 1949. Scattergram, regression line, and coefficient of correlation (*r*) are given for each collection group. Each graphic symbol represents one female from which the number of ova was estimated. Venard-Lake warmouths belonged to a population of fish that was expanding rapidly. In Park Pond the warmouths were subjected to severe competition for food and space, and many were heavily parasitized. [From Larimore, R.W., *Ill. Nat. Hist. Survey Bull.*, 27(1) (1957)]

Lake was supporting a rapidly expanding fish population, while the fish in Park Pond were more crowded and more heavily parasitized (Figure 5.6).

COMPETITION FOR SPECIFIC HABITATS

This type of competition may be more common than is the general crowding of fishes, particularly in the case of competition for spawning areas by sunfishes, or competition for limited shallow bottom areas for bottom-loving bullheads. Control of a specific habitat within an aquatic environment may allow a single species of fish to hold dominance over other components of a fish population.

STARVATION

Most fishes are well equipped to withstand prolonged periods of starvation. In some laboratory experiments by Dr. Marian F. James,[38] bass were held in aquaria at room temperature without food for several months. During this period they lost nearly half of their body weight, and some died of starvation. Some were brought back to their original weights through repeated force feeding of small amounts of food. After having been starved for 2 or more months, these bass were no longer interested in food and would pay little or no attention to live minnows released in the aquaria with them.

Other laboratory experiments indicated that in order to maintain a constant weight bass required about 1 per cent of their body weight per day in the form of fish. These fish were able to live for an indefinite period on a maintenance diet with no indication of ill health. It is not unlikely that food ingestion at this level may occur frequently in populations of stunted fish.

INTER- AND INTRASPECIFIC COMPETITION

In considering competition among the fishes in an aquatic habitat, one usually considers competition between the several species first, but intraspecific competition—competition between individuals belonging to a single species—may be more continuous or severe than that between species. In describing the fish inhabiting Lake Gogebic, Eschmeyer [29] stated that walleye and the northern pike dominated the game fish population. Other species of game and pan fish were present in small numbers: largemouth and smallmouth bass, black crappies, rock bass and seasonally, brook trout. Young of the yellow perch were abundant, but adults were relatively scarce. On the basis of Eschmeyer's study of various phases of the life history of the walleye in this lake, it is probable that intraspecific competition among walleyes was more severe than interspecific competition between walleyes and other kinds of fish.

In Onized Lake (Illinois) where heavy fishing controlled the numbers of larger fish, except largemouth bass and bluegills,[7] there appeared to be severe inter- and intraspecific competition among the young of all species present. Once these small fishes reached sizes large enough to interest anglers they were thinned by fishermen.

A suggestion of intraspecific competition was indicated among the bluegills of Fork Lake (Illinois)[13] where older bluegills were eating a higher percentage of plants than were the yearlings. Here the older bluegills were believed to be less active than the yearling fish in seeking animal foods, and they were apparently using plant material as a substitute.

REPRODUCTION, COMPETITION, AND PREDATION

In the preceding paragraphs I have attempted to illustrate several aspects of the life cycles of fishes—reproduction, predation and competition—which, when integrated with one another and with other forces, constitute the dynamics of any fish population in any body of water. These forces may result in cycles of abundance of certain fishes, or they may assure that one species eventually becomes dominant and stays so, until some unusual or catastrophic event occurs.

Thompson [79] reported a population study of the fish of Lake Senachwine (Illinois) where very abundant year classes of black crappies not only controlled the survival of their own young for the next four spawning seasons, but they also controlled the survival of young of most other species of fish in this lake. During the fourth year of their dominance, the natural death rate of this year class of crappies was high. When the next spawning period arrived, the 5-year-old crappies were no longer numerous enough to dominate the fish population, but there were enough of them to produce a new dominant year class of crappies.

Starrett and McNeil,[69] while studying the fish population of Chautauqua Lake (Illinois), which in some ways is similar to that of Lake Senachwine, found that the relative abundance of several species of fishes fluctuated over periods of several years, but that no one year class of any species dominated the fish population as did the black crappie broods in Lake Senachwine. In Chautauqua Lake, the 1948 year class of white crappies was much larger than any other year class of that species produced in any year from 1949 to the present (1961), but large year classes of other species were produced in some years.

Only occasionally are predatory fishes confronted by a shortage of prey fishes; when this does occur, it is often the result of pressure from a dominant year class of the predatory species. Such a situation occurred with largemouth bass in Ridge Lake in 1941 and 1942.[11] The 1951 angler's catch of walleyes in Clear Lake (Iowa) was unusually high, apparently because of a failure in the perch crop in 1949 and 1950 which in turn was believed to have been related to a shortage of aquatic vegetation during those years.[20]

In this same lake a very large yield of northern pike occurred in 1954, as a result of the transference in 1953 of some 17,000 young pike 10 to 16 inches long into Clear Lake from Ventura Marsh lying adjacent to the lake. This amounted to 5 pike per acre, or by the spring of 1954, to 7 pounds of pike per acre—a rather abrupt increase of at least 10 per cent in the predator population of the lake. The pike caught were thin and later in the summer some were found dead along the shore.[20]

Still another type of interplay of reproduction, competition, and predation results in a progressive increase in one or two species of fishes until they become so numerous as to exceed the normal food resources for these species in their habitat. These abundant species spill over their habitat niches into those of other less aggressive species and crowd them sufficiently for food and space to prevent the survival of adequate young to maintain a level of population of the less aggressive fishes. It follows that the latter species eventually may be represented by a few old fish, and they may disappear entirely. This type of population change is non-reversible and is characteristic of fish populations subjected to limited or ineffectual predation. Only catastrophic changes in the habitat will modify the overpopulated and stunted condition of the dominant fishes. No known instances of over-use of habitat resources, followed by population collapses, such as are cited by Errington[27] for overpopulations of deer, muskrats, and some other mammals, have been reported for fishes, although diseases or parasites sometimes wipe out or severely reduce overpopulations of fishes that are characteristic of hatchery ponds before fish distribution is begun.

BALANCE

Balance is a term used by some biologists to describe natural fluctuations of animal populations around a constant numerical level. Other biologists have expressed the opinion that the term is inappropriate[68] because balance refers to a state of equipoise and is synonymous with equilibrium. Nicholson[59] believes that "balance refers to the state of a system capable of effective compensatory reaction to the disturbing forces which operate upon it, such reaction maintaining the system in being."

Others, for example Swingle,[73, 74] use the term balance to define fish populations that yield satisfactory crops of harvestable fish in relation to the basic fertilities of the bodies of water containing these fish. According to Swingle, fish in a balanced population (1) must reproduce periodically, (2) must produce a sustained yield (presumably by angling), and (3) must contain a combination of species including at least one piscivorous species. Unbalanced populations are those unable to produce succeeding crops of harvestable fish.

This concept of balance [74] is somewhat different from that of biologists who have applied this term previously. It visualizes a simple predator-prey relationship between carnivorous fishes (piscivorous) and omnivorous ones (prey species) in which the prey species make the maximum use of the food resources to produce adults of harvestable sizes and small fish to serve as food for the carnivorous fishes. The carnivorous fishes produce young to maintain stocks of adults for fishing and control the potential overproduction of stocks of both omnivorous and piscivorous fishes. In practice, this relationship of predator fish to prey fish may maintain itself for a number of years, but eventually it will change to become overbalanced, usually in favor of the prey fish, and human intervention will be required to restore the original relationship. This is not the "balance" of Nicholson because this system in itself is not capable of compensating for changes that may take place through natural variation of reproductive and survival rates, unless one is willing to include the management activities of man as part of the system.

The sustained yield requirement of "balance" should be based on fish of sizes large enough to interest anglers. The smaller the minimum useful size set by biologists the larger will be the number of ponds that are acceptable ("in balance"). Harvestable-sized fish according to Swingle [74] are given by weights in the following table. The approximate lengths of these fish have been interpolated from these weights.

	Minimum weight, pounds	Estimated length, inches
Bluegills and other sunfish	0.10	5.0
Crappies	0.26	7.5
Largemouth bass	0.40	9.5
Bullheads	0.30	8.0
Gizzard shad	0.50	11.0
Channel cats	0.50	12.0
Gar	1.00	16.0
Buffalo	1.00	12.0
Carp	1.00	14.0

Youthful fishermen are likely to accept fish of any size; adult experienced fishermen are more conservative, possibly because they have to process the fish and perhaps have to eat them once they are cooked. Although one may eat smelt of relatively small sizes, because their bones are fine and become soft with cooking, the same cannot be said for small crappies, bluegills, and other sunfish. Bluegills or sunfish of 0.10 pound and crappies of 0.26 pound are listed as being harvestable. Converted to inches, these weights would represent lengths of 5.0 inches and 7.5 inches, respectively, for bluegills and crappies; for most parts of this country these minimum lengths for harvestable fish should be increased to at least 6.0 inches (0.18 to 0.20 pound) for bluegills and other sunfish and 8.0 inches for crappies (0.30 to 0.35 pound). Neither gizzard shad nor gars are usually considered harvestable in a practical sense, and buffalo cannot be harvested by hook-and-line except by accidental snagging. Disagreement on minimum harvestable (useful) sizes for bluegills and other sunfish by only one inch (5 inches to 6 inches) might make a great deal of difference in designating a population of fishes as desirable or undesirable (e.g., balanced or unbalanced).

The use of the term "balance" in referring to fish populations that produce satisfactory yields is untenable because:

(1) Balance has already been defined in biological terminology, so that the term should not be applied with specific reference to pond fish populations.

(2) The simple predator-prey relationship which is the basis for "balance" in fish populations is an oversimplification of what actually is taking place.[13, 45] Fishery biologists should be no more willing to accept such a relationship than are game biologists to accept a fox-rabbit "balance" or a prairie dog-coyote ratio.

(3) Selected species, numbers, and sizes of fishes released in an artificial lake habitat represent the ultimate in artificial ecosystems and can hardly be expected to show any great stability or "effective compensatory reaction to the disturbing forces which operate upon it."[59] Therefore, "balance" is quite without meaning when applied to such a population.

LITERATURE

1. Allen, K. R., *Am. Fish. Soc. Trans.*, **71**, 275-283 (1942).
2. Ball, R. C., *Jour. Wildl. Mgt.*, **16**(3), 266-269 (1952).
3. Ball, R. C., and Ford, J. R., *Mich. St. Coll. Ag. Exp. Sta. Bull.*, **35**(3), 384-391 (1953).
4. Ball, R. C., and Tait, H. D., *Mich. St. Coll. Ag. Exp. Sta. Tech. Bull.*, **231**, 1-25 (1952).
5. Ball, R. C., and Tanner, H. A., *Mich. St. Coll. Ag. Exp. Sta. Tech. Bull.*, **223**, 1-32 (1951).
6. Barney, R. L., and Canfield, H. L., *Fins, Feathers and Fur*, **30**, 3-7 (1922).
7. Bennett, G. W., *Ill. Nat. Hist. Surv. Bull.*, **23**(3), 373-406 (1945).
8. Bennett, G. W., *Ill. Nat. Hist. Surv. Bull.*, **24**(3), 377-412 (1948).
9. Bennett, G. W., *Am. Fish. Soc. Trans.*, **80**, 231-239 (1951).
10. Bennett, G. W., *Jour. Wildl. Mgt.*, **16**(3), 249-253 (1952).
11. Bennett, G. W., *Ill. Nat. Hist. Surv. Bull.*, **26**(2), 217-276 (1954).

12. Bennett, G. W., and Childers, W. F., *Jour. Wildl. Mgt.*, **21**(4), 414-424 (1957).
13. Bennett, G. W., Thompson, D. H., and Parr, S. A., *Ill. Nat. Hist. Surv. Biol. Notes*, **14**, 1-24 (1940).
14. Breder, C. M., Jr., *Zoologica*, **21**(1), 1-48 (1936).
15. Brown, W. H., *Am. Fish. Soc. Trans.*, **80**, 210-217 (1951).
16. Brown, W. H., *Prog. Fish-Cult.*, **14**(2), 79-80 (1952).
17. Brown, C. J. D., and Thoreson, N. A., *Jour. Wildl. Mgt.*, **16**(3), 275-278 (1952).
18. Carbine, W. F., *N. A. Wildl. Conf. Trans.*, **4**, 275-287 (1939).
19. Carbine, W. F., *Am. Fish. Soc. Trans.*, **71**, 149-164 (1942).
20. Carlander, K. D., *Am. Fish. Soc. Trans.*, **87**, 34-38 (1958).
21. Carlander, K. D., Whitney, R. R., Speaker, E. B., and Madden, K., *Am. Fish. Soc. Trans.*, **89**(3), 249-254 (1960).
22. Clark, M., *Jour. Wildl. Mgt.*, **16**(3), 262-266 (1952).
23. Cooper, G. P., *N. A. Wildl. Conf. Trans.*, **13**, 188-193 (1948).
24. Childers, W. F., and Bennett, G. W., *Ill. Nat. Hist. Surv. Biol. Notes*, **46**, 1-15 (1961).
25. Durham, L., "A Study of the Largemouth Bass-Bluegill Population of Martin's Pond, McLean Co., Illinois," Master's Thesis, unpub., Univ. of Ill. Library, 1-47, 1949.
26. Dyche, L. L., *Kan. Dept. Fish and Game Bull.*, **1**, 1-208 (1914).
27. Errington, P. L., *Science*, **124**(3216), 304-307 (1956).
28. Eschmeyer, R. W., *Jour. Tenn. Acad. Sci.*, **19**(1), 31-41 (1944).
29. Eschmeyer, P., *Mich. Dept. Cons. Inst. for Fish. Res. Bull.*, **3**, 1-99 (1950).
30. Hall, J. F., *Proc. 12th Ann. Conf. Southeast Assoc. Game & Fish Comm.*, **116**, 91-116 (1958).
31. Hansen, D. F., *Ill. Nat. Hist. Surv. Bull.*, **25**(4), 211-265 (1951).
32. Hansen, D. F., Bennett, G. W., Webb, R. J., and Lewis, J. M., *Ill. Nat. Hist. Surv. Bull.*, **27**(5), 345-390 (1960).
33. Harrison, A. C., *Inland Fish. Rept., Union of S. Africa*, 1-19 (1940).
34. Heard, W. R., and Curd, M. R., *Proc. Okla. Acad. Sci.*, **39**, 197-200 (1959).
35. Hess, A. D., and Swartz, A., *N. A. Wildl. Conf. Trans.*, **5**, 162-164 (1940).
36. Hubbs, C. L., *Systematic Zool.*, **4**, 1-20 (1955).
37. Hubbs, C. L., and Hubbs, L. C., *Pap. Mich. Acad. Sci., Arts & Letts.*, **13**, 291-301 (1933).
38. James, M. F., *Jour. Morph.*, **71**(1), 63-92 (1946).
39. James, M. C., Meehean, O. L., and Douglas, E. J., *U.S.F.W.S. Cons. Bull.*, **35**, 1-22 (1944).
40. Jenkins, R. M., *Proc. Okla. Acad. Sci.*, **36**, 70-76 (1955).
41. Jenkins, R. M., *Proc. Okla. Acad. Sci.*, **38**, 157-172 (1958).
42. Jenkins, R. M., "Reservoir Management—Progress and Challenge," Sport Fish. Inst., Washington, D.C., 1-22, 1961.
43. Johannes, R. E., and Larkin, P. A., *Jour. F. R. Bd., Canada*, **18**, 203-220 (1961).
44. Johnson, L. D., *Wisc. Cons. Dept. Tech. Bull.*, **17**, 1-54 (1958).
45. Johnson, R. E., *Conv. Int. Assoc. of Game, Fish & Cons. Comms. Proceed.*, **38**, 35-42 (1949).
46. Kawamoto, N. Y., *Prog. Fish-Cult.*, **23**(2), 70-75 (1961).
47. Krumholz, L. A., *N. A. Wildl. Conf. Trans.*, **15**, 251-270 (1950a).

48. Krumholz, L. A., *Am. Fish. Soc. Trans.*, **79**, 112-123 (1950b).
49. Krumholz, L. A., *Jour. Wildl. Mgt.*, **16**(3), 254-257 (1952).
50. Kutkuhn, J. H., *Proc. Iowa Acad. Sci.*, **65**, 571-579 (1958).
51. Lagler, K. F., and DeRoth, G. C., *Pap. Mich. Acad. Sci., Arts & Letts.*, **38**, 241-250 (1953).
52. Larimore, R. W., *Ill. Nat. Hist. Surv. Bull.*, **27**(1), 1-83 (1957).
53. Leonard, J. W., *Am. Fish. Soc. Trans.*, **71**, 219-227 (1942).
54. Luce, W. M., *Ill. Acad. Sci. Trans.*, **30**(2), 309-310 (1937).
55. Marzolf, R. C., *Jour. Wildl. Mgt.*, **21**(1), 22-28 (1957).
56. McCaig, R. S., Mullan, J. W., and Dodge, C. O., *Prog. Fish-Cult*, **22**(1), 15-23 (1960).
57. McCarraher, D. B., *Prog. Fish-Cult.*, **21**(4), 188-189 (1959).
58. Mraz, D., and Cooper, E. L., *Jour. Wildl. Mgt.*, **21**(1), 66-69 (1957).
59. Nicholson, A. J., *Australian Jour. of Zool.*, **2**(1), 9-65 (1954).
60. Oehmcke, A. A., Johnson, L., Klingbiel, J., and Wistrom, C., *Wis. Cons. Dept. Pub.*, **225**, 1-12 (1958).
61. Petriarche, M. H., and Ball, R. C., *Mich. St. Coll. Ag. Exp. Sta. Tech. Bull.*, **207**, 1-35 (1949).
62. Rawson, D. S., and Ruttan, R. A., *Jour. Wildl. Mgt.*, **16**(3), 283-288 (1952).
63. Ricker, W. E., *Am. Fish. Soc. Trans.*, **75**, 84-96 (1948).
64. Rose, S. M., *Science*, **129**, 1026 (1959).
65. Saila, S. B., *Jour. Wildl. Mgt.*, **16**(3), 279-282 (1952).
66. Smith, W. A., Kirkwood, J. B., and Hall, J. F., *Ky. Dept. Fish & Wildl. Res. Fish. Bull.*, **16**, 1-42 (1955).
67. Smith, E. V., and Swingle, H. S., *Am. Fish. Soc. Trans.*, **72**, 63-67 (1943).
68. Solomon, M. E., *Jour. Anim. Ecol.*, **18**, 1-35 (1949).
69. Starrett, W. C., and McNeil, P. L., Jr., *Ill. Nat. Hist. Surv. Biol. Notes*, **30**, 1-31 (1952).
70. Stroud, R. H., *Prog. Fish-Cult.*, **17**(2), 51-62 (1955).
71. Surber, E. W., *Am. Fish. Soc. Trans.*, **77**, 141-151 (1949).
72. Swingle, H. S., *Ala. Exp. Sta. Bull.*, **254**, 1-23 (1942).
73. Swingle, H. S., *N. A. Wildl. Conf. Trans.*, **10**, 299-308 (1945).
74. Swingle, H. S., *Ala. Agric. Exp. Sta. Bull.*, **274**, 1-77 (1950).
75. Swingle, H. S., *Eighth Pac. Sci. Cong. Proceed.*, **IIIA**, 865-871 (1956).
76. Swingle, H. S., Prather, E. E., and Lawrence, J. M., *Ala. Poly. Tech. Inst. Ag. Exp. Sta.*, **113**, 1-15 (1953).
77. Swingle, H. S., and Smith, E. V., *Ala. Poly. Inst. Ag. Exp. Sta. Bull.*, **254**, 1-30 (1947).
78. Thompson, D. H., *Ill. Nat. Hist. Surv. Bull.*, **20**(5), 492-494 (1935).
79. Thompson, D. H., "A Symposium on Hydrobiology," pp. 206-217, Univ. of Wis. Press, Madison, Wis., 1941.
80. Vincent, R. E., *Am. Fish. Soc. Trans.*, **89**, 35-52 (1960).
81. Viosca, P., Jr., *Am. Fish. Soc. Trans.*, **73**, 274-283 (1945).
82. Yashouv, A., *Bamidgeh*, **10**(4), 90-95 (1958).

6 ～～～

Theories and Techniques
of Management

The objectives of management are to produce and maintain a fish population that will supply a satisfactory sustained return to those with the authority to take an annual crop. Few populations are handled with sufficient intensity to keep them producing at peak level, although many provide a fairly adequate sustained yield. Probably, private and public demand for angling would be satisfied if all available waters offered a moderate sustained yield. However, in many regions unproductive ponds and lakes (those that supply little or no fish) predominate. This is particularly true of small artificial lakes and reservoirs located near centers of population.

Most unproductive lakes or reservoirs contain "problem" fish populations. Obviously, management effort should first be directed to restoring reasonable production to these bodies of water; the application of intensive fish management can come later.

There are two methods of handling a "problem" population in a pond or lake. One is to eliminate the population entirely and start anew with fish from an outside source; the other is to change the problem population, either by direct action upon it or through indirect action, brought about by modifying the fishes' environment. Both of these approaches are in common use. However, before deciding on a management procedure, a rather careful diagnosis, requiring one or several methods of sampling the population, must be made. Following is a dicussion of the uses of fish samples and some common methods of taking them.

FISH SAMPLING

The fisherman or fisheries manager can rarely see beneath the water sufficiently to identify and count the fishes in a lake or pond. Consequently, to determine the numbers and species present, he must resort to live-trapping techniques. It is seldom necessary to kill these specimens, whether or not their number is large enough to have any significance in relation to the remaining population.

REASONS FOR SAMPLING FISH POPULATIONS

There are several justifiable reasons for sampling fish populations. An adequate sample allows an appraisal of the components of a population, and exposes those segments of it, having sizes and numbers satisfactory for angling. As described in another chapter, the main causes of poor fishing are (1) overpopulation and stunting of desirable species, and (2) an overabundance of undesirable species with a concurrent shortage of acceptable ones. Hence, once the causes of poor fishing have been exposed, it is possible to plan a method of improving the population. For example, an excessive number of stunted crappies can be thinned out by partial poisoning; however, if there are overabundant and stunted bullheads as well, complete elimination and restocking may be necessary. Obviously, a sampling method that will expose only the crappies does not provide a satisfactory diagnosis.

It is frequently necessary to demonstrate to fishermen and owners that lakes are not "fished out." This is commonly called for in waters close to urban centers where species exposed to heavy fishing pressures may know a frog from a frog "popper" and a worm on a hook from a free one. These "fished-out" lakes are often filled with "wise" fish and fishermen will keep trying to catch them (at the same time receiving health and aesthetic benefits) if the fishery biologist can demonstrate that desirable species are present.

Regular annual sampling should be done on important impoundments not only to record changes in the relative abundance of species, but also in their length-frequency distribution and their condition from year to year. Fish taken with various sampling techniques should be measured and weighed individually, and scale samples obtained where there is an indication of stunting or of exceptionally rapid growth. These data allow an annual appraisal of the status of all important species. When this information is integrated for several successive years, it shows unmistakable trends that may call for certain management practices.

Table 6.1 shows a hypothetical length-frequency distribution for bluegills in an imaginary lake. In 1955, there were adequate numbers of large bluegills belonging to the 1953 year class (determined from scales). These fish showed an average Index of Condition (C) of 8.0 or higher which demonstrated that the fish were relatively fat. In collections of 1955 and 1956 no excessively large year class more recent than 1954 was present although this year class was fairly well represented. However, the collections of 1957 showed very large numbers of 1956 year-class fish that, after two growing seasons, were only about 3.0 inches in length. This would indicate a dangerous situation that might mark the beginning of overpopulation and stunting of bluegills. Further evidence of population pressure in 1957 was found among the 1954 and 1953 year-class bluegills which had Indexes of Condition of 7.0 and 7.4 respectively, indicating that the larger fish were thinner in 1957 than in previous years.

TABLE 6.1   LENGTH-FREQUENCY DISTRIBUTION OF BLUEGILLS IN CLEAR LAKE FROM SEPTEMBER COLLECTIONS TAKEN WITH WIRE TRAP NETS.

Total length in inches	1955	1956	1957	1958	
3.0	13	4	256	18	
3.5	27	3	140	36	
4.0	33	63	27	216	1956 year class
4.5	12	72	47	84	
5.0	15	18	45	62	
5.5	62	17	52	14	
6.0	128	26	11	30	1954 year class
6.5	47	102	10	3	
7.0	12	13	47	4	
7.5	1	2	9	10	1953 year class
8.0	5	2	1	1	
8.5	3	1	1		
9.0	1		1		

By September of 1958, the 1956 year class was severely stunted. After three growing seasons (summers) they averaged only 4.0 inches in length and were thin with abnormally large eyes (an indication of stunting). Bluegills of 6 inches or larger were still fairly common, but were very thin with Indexes of Condition ranging from 6.5 to 6.9. This bluegill population needed to be drastically reduced, particularly those fish belonging to the 1956 year class. Furthermore, since the 1957 sampling disclosed an abnormally large 1956 year class, measures should have been taken then to reduce its size.

SAMPLING METHODS

Many types of gear have been used for sampling populations. Most of these are selective for one or more kinds of fish, and may give a faulty impression of the relative abundance of species—both those too easily caught and those not taken in proportion to their numbers.

Table 6.2 gives a rough appraisal of the efficiency of several kinds of sampling methods in relation to a number of kinds of warm-water fishes.

These represent the combined experiences of Starrett and Barnickol [96] and the members of the Illinois Natural History Survey staff who have fished with these methods for many years.

Gill Nets. These nets are made with linen or nylon thread, fine enough so that fish, not seeing them will become gilled or entangled (Figure 6.1). Gill nets are tied to give bar measurements (one side of a square mesh) ranging from 1 to 4 inches; sometimes special sampling nets are made by splicing 50-foot sections of increasing mesh sizes from 1 inch up to 3 or 4 inches. Gill nets can be set at various depths from surface to bottom. They are selective for pelagic fish such as herring and trout and are seldom used in shallow lakes.

TABLE 6.2 AN APPRAISAL OF THE EFFICIENCY OF SEVERAL FISH SAMPLING METHODS COMMONLY USED IN ARTIFICIAL LAKES, AS RELATED TO COMMON WARM-WATER FISHES (IN PART FROM STARRETT AND BARNICKOL [96]).

	Method of Sampling					
Kind of fish	Trammel nets	Wing nets Trap nets	Seines	Spot poisoning	Boat shocking	Angling
Largemouth bass	poor	poor	fair	good	fair	good
Smallmouth bass	poor	fair	fair	good	fair	good
Sunfish [1]	good	good	good	good	good	good
Crappies	good	excellent	good	good	fair	poor
Carp	good	good	good	good	fair	poor
Gizzard shad	fair	good	good	good	good	—
Gar fish	good	fair	good	good	poor	poor
Bullheads	fair	good	poor	fair	poor	good
Channel catfish	poor	good	good	good	poor	poor

[1] Bluegills, green sunfish, red-ear sunfish, etc.

Trammel Nets. A light gill net of small mesh is hung with plenty of extra webbing between two walls of netting consisting of very large mesh of heavy twine. A fish hitting the light net carries a pocket of this net through an opening in the larger net and so becomes trapped. Trammel nets are supplied with floats and weights; they are set across and/or floated in a current (in a river) or set around a school of fish (in a lake). These nets are selective for fish that can be frightened into hitting the net. They are commonly used for commercial fish—carp, buffalo, and catfish.

Seines. These are pieces of webbing of various mesh sizes and lengths held upright in the water by floats and weights and pulled through the water to encircle fish. They are somewhat less selective than most other types of gear. Seines can be used only where the water depth is less than the depth of the seine and where the bottom is clear of snags. When confined within a small area, certain fishes such as largemouth bass will jump over the top of a seine unless the cork line is held up above the surface of the water.[112] Other kinds of fishes attempt to go under the lead line at the bottom so that if the seine becomes snagged or rolls up, they may escape from it. Large seine hauls repeated annually on a specific lake may be used for predicting standing crops of fish in pounds per acre; isolated seine hauls are of little value in this respect.[78]

Figure 6.1. TVA biologists use gill nets for sampling fish in large deep reservoirs.

Hoop Nets, Wing Nets, and Trap Nets. A hoop net consists of a cylinder of webbing supported by hoops, open at one end and closed at the other. Inside are two funnels, one just inside the open end of the cylinder and the other midway between the open and closed ends. Hoop nets are set in rivers with the tail upstream and the open end downstream. The current keeps the hoops separated and the net stretched. Fish move into the net easily through the funnel openings, but have some difficulty in finding their way out again.[39] Usually in swimming around inside of the net after passing through the first funnel, some wander through the second funnel and are then inside the closed end of the cylinder called the pot. Fish are removed from the pot by releasing a drawstring after the net or pot has been lifted into a boat.

Wing nets are modified hoop nets with short wings of webbing attached to the hoop at the open end of the net. They are used in quiet water where the wings guide fish into the net opening, and are held in a stretched position by stakes or weights.[40] Wing nets are sometimes fished with a long lead net set upright between the wings at the net opening. This lead net acts as a "drift" fence and fish following it soon find themselves in the wing net.

Hansen [41] found considerable variation in the catch of wing nets at various times of the year and under varying physical and chemical conditions associated with water—temperature, turbidity, dissolved oxygen, and carbon dioxide.

Trap nets are usually modified wing nets with wings arranged in loops to direct fish toward the opening of the net no matter which way they attempt to go, and with a lead net attached inside a forebay so that fish following the lead net to its proximal end are already inside of the front of the trap.

Mesh covering these nets is composed of nylon or cotton webbing squares varying in size from ½ inch to 4 inches. Hoop diameters range from 2½ to 6 feet. Trap nets of larger sizes are not used for sampling.

"Hoop nets" made of hardware cloth are more useful for fishing in ponds and small lakes than are hoop nets or wing nets made of string because the wire nets are not subject to muskrat damage. The nets are constructed of ½-inch hardware cloth and consist of a cylinder of wire, 2 feet in diameter and 4 or 5 feet long, with a single funnel leading into the open end and wire mesh across the closed end. Fish are removed through a small door covering an opening on one side, or through the open end of the cylinder after the funnel has been lifted out.

Thompkins and Bridges [110] found that low doses of copper sulfate (0.15 ppm) in soft water irritated the fish and caused them to move about, thereby increasing the catch of wing nets set in the area of treatment. Some fish may be attracted into a net by bait [6, 23] or by the darkness of the water inside of it. However, other fish, that avoid nets of small mesh, will enter those of larger mesh because their interiors are scarcely darker than the surrounding water. Certain kinds of fish such as largemouth bass will seldom enter hoop nets, wing nets, or trap nets in clear water, whether the mesh size is large or small.[84] Because these nets are attractive to certain kinds of fish and are avoided by others, the nets are extremely selective and samples of fish taken by them will not be representative of the fish population from which they were taken.

Minnow Seine Sampling. Minnow seines are often used to catch the young of various kinds of fish in order to gather information on the number of species of fish present in a body of water and to determine spawning success (relative abundance of young) of the several kinds of fish present. Usually when a dominant year class of one species of fish has been spawned, it will show up almost at once in early summer minnow seine hauls.

Anyone who has made an intensive study of a fish population inhabiting a pond or lake will discover after a few years of sampling of young that the total numbers and relative abundance of these young may vary greatly from year to year. Also, the young of a given species may appear to be very abundant in the early summer when the young are small, but later, if the rate of survival was low, they may have become relatively scarce.

Minnow-Seine Method of Pond Analysis. According to the minnow-seine method of testing ponds containing largemouth bass and bluegills,[102] the condition of the fish population ("balance") may be judged on the basis of the success of reproduction of bass and bluegills for the current year and the past survival of bluegill spawn beyond the first year (3-, 4-, and 5-inch length groups of bluegills). The method is based on the hypothesis that with an overabundant stunted population of bluegills, the bass (and sometimes bluegills, too) will be unable to produce enough to assure their appearance among fish caught in a reasonable number of minnow-seine hauls. On the other hand, with an overabundant stunted population of bass, there will be no intermediate-sized bluegills, and a scarcity or absence of small bluegills and perhaps small bass. These assumptions are valid if interference in spawning has not come from water too cold, turbid, or saline, with a pH too high or low, and if there is no great rise or drawdown of water levels at the wrong time.[102]

In 1950, an airing of conflicting ideas on minnow-seine sampling occurred when Dr. Gustav A. Swanson, editor of the *Journal of Wildlife Management*, published some pro and con opinions of it.[1] Long-term intensive studies of populations, in which minnow-seine collections were interpreted by the minnow-seine hypothesis, often failed to accurately define the type of population present. If these studies could not demonstate the consistent validity of the method, one may doubt the value of less intensive investigations, regardless of the number of ponds sampled and catches subjected to the test formula. As stated in 1950,[1] the author has found no published information (an adequate series of experiments in which minnow-seine analyses were followed by draining or poisoning censuses of the adult fish populations) to prove the value of the minnow-seine method. Tests of the method in Iowa,[21] through use of a larger seine and age analyses of fish, demonstrated errors in interpretation of results from minnow-seine collections.

However, shoreline seining with a fine-mesh seine to catch the smaller fish in a body of water can furnish a great deal of information about a fish population. Some acceptable values are as follows:

(1) In previously unsampled waters it will give a partial, and in some instances, a complete list of species inhabiting these waters.

(2) The collection of the young of bass, walleyes, northern pike, or other game fish not only indicates their presence in the water but also their

ability to reproduce under current conditions. However, their absence from waters containing adults does not necessarily mean that these populations cannot reproduce and are "on their way out."

(3) The production of dominant year classes of fish may be recorded first through minnow seining.

(4) Some indication of overpopulation and stunting may be gained from minnow seining, although a larger seine is much more useful for this.

Spot Poisoning. One of the more satisfactory methods of obtaining an unbiased sample of the fish population of a large lake is to poison a bay or lagoon connected with the larger body of water by a narrow channel. If the bay is not too small or too shallow, it will probably contain a population fairly comparable (in composition) to that of the larger lake,[38] particularly if the fish are warm-water species and the bay is treated with the chemical during the night when they are moving about in the shallower parts of the lake.

A seine or block-off net [67] deep enough to reach from the top to the bottom of the bay is set across the channel connecting the bay with the main lake. Fish disturbed by the chemical treatment or frightened by the noises of boats are prevented from escaping by this seine. Following its placement, a canvas strip approximately its same depth can be staked across the channel adjacent to the seine. This canvas strip prevents the circulation of rotenone-treated water from the bay into the main part of the lake. The bay is then treated with derris or cubé powder, 5 per cent rotenone, or emulsifiable rotenone with a dosage of sufficient strength to kill all of the fish trapped in the bay. These poisoned fish are picked up, counted, measured, and weighed, as in a regular census. Following the rotenone treatment the seine and canvas strip are left in place until the rotenone has disappeared from the water, so that no fish are killed outside of the bay.

Spot poisoning may be done in open water by treating the circumference of an arbitrary one-acre circle and then applying the rotenone inward throughout its area. However, work in open water is not as satisfactory as in an isolated bay because in the former instance the treated water may move downwind out of the original circle, causing fish affected by the rotenone to disperse beyond the original area of treatment. In any case, it is well to pick a time when wind velocity is at a minimum to prevent, as much as possible, the mixing of treated and untreated water.

As the behavior of fishes is influenced by seasons, several spot treatments of the same bay, made several weeks or months apart, will give a better population sample than a single spot poisoning.

Boat Shocking. In 1949, an AC row boat shocker was developed for the purpose of sampling fish in lakes.[69] This apparatus is useful for obtaining quickly a fish sample from lakes and ponds that are sufficiently shallow and have a water hardness of 25 or more parts per million (Figure 6.2). If the hardness is less than 25 ppm, the effective field of the electrodes is too small for the shocker to function efficiently. A boat shocker is often much more effective in taking fish at night, when fish are in the shallows, than in the daytime. A lighting system presents no problem because lights may be powered from the generator.[75]

Figure 6.2. An electric fish shocker mounted on an aluminum work boat. Biologist standing in front of boat controls a 220-volt generator, keeps electrodes in position, and picks up stunned fish. Biologist in rear runs outboard motor and cares for stunned fish which are placed in the tank amidship.

The boat shocker is selective in that it may stun fish attempting to hide in vegetation or on the shallow bottom; whereas fish swimming ahead of the advancing edge of the electrical field may escape unless they are cornered at the end of a bay or channel and forced to swim through the field. In general, bass tend to swim ahead of the shocker boat while other smaller centrarchids often try to hide in vegetation. Catfish and bullheads are seldom taken with an alternating current shocker because they are stunned on the lake or pond bottom where they are difficult to see and pick up. Certain kinds of fishes attempt to escape the shocker by diving into brush and into pockets at the base of rocks, stumps, and logs lying in the water, making these ideal collecting locations. Most fishes revive within a period of 30 seconds to 2 minutes. Occasionally a fish is killed by direct contact with an electrode. The shocker is not only used for sampling but also for collecting fish with "full" stomachs (food-habit studies) and for taking live specimens for stocking other waters. For some reason, many laymen have an idea that the electric shocker can be used to clear lakes of undesirable fishes. When they discover that the fish stunned by the shocker represent only a sample, they are often disappointed.

Both direct and alternating current are used on boat shockers. For collecting most kinds of fishes in shallow ponds, alternating current appears to be more effective. However, some biologists prefer a pulsating direct current to give a combination of electrotaxis and forced swimming.[20] Tests made in a webbing enclosure in a shallow lake (Minnesota) indicated that about 240 interruptions per minute was most effective for catching fish.[93]

Angling. Fishing with certain kinds of gear (fly rod, spinning rod, etc.) and certain types of artificial or natural baits may be highly selective for certain kinds and sizes of fish. For this reason, angling is sometimes very important as a method of sampling. Largemouth bass are usually taken more readily on hook-and-line than by any known type of net or trap. Several years ago I attempted to catch largemouth bass in a lake, at a time when it contained almost no fish other than bass of about 7.5 inches total length, by using 1-inch mesh wing nets with 60-foot lead nets. Six nets were set and raised daily on six consecutive days. The catch of all nets for the six-day period (36 net-days) was 6 of these small bass; on the last day that the nets were set I caught 47 bass on fly rod "poppers" in less than three hours.

The ability to avoid nets and seines is shared also by smallmouth bass, although they are somewhat more vulnerable than are largemouths. For sampling smallmouths, a fly rod and artificial "popper" may serve efficiently. For example, biologists captured 192 smallmouth bass (6 to 11 inches) in 22 hours of fishing at the rate of 8.7 per hour.[12] The fish were used to restock a renovated lake. They probably could not have been taken from the source lake (a deep quarry lake) at this rate by any other method.

Hook-and-line fishing may be useful for sampling specific fishes such as male bluegills guarding nests, or for taking fishes that inhabit a certain weed bed or lie beneath a log.

Many kinds of fishes become trap-wise as well as hook-wise, so that most types of fishing gear become less efficient with intensive use.

MANAGEMENT TECHNIQUES

Once sufficient sampling of a fish population has indicated that management is necessary, one should investigate the known techniques and decide which are applicable. Often several methods seem justifiable and one or more must be selected on the basis of expediency.

COMPLETE FISH POPULATION REMOVAL

Complete removal of a population is usually desirable when a lake or pond becomes contaminated with species of no value for angling or fish production. Such fishes as buffalo, suckers (of several kinds), gizzard shad, and sometimes stunted black bullheads may have limited sport fishing value. These species often crowd out more desirable game and pan fishes. Even if these undesirable fishes are present in small numbers, they are always a potential danger to the production of a high sustained yield of more desirable species because of their capacity for producing tremendous numbers of young at a single spawning and their ability to modify their environment (by stirring silt) in their search for food. These fishes, and some others unlisted, are completely under control only when they are absent.[62]

Population Removal by Draining. All artificial ponds and lakes should be built with drain outlets of sufficient size to allow their basins to be drained within a period of 3 to 10 days. If a lake with a drain becomes contaminated with undesirable species or must be drained for any other purposes (such as the recovery of stolen goods), a Wolf-type weir (Figure 6.3) can be placed across the outlet, the live fish separated from the water, and the valuable fish saved alive for restocking.[117] A Wolf-type weir is more satisfactory than any other type of screen because the water falls through the bottom of the wire-mesh weir instead of flowing through a perpendicular screen. The fish either are left exposed on the wire mesh of the weir bottom or they flop across the bottom screen into a holding box. This is the only type of screen that can handle a large flow of water without frequent shutoffs for cleaning the screen. A Wolf-type weir can be constructed below almost any outlet that will give 6 inches to 2 or more feet of working space below the level of the outflowing water. If it is necessary to catch very small fish or plankton organisms, such a weir may be covered with copper window screening or MS-904 Saran Screen.[18] Usually it is not desirable to use mesh of smaller than one-fourth to three-eighths of an inch.

Before draining, it is necessary to make some arrangements, either temporary or semi-permanent, for storing desirable fishes. The surface spillways of some artificial lakes may terminate in stilling basins of sufficient size and depth to hold fish. Such an arrangement was used at Ridge Lake where, in cool weather, all of the larger fish from 18 acres of water could be held for several days in a concrete stilling basin 70 feet wide, and 30 feet long, with a maximum depth of 4 feet when the basin was pumped full.[11] Where no holding basin is available near the outlet, arrangements should be made to hold the fish in portable tanks of metal or canvas or in nearby ponds, a count being kept of the fish moved

Figure 6.3. Small Wolf-type weir built across the concrete flume below drain valve for 2.5-acre pond. This weir will handle a comparatively large flow of water and allow capture of the fish alive because water drops through the bottom screen as well as flowing through the sides.

to these ponds. Later, when a small amount of water has become impounded in the drained lake basin, fish in the tanks may be returned or, those released in the ponds may be recollected by seining. The cool days of early spring and late fall are best for lake draining operations, because fish can be handled at these times with a minimum of loss.

Most lakes and ponds will not drain completely, and it is usually necessary to treat the water remaining in pockets or channels in the basin with some chemical to kill the small fish that may remain in this water and escape to the lake as the basin refills. For this purpose one can use H.T.H.

powder (calcium hypochlorite) to give several parts per million * of free chlorine, or rotenone (as 5 per cent cubé powder) or emulsifiable rotenone (2 to 5 per cent) to give 1 ppm or more. It is desirable to use a fish poison that disappears rapidly so that fish can be restocked within a few days.

After the fish and water have been removed from a lake basin and the water pockets and channels treated, the outlet valve can be closed so that water will collect in the basin. However, the basin may be allowed to dry for several months before reimpoundment is begun, if the fish to be restocked can be held for this length of time.

Population Removal by Rotenone Treatment. The use of rotenone containing plants as an aid in catching fishes is common to the native inhabitants of many widely separated tropical and subtropical countries. Leonard [72] and Krumholz [65] described the catching of fish by natives of Australia, Oceania, and southern Asia by the use of tuba, the local name for a substance (rotenone) originating from plants (Genus *Derris*) native to those regions. In tropical South America, the same substance, extracted from plants belonging to several genera such as *Lonchocarpus* and *Trephosia,* is known as cubé, timbo, barbasco, and by other names, depending upon the plant source and locality. Both Dr. Leonard and Dr. Krumholz recount descriptions of tuba fishing parties from the writings of early explorers in Sumatra, Sarawak, and Brazil.

The insecticidal properties of rotenone are well known and for many years there has been a large importation of rotenone-bearing plants into the United States. Probably Professor Eigenmann was the first to use native fishing methods with rotenone for collecting specimens of fishes in South America. Dr. Carl L. Hubbs used powdered derris root with 5 per cent rotenone content for collecting fish in Guatemala in 1934.

Rotenone was first used in fisheries management in the United States in 1934 when Milton B. Trautman at the suggestion of Dr. Hubbs attempted to eliminate goldfish from two small ponds on the W. O. Briggs estate near Birmingham, Michigan. The attempt was not entirely successful because the dosage was too light.

In September, 1934, Michigan fisheries biologists attempted to eliminate a population of stunted yellow perch from a 4.3-acre lake in Otsego County, Michigan.[29] After 1937 the technique of killing fish with rotenone spread rapidly to other states. In 1938, biologists with the Illinois Natural History Survey censused 6 ponds using rotenone treatment.[8]

Leonard's laboratory studies of the toxicity of rotenone to fishes in-

* Parts per million is promulgated on a weight basis, i.e., one pound of a chemical added to a million pounds of water equals one part per million. This is not too difficult to visualize if one will remember that an acre of fresh water (43,560 square feet), one foot deep, will weigh about 2.7 million pounds. Thus, 2.7 pounds of a chemical applied to one acre of water, one foot deep (one acre-foot), will give a dosage of one part per million (ppm).

dicated that a concentration of 0.5 ppm of derris powder with 5 per cent rotenone content should be lethal to all kinds of fishes. Also, a 14-degree elevation of water temperature from 60°F to 74°F decreased the reaction time to equilibrium loss and death of the fish by one-half, and rotenone was found to be somewhat more toxic in acid than in alkaline water.

Biologists soon discovered that derris and cubé mixtures with water were slow in penetrating the deeper waters of thermally stratified lakes. For this reason it was physically possible to kill warm-water fishes such as yellow perch, rock bass, and largemouth bass inhabiting the upper warmer layers of water without killing many brook or rainbow trout,[25, 57, 111] inhabiting the colder strata below (Figure 6.4). Hayes and Livingstone [45] combined the technique with the stocking of brook trout in a Nova Scotia lake and were able to increase the trout yield by 230 per cent.

Wide experience with rotenone-bearing compounds including the newer emulsions formulated by several chemical manufacturing companies has shown that it is risky to depend upon a dosage of material containing 5 per cent rotenone of less than 1 ppm to give a complete kill of fish.[19] In Illinois we have used a standard dosage of 3 pounds of 5 per cent rotenone-bearing material or 3 pints of emulsifiable rotenone, 5 per cent, per acre-foot of water, a dosage somewhat larger than 1 ppm. The extra chemical takes care of: (1) inaccuracies of lake volume estimates, (2) fishes showing high resistance to rotenone, (3) water of high organic content and/or alkalinity, and (4) unevenness of spreading. It is better to use too much rotenone than too little when all of the population must be killed (Figure 6.5) because if a few fish survive, both the cost of the rotenone and the treatment time of the crew have been lost, and the lake must be retreated.

In every case special methods of application should be used to carry the rotenone into deeper parts of a lake. One of the simplest is to introduce the rotenone mixture or emulsion through a weighted hose connected to a tank supported in the boat a foot or two above the water level. The movement of the boat (driven by an outboard motor) and the action of gravity forces the liquid into the deeper waters. The surface and edges of the pond or lake can be treated by the use of any type of small-power sprayer apparatus, and this same equipment can be used to pump the liquid into deep water. A hand sprayer is sometimes effective for covering edges of a small pond; for treating open surface water, the material can be poured over the side of the boat in advance of an outboard motor. Bilge-pump attachments available with some makes of outboard motors have been used for spreading emulsifiable rotenone. Powdered derris or cubé suspended in water might clog a bilge-pump attachment.

Care must be exercised to spread the fish-killing material as evenly

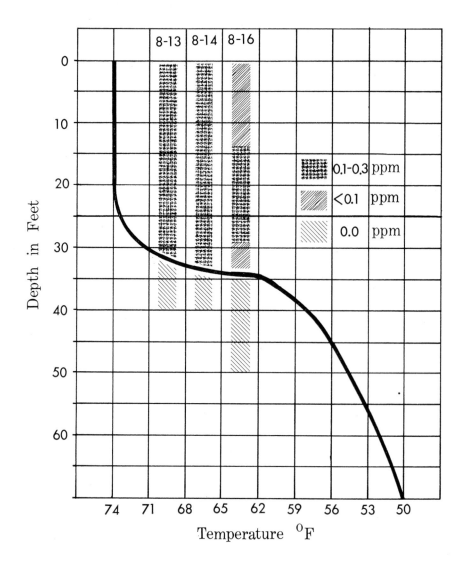

Figure 6.4. Selective poisoning of warm-water fish in trout ponds in Massachusetts by the use of rotenone. Tests indicated that the rotenone did not penetrate below the zone of rapid-temperature transition at 30 to 35 feet. Trout that remained at depths below about 35 feet were unaffected, while most of the warm-water fish above 30 feet were killed. [From Thompkins, W. A., and Mullan, J. W., *Prog. Fish-Cult.*, 20(3) (1958)]

as possible throughout the lake from surface to bottom. This can be done by following a grid pattern which divides the lake surface into parallel and crossing lines of treated strips (Figure 6.6). A fish has little chance to escape the treated strips in the grid.

Treatments for complete kills of fish should be made during seasons when the surface water of the pond or lake is 70°F or higher, because, as cited above, the efficiency of rotenone is much reduced in cold water.

Figure 6.5. Carp, bullheads, and green sunfish killed by rotenone treatment of a small pond.

Sometimes it is impossible to do a rotenone treatment during warm weather; if such is the case, an extra amount of rotenone should be used and special care should be taken in spreading it evenly.

Where lakes and ponds to be poisoned contain significant numbers of desirable fish, it is often practical to attempt their removal by seining or the use of a boat shocker. These fish are stored in other waters during the treatment and post-treatment period, and are restocked after the rotenone has disintegrated. Sometimes water levels of lakes may be lowered prior to treatment. Such a procedure is beneficial if it does not endanger the survival of desirable fishes returned to the lake after treatment is completed. Lowering the water level often increases the efficiency of

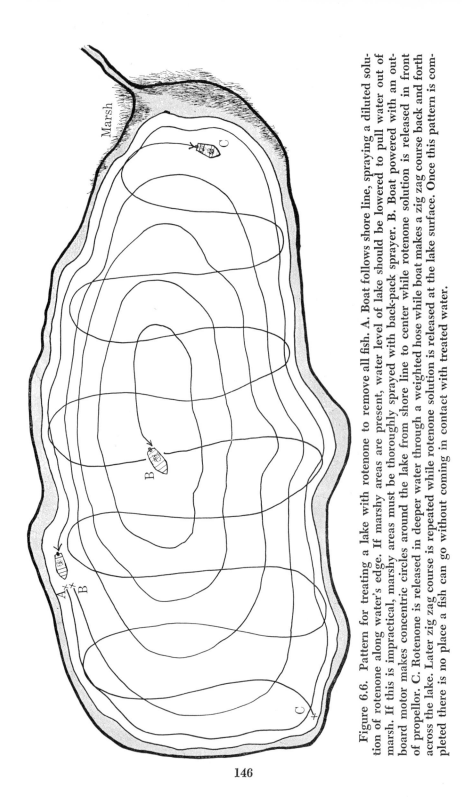

Figure 6.6. Pattern for treating a lake with rotenone to remove all fish. A. Boat follows shore line, spraying a diluted solution of rotenone along water's edge. If marshy areas are present, water level of lake should be lowered to pull water out of marsh. If this is impractical, marshy areas must be thoroughly sprayed with back-pack sprayer. B. Boat powered with an outboard motor makes concentric circles around the lake from shore line to center while rotenone solution is released in front of propellor. C. Rotenone is released in deeper water through a weighted hose while boat makes a zig zag course back and forth across the lake. Later zig zag course is repeated while rotenone solution is released at the lake surface. Once this pattern is completed there is no place a fish can go without coming in contact with treated water.

146

seining and boat shocking and reduces the amount (and cost) of rotenone needed to give a complete kill of undesirable fish. It may also pull the water out of cattail marshes and shallow bays overgrown with aquatic vegetation and pond weeds, and thereby eliminate the danger that a few small fish might survive in these areas.

Fish are more sensitive to rotenone than are most other aquatic organisms except entamostraca.[16, 73] The length of time that rotenone-treated water will remain toxic to fishes depends largely upon water temperature; at 70° to 80°F waters can be restocked with fish within 4 to 5 days after treatment. Lakes treated during cold weather may remain toxic for much longer periods—as much as 30 days. A color test has been developed for measuring the amount of rotenone in water.[86] Potassium permanganate ($KMnO_4$) or chlorine (Cl_2) will quickly oxidize rotenone and disappear from treated water.[61, 71]

Prevost, Lanouette, and Grenier[88] have demonstrated that the toxicity of some preparations decreases after an initial group of animals has been in it for a time. Thus, the disappearance of toxicity in a derris-powder suspension after 48 hours reported by Leonard[72] is not entirely an effect of time but is certainly related to the fact that the first two sets of fishes killed in the preparation had caused the toxicity to drop below the lethal point. This may in part account for the fact that most preparations appear to be less toxic out-of-doors than in laboratory aquaria.

Selective Poisoning. Recently a search has begun for selective poisons toxic to certain kinds of fish but not to others. The U. S. Fish and Wildlife Service began this search while looking for a chemical to kill larval sea lampreys, and after testing more than 4000 chemicals, they found an effective lamprey poison, as well as other chemicals that were toxic to certain other species.[2] As yet, selective poisoning of fishes is still in experimental stages.

DDT and Other Insecticides. The release and widespread use of DDT after World War II caused apprehension among conservationists and numerous studies were made of the effects of small and large scale applications of DDT on fish and wildlife.[28, 52, 53, 54, 74, 108, 109] As with many other chemicals, DDT was more toxic to fishes in laboratory tests than in field tests. On land it was often applied in dosages calculated in pounds or fractions of a pound per acre. These same dosages, based on surface area, were tested on shallow ponds containing miscellaneous fishes. In one series of experiments where DDT in the emulsifier Triton X-100 was followed by a treatment of rotenone applied at 1 ppm to kill all remaining live fish, a dosage of DDT at the rate of 1 pound per acre was found to kill all fish. A similar application at the rate of one-half pound per acre killed bass, crappies, bluegills, and some carp, but enough carp survived to repopulate the pond had they been allowed to spawn.

Since the appearance of DDT, many other chlorinated hydrocarbon insecticides have been developed. Some are more toxic to fish than DDT and others are less toxic. The development of organic phosphorus insecticides soon followed the chlorinated hydrocarbons. Many of the organic phosphorus compounds were more dangerous to handle than the chlorinated hydrocarbons but applied to waters containing fish they were somewhat less toxic. Table 6.3 shows the amounts of 10 chlorinated hydro-

TABLE 6.3   COMPARATIVE TOXICITY OF CHLORINATED HYDROCARBON AND ORGANIC PHOSPHOROUS INSECTICIDES TO FATHEAD MINNOWS IN HARD WATER AT 25°C. (FROM HENDERSON, PICKERING, AND TARZWELL [48])

Chlorinated Hydrocarbon		Organic Phosphorous	
Insecticide	96 hr. TLm ppm (mg/l) active	Insecticide	96 hr. TLm ppm (mg/l) active
Endrin	0.0013	EPN	0.25
Toxaphene	0.0051	Para-oxon	0.25
Dieldrin	0.016	TEPP	1.00
Aldrin	0.028	Parathion	1.60
DDT	0.034	Chlorothion	3.20
Methoxychlor	0.035	Systox	4.20
Heptachlor	0.056	Methyl parathion	7.50
Lindane	0.056	Malathion	12.50
Chlordane	0.069	Dipterex	51.00
BHC	2.000	OMPA	135.00

carbon and 10 organic phosphorus insecticides in ppm required to give a 50 per cent mortality (median tolerance limit, TLm) in 96 hours.[48] Of these chlorinated hydrocarbons, Toxaphene which holds second place to Endrin in its toxicity to fish has been used as a fish poison to clear all fish from lakes. Both Endrin and Thioden have been tested as fish poisons by Canadian biologists.[87]

Toxaphene. According to information furnished by Mr. Lynn H. Hutchens (U. S. Fish and Wildlife Service) in 1953, Messrs. Jack Hemphill and Jack Killian of the Arizona Game and Fish Commission first used toxaphene for killing fish. They used a dust containing 40 per cent toxaphene, and the cost of treating a lake was found to be only 15 per cent of the cost of treatment with derris or cubé powder containing 5 per cent rotenone.

In this treatment of Becker Lake (Arizona) with toxaphene, several horses were deliberately allowed to drink the water and no losses resulted. No dead deer, raccoons, or other wild animals have been observed around such lakes. There is apparently no danger in human consumption of fish so destroyed.[46]

Under alkaline conditions toxaphene is said to break down into hydrochloric acid and water. Shallow ponds lose their toxicity more rapidly than deep, and the former treated before the fall overturn of one year might be ready for restocking the next spring or early summer. In contrast, 8 alkaline, relatively deep lakes in British Columbia remained toxic for more than 9 months.[97] Alkalinity, the action of microorganisms, and turbidity [98] are important in the rate of detoxification of toxaphene.[56, 77]

A variety of dosages of toxaphene have been tested for killing fish, ranging from 0.1 ppm to 5 ppb * (.005 ppm). Usually a dosage of not less than .05 ppm of emulsifiable toxaphene in hard water applied when the temperature is in the 70° to 80°F range is to be recommended. Toxaphene is more toxic to small fish than large ones, and to black, yellow, and brown bullheads than to channel catfish, which show a great deal of resistance to it.[56] Thus it may be used at a dosage of 5 ppb (.005 ppm) as a poison for small fish or at a somewhat higher dosage as a selective poison for bullheads. Toxaphene is roughly 3 times as toxic to fish as rotenone and can be used at concentrations one third as great.[55]

Toxaphene seems to have little effect on phytoplankton, and zooplankton usually reappears within 3 or 4 weeks after treatment.[46] Most invertebrates seem to be quite sensitive to toxaphene and bottom fauna may be killed (except for oligochetes [24]) by a dosage of 0.1 ppm.[56] This might result from the tendency of toxaphene to collect at the bottom (specific gravity 1.6). Among the invertebrate bottom organisms, dragonfly nymphs were the earliest to reappear after treatment. Chironomidae were absent for more than 9 months.[24, 46, 56, 64, 77, 97, 98]

Most aquatic biologists have hesitated to use the newer insecticides for killing fishes because of the residual toxicity of these materials, and the unpredictable length of time required after treatment before a lake or pond can be restocked.

Sodium Cyanide. Sodium cyanide is useful as a fish poison in ponds and small lakes, primarily because the poisoned fish may be revived by placing them in fresh water if the fish are removed while still active. Ponds dosed at the rate of 1 ppm sodium cyanide become nontoxic to fish in about 4 days. Fish to be revived are usually collected within the first hour or two after treatment.[15]

As cyanides can be fatal to humans, this method of fish poisoning should be done only by competent technicians. Sodium cyanide, once applied to to the pond, offers little danger to wild or domestic animals. At 1 ppm, it has no noticeable effect on tadpoles, frogs, snakes, turtles or aquatic insects.

Sodium Sulfite. Sodium sulfite at a dosage of 168 ppm had been used experimentally to salvage fish in a small pond. The sulfite reduced the

* ppb = parts per billion.

dissolved oxygen and forced the fish to gulp air at the surface. Fish recovered fully when placed in fresh water if they were collected when still gulping air. This method is practical only in small ponds because of the cost of the sulfite (10 cents per pound).[116]

FISH POPULATION ADJUSTMENT

As mentioned above, there are a number of ways that a low-producing population may be adjusted to achieve a higher yield without eliminating and replacing the entire population. These methods are applicable when:

(1) A population consists of desirable fishes, but with some species stunted and others becoming scarce due to excessive competition.
(2) There is high demand for one or two species and low demand for one or more other species inhabiting the same water.
(3) Eliminating the indigenous population and starting over with a new one is impossible or impractical.

USE OF NETS AND SEINES

In small ponds, wire traps or wing nets are used to reduce excessive populations of crappies, bluegills, and other sunfishes and to permit an increase in the largemouth bass. Wing nets employed in Fork Lake controlled bluegills and allowed the development of a very large bass population. The very same type of selective cropping may be done with intensive seining provided the pond or lake basin lends itself to the making of a productive seine haul, and the seine and crew are available.[112] The main drawback to either of these methods is that they both entail a great deal of work, and some rather expensive equipment. Also, relatively few lakes or ponds are well adapted to cropping with wing nets or seines, and the average pond or lake owner does not have access to this equipment.

PARTIAL POISONING

Soon after the use of rotenone to poison an entire population became widespread fisheries biologists noted its differential toxicity to various species and sizes of fishes. This led to the development of the selective or partial poisoning technique with rotenone, designed to kill certain parts of a population without seriously damaging the remainder of it. This technique for removing warm-water fishes from trout lakes has been described on page 143.

In 1945 and 1946, I applied a shoreline treatment of rotenone to Park Pond of the South Pollywog Association holdings of a stripmine pond area in east central Illinois, in order to reduce an excessive population of gizzard shad and small sunfish. Later, when Dr. R. Weldon Larimore was studying the growth of warmouth in Park Pond,[68] he found that the warmouth had made unusually rapid growth (114 and 128 per cent of expected annual length increment) during 1945 and 1946. This he could not explain until it was discovered that the years of good warmouth growth corresponded to years of population thinning through partial poisoning.

Experience in partial poisoning operations has shown that gizzard shad are killed with lighter dosages of rotenone than almost any other warmwater fish.[14] In general most of the centrarchids (sunfishes) are moderately sensitive to rotenone, but smaller individuals of a species are generally more susceptible than larger ones. For this reason and because young fishes of many species inhabit the warm, quiet, shallow waters near the shore on bright summer days, a shoreline rotenoning operation can be used to kill numerous fish too small to interest anglers.[103]

Timing in Partial Poisoning. The timing of a partial treatment is important because the final effect may vary, depending upon whether the operation is done in the spring, mid-summer, or early fall. Suppose, for example, that a lake contained an excessive number of small bass and one wished to thin this population to allow for an expansion of a relatively small population of bluegills. A partial poisoning operation in May or June, but *after* the bass had spawned, would reduce the severity of predation by young bass on newly-hatched bluegills (the spawning season for bluegills lasts from late May to mid-September in the latitude of central Indiana and Illinois) and would allow a greater survival of these young in June, July, and August. Many of these bluegills might grow fast enough to exceed the size of easy predation before the next year class of bass was produced the following spring.

In another instance, a lake might contain a large population of stunted bluegills and a few large bass unable to reproduce successfully because of predation on bass eggs and fry by hoards of hungry bluegills. In such a situation partial poisoning should be performed either (1) immediately before the bass spawning season in the spring or (2) at the end of the bluegill spawning season, in September or early October. If the operation were done between these specific times, the food and space gained by the removal of a portion of the excess of bluegills would be taken up almost immediately by new hatches of young bluegills. However, population reduction by partial poisoning, just prior to the bass spawning season (and the bluegill spawning season as well), would curtail bluegill predation on the bass eggs and fry, resulting in a proportionate increase in the survival of young bass. Similarly, if partial poisoning were performed in early fall after the bluegills had stopped spawning, the space gained at the expense of a part of the population would not be filled, either through the production of new bluegills or growth of those escaping poisoning. Much of this space would still be available when the bass spawned the following spring, insuring improved survival of young bass. In the instances cited above, timing is of utmost importance if the desired results are to be forthcoming.

The greatest weakness of the partial poisoning technique is that without supplementary information on the standing crop of fish, it is impossible to gauge accurately the extent of the operation in terms of the per cent of a fish population removed.[63] Usually the operation is too conservative for optimum results, and a repetition may be necessary. In some instances it is useful and practical to do a partial poisoning operation just prior to the spawning season each year for as long as 5 successive years. Each treatment insures the production and survival of a year class of bass for that year and before the end of 5 years the bass population should be approaching the maximum that the water will support.

Swingle, Prather, and Lawrence [103] recommend the stocking of 150 to 200 fingerling bass per acre following a summer marginal poisoning operation. Such a stocking might check the success of sunfish reproduction which could be expected to fill up the space created by the poisoning with a new year class of small bluegills, green sunfish or other kinds of sunfish present. As mentioned above, this restocking is unnecessary if the poisoning operation can be done in spring before the bass have spawned or in the fall near the end of the fish-growing season.

Shoreline vs. Sectional Treatment. In partial poisoning operations one may poison completely a bay or an arm of a lake, using a dosage of rotenone of sufficient strength to kill all fish. In such a case it may be practical to separate the rest of the lake from the treated bay by blocking the opening with a canvas strip, long and deep enough to reach across the mouth of the bay (Figure 6.7). This strip can be hung on a wire supported by posts driven into the lake bottom.

Beckman [7] demonstrated an increase in the growth rate of rock bass after he had poisoned the fish in half of a lake having a natural constriction near the center. Unless the arm or bay to be treated represents one half or more of the total lake surface area, such a fish poisoning operation may be insufficient to reduce a stunted fish population.

Swingle, Prather, and Lawrence [103] do not favor sectional poisoning because more desirable fish are killed by this method than by marginal poisoning. This may or may not be a valid argument. Sectional poisoning removes fishes in proportion to the relative abundance of kinds and sizes in a pond or lake and, therefore, is a useful method of cropping. It is probably the only technique short of complete poisoning that is effective in reducing stunted populations of bullheads.

It is often practical to combine marginal poisoning with sectional poisoning. In such a combined operation the section of lake receiving complete treatment should represent 20 to 80 per cent of the total lake area (Figure 6.8). In calculating the dosage of rotenone to be used, the part of the lake to receive complete treatment should be dosed at 1 ppm— the remainder being given a marginal treatment with an amount required to treat it at the rate of 0.25 ppm. This marginal amount is sprayed within

Figure 6.7. Canvas "fence" used in partial poisoning of a lake. Water to right of canvas was treated with sufficient rotenone to kill all of its fish. Several fish in the "live box" on the left side of the canvas were unaffected.

a 20-foot strip parallel to the shore and completely encircling the lake exclusive of the section receiving the heavier dosage (Figure 6.8).

When a sectional poisoning is combined with marginal treatment, the fish collected from the sectional part may be considered a representative sample of the entire population of the lake. From the kinds and sizes of fish in this sample it may be possible to estimate the extent of artificial cropping in the current treatment and what further measures may be required to thin out the more severely stunted components of the population.

In planning the partial poisoning it is well to calculate the dosage, order

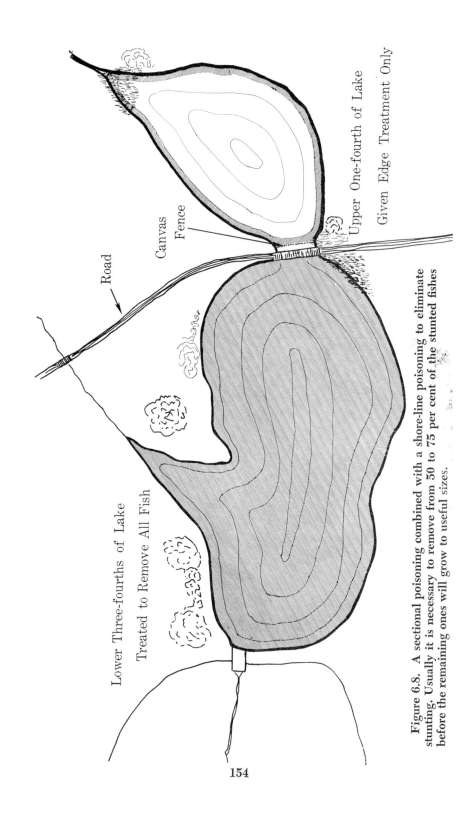

Road

Canvas
Fence

Upper One-fourth of Lake
Given Edge Treatment Only

Lower Three-fourths of Lake
Treated to Remove All Fish

Figure 6.8. A sectional poisoning combined with a shore-line poisoning to eliminate stunting. Usually it is necessary to remove from 50 to 75 per cent of the stunted fishes before the remaining ones will grow to useful sizes.

the chemical, and plan the mechanical aspects of the operation well in advance. If this has been accomplished, the operation can be performed on short notice—at a time when wind and weather conditions are favorable.

ARTIFICIAL FLUCTUATION OF WATER LEVELS

In Chapter 4, I described certain experiments that demonstrated that the total weight of a population was related to the size of the water area it inhabits. Thus, if a body of water devoid of fish is stocked with a few sexually mature individuals, these fish will reproduce and they and their offspring will add flesh until their total weight approaches the poundage of fish that the water area will support. This process may require one or more growing seasons, but eventually the poundage of fish will level off at some figure related to the size of the habitat and its food-producing capacity (natural fertility). This poundage adjustment may be downward if more pounds of fish were stocked originally than the lake would support.

Various levels of population density favor certain species, that is, some are better able to compete for food and space than others. Under extreme competition some become dominant and others, if exposed to this competition for several years, may entirely disappear from a population. These species that do poorly when subjected to severe competition may actually become very abundant if stocked with other fishes in a body of water with plenty of space.

Suppose then, that instead of adjusting the population by netting, seining, or partial poisoning, we subject it to extreme crowding for weeks or months through the release of much of the total volume of water (Figure 6.9). When the fish are crowded during warm weather, the entire population is under stress. Smaller and weaker fishes of many species starve or are killed through food competition, strife, or predation; the total poundage of the population is adjusted downward to conform with the smaller habitat and reduced food supply. The species, which as adults or fingerlings are best able to withstand crowding, will remain dominant although they may have stopped growing entirely.

Then the habitat is rapidly expanded by the addition of new water! The exposed lake bottom is reflooded and there is suddenly plenty of space and more food. All fish that have survived the period of crowding begin to grow rapidly. Under conditions of unlimited food and space, certain species that were adversely affected by crowding, produce large broods of young. If these young are piscivorous they may actually check the expansion of some of the species formerly so successful. Thus, there has been a sudden shift in dominance brought about by a drastic change in the habitat.[10] If this change is man-made, we have only taken our cue

Figure 6.9. Aerial view of fall drawdown shows lake area reduced by more than 50 per cent.

from nature where water levels are rarely stable, but are usually in a state of fluctuation, often mild, but sometimes very severe during floods. Flood-plain lakes in the valleys of rivers are subject to the rivers' fluctuations and, because these lakes are relatively shallow, these fluctuations may cause extreme changes in the surface areas of these lakes.

Prior to 1920, changes in water levels similar to those described above commonly occurred as a natural cycle in many of the flood-plain lakes along the Illinois River in Illinois. Professor Stephen A. Forbes [37] described the changes in water levels in the Havana region where in late summer the lakes, which extended over thousands of acres in spring when the river was high, covered only hundreds of acres; and many connecting channels were so low that it was often difficult to move a boat from the river into these lakes. According to the average gauge readings at Havana, water levels were usually highest in spring, gradually diminishing throughout the summer until they reached a low point in early fall. Levels usually rose in fall and winter but floods seldom occurred before spring. There were notable exceptions to this cycle, and floods have occurred in summer, fall and winter.

After World War I, most of the bottom land lakes of the Illinois River valley were surrounded by earthen levees and pumped dry, and the lake basins were used for farming. The few lakes that were left or reconverted after agricultural use were more or less stabilized through the construction of levees and spillways that kept the river water out unless it rose above the spillways' crests and held the lake water in when the river was lower than the crests.

During the pre-leveeing period of wide fluctuations of lake levels and areas, the lakes in the Havana region were famous for their fishing, particularly for their largemouth bass fishing. Presidents of the United States have fished there; fishing trains brought anglers from distances beyond the range of the horse and wagon. Records show that it was not considered unusual for fishermen to catch 100 bass in a day.

There are still plenty of fish in the Illinois River and adjacent undrained bottomland lakes,[95] but the populations are composed largely of crappies, bluegills, yellow bass, sheepshead, buffalo, carp, bullheads, and channel catfish, and where vegetation is abundant yellow perch may be common. Although largemouth bass are sometimes caught by bass fishing experts, the average angler does not go to the Illinois River for bass except in a few special locations.

Interest in the effects of fluctuating water levels upon fishes was stimulated by the late Dr. R. W. Eschmeyer and his colleagues,[30, 31, 32, 33] through their investigations of TVA waters. In 1947, Dr. Eschmeyer stated that several permanent-level pools on TVA impoundments had provided poorer fishing than other reservoirs subjected to wide fluctuations of water levels. He suggested that "the winter drawdown apparently limits the abundance of rough fish (by limiting their food) without serious injury to the game fish population." Drawdowns on TVA lakes followed no definite schedule, but most of the drop in level occurred in winter following needs for power.

The sudden lowering of the water level of a lake with the accompanying reduction in water volume and surface area affects all parts of an aquatic habitat and all components of the animal and plant communities that inhabit the water.

Effects Upon the Exposed Lake Bottom. According to Neess [80] the bottom of a lake or pond is divided into regions, "an upper, loose well aerated, and often highly colloidal layer of decomposed organic material, plant debris . . . and a lower anaerobic zone, differing widely in composition from place to place and often containing a large proportion of mineral matter." These soil layers have the ability to direct certain processes in the pond because the mineral composition of water is largely a reflection of the mineral composition of the soils of the pond bottom and the surrounding basin; also the colloidal fraction of the bottom materials consisting of humic substances, ferric gels, and clay is capable of absorbing certain soluble nutrient elements and governing their later distribution.

In a pond or lake where there is a shortage of oxygen near the bottom, decomposition of organic matter is slow and the products are reduced to incompletely oxidized compounds such as hydrogen sulfide, methane, and short-chain fatty acids. When the water is drawn off of a lake bottom and the bottom is allowed to dry out and crack open, an abundance of oxygen becomes available, the processes of decomposition are stepped up, and the pH of the bottom soils is raised. Under these conditions there may be a release of certain fertilizing substances from organic colloidal systems, making available greater quantities of potassium and phosphate. In European pond culture it was once considered important to grow a crop plant or a legume on the exposed pond bottom. Later the need for this practice was questioned [27] although the crop furnished income to the pond owner when the pond was not producing fish.

Whether a lake or pond bottom exposed by a drawdown will develop a vegetative cover depends upon the length of time the bottom lies exposed and the season of the year when the drawdown is made. A winter or early spring drawdown, which is prolonged by drought or purposely extended throughout the following plant growing season, will insure a luxuriant growth of terrestrial weeds on the exposed lake bottom. These weeds will reflect the fertility of the exposed lake bottom by their height and the density of the stand. Drawdowns made in July and August will be followed by some germination of seeds and growth of terrestrial plants, but drawdowns made as late as early September in the north are not followed by growth of terrestrial vegetation in the basin.

Whether or not plants grow upon the exposed bottom seems to be unimportant; of primary significance is the exposure of the bottom to rapid and complete oxidation.

Effects Upon Rooted Aquatic Vegetation. Most forms of submersed rooted aquatic plants are not greatly affected by a drawdown, e.g., exposure of such relevant portions of the bottom may not free them from this vegetation if water levels are normal by the next growing season, although it may be somewhat more sparse and scattered. The drawdown is not an effective method of controlling rooted aquatic plants. In some instances it may be responsible for increasing the extent of beds of rooted aquatics, because plants may gain a root hold in parts of a lake when the water level is down, that ordinarily are too deep for them. For example, in Allerton Lake near Monticello, Illinois, a September drawdown of six feet (maximum depth of lake 14 feet) was maintained throughout a long warm fall (1955). During this period, curly-leaved pond weed, *Potamogeton crispus*, gained a start in parts of the lake where the water was seven to eleven feet in depth when the lake was full. Then, as the lake refilled over winter and spring, this pond weed continued to grow so that in the summer of 1956 it reached the surface in all areas seven to eleven feet deep. This created a severe nuisance for boating and swimming and, when the lake was drawn down again in the fall of 1956, the drawdown had a minimum effect upon small green sunfish, red-ear sunfish, and bluegills, because they were protected from bass predation by the dense mats of vegetation in the deeper waters. A fish census made by draining the lake completely a month after the drawdown, exposed excessive populations of small green and red-ear sunfish and demonstrated the importance of pulling the water out of beds of vegetation if a drawdown is to be effective in ridding a lake of small sunfish.

Effects Upon Invertebrates. When water is released from the basin of an artificial lake through an outlet valve, all motile aquatic animals are either stranded or forced to move down with the water. Animals that escape being stranded are concentrated and exposed to new environmental conditions. Such weak swimmers as many kinds of entomostraca, rotifers, and small insects, particularly those that are littoral, are stranded as the water recedes. Larger aquatic insect larvae, such as dragonfly and mayfly nymphs, may attempt to crawl along with the receding water, but most of them eventually are stranded and die or are eaten by birds or other vertebrates. Some crayfish may be stranded, but most of them burrow into the lake bottom or move down with the receding waters. In draining Ridge Lake,[11] it was not unusual to find 200 to 300 pounds of crayfish in the stilling pit below the gate valve in the outlet tunnel, after all the water had escaped from the basin. These crayfish came through the outlet gate with the water during the time the lake was being drained.

Effects Upon Fishes and Other Vertebrates. The receding water not only strands small invertebrates but many small fishes as well, particularly in the littoral zone where sticks, debris, and mats of rooted vegetation trap these small fishes in temporary water pockets which soon dry up. Certain kinds of small fishes are stranded more often than others. For example, small green sunfish are stranded more often than are small blue-gills and small bluegills more often than small red-ear sunfish. Green sunfish are commonly found in shallow water along the lake edges, as are bluegills. The red-ear prefers deeper water and shows a tendency to move away from the water's edge as the lake level moves down. Neither young largemouth nor young smallmouth bass are ordinarily stranded with receding lake levels, although both may be trapped by dense mats of vegetation. Few large fishes are stranded unless they become trapped in shallow basins on the lake bottom and die later when the water in which they are trapped dries up.

Small fishes that are not stranded and move down the lake basin with the water are forced from the protection of rooted vegetation and shallow-water debris into the open water of the lake where they are subject to predation from larger fishes, bullfrogs, and fish-eating reptiles, birds, and mammals. These forces and the mechanical stranding of small fish materially reduce the populations of smaller fishes without greatly reducing numbers of the larger ones. The result is a selective culling action which is more specific for sunfish than for bass, and which may not be extensive enough to be beneficial unless the drawdown: (1) reduces the lake surface area by more than 50 per cent (Figure 6.9) and (2) forces the fish from the protection of beds of aquatic plants. The selective culling action resulting in a reduction of sunfish may set the stage for high survival of bass at the next bass-spawning season. Thus, fall drawdowns in several successive years may result in such a numerical buildup of bass that they will be of smaller average size than under more stable water levels (Figure 6.10).

Heavy predation on the small fish during a fall drawdown may continue as long as their numbers are concentrated and the water remains warm enough for rapid digestion. When the lake cools below 55°F, digestion is greatly slowed and the rate of predation diminishes accordingly.

Although small fish concentrated by a drawdown are vulnerable to predation by many aquatic animals, it seems probable that piscivorous fish account for the death of more small fishes than all other predators together. As yet, no one has been able to evaluate the element of time in relation to the culling of small fish following a drawdown, but it is reasonable to assume that small fish losses, while heaviest at first, may continue with reduced intensity over a period of several weeks or months.

Flat areas in the bottoms of reservoirs suitable for making seine hauls are sometimes cleared of stumps and debris before the reservoirs are filled. Then, later, when the reservoirs are drawn down, seines may be used to harvest concentrations of carp, buffalo, and other commercial fish, thereby giving an additional assist in the process of population improvement.

Types of Drawdowns. From the standpoint of angling there is some evidence to suggest that prolonged droughts affect fish populations favorably. In droughts extending over several years, lakes may gradually decrease in area. This gradual decrease must cause adjustment in the fish population. However, it is difficult to see how a slow drawdown would have a selective effect in eliminating excessive small fish.

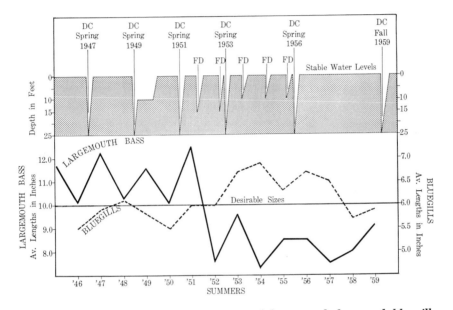

Figure 6.10. Changes in average sizes of largemouth bass and bluegills caught by fishermen at Ridge Lake (Illinois) under several types of management: 1945-1950 biennial draining and culling of small fish; 1951-1955, fall drawdowns with draining censuses in spring of 1953 and spring of 1956; 1956 to fall of 1959, stable water levels. DC = draining census; FD = fall drawdown. Fall drawdowns increased the number of bass but reduced their average size. Under stable water levels following the drawdown period, the number of bluegills expanded more than 500 per cent and their average size decreased. After 1957, the average size of the bass increased and their number declined.

Annual cycles of water levels, such as were described above for the Illinois River and adjacent bottom-land lakes, can be shown to have a pronounced effect on the fish population. Reservoirs with the greatest water-area fluctuations contained the largest per cents (by weight) of predatory species, which included many of our game species.[118, 119] Large man-made and controlled reservoirs have various types of annual cycles of water fluctuation; these cycles may be only remotely related to cycles of rainfall and runoff. Man-made cycles may vary from one lake to the next, depending upon purposes of water release. If the reservoir is designed to control floods, water will be expelled between floods or prior to anticipated high runoff so that the lake may be partially empty for the storage of excess runoff water. However, if its purpose is to supply water for navigation, the drawdowns occur during the drier parts of the year. In most parts of North America, dry periods correspond to late summer and early fall. However, in some cases, where there is an annual cycle of need for power, the water may be used to generate it, and the drawdown may conform to no schedule, or follow one bearing no relationship to rainfall and runoff in the watershed of the reservoir.

More experimental work must be done on drawdowns to allow biologists to predict the exact effects of these operations upon fish populations. Nearly all of the experimental work has been on drawdowns made at the end of the summer fishing season. As yet, no one can say whether a drawdown made in mid-summer would be more beneficial than one made in early September.

Where fishing is an important use for a "waterfowl" lake, there has been severe conflict between fishermen and those concerned with waterfowl, relative to the time that a drawdown is made. Waterfowl managers usually favor a mid-summer drawdown to allow the planting of millet or other quick-maturing grain on exposed mud flats. Fishermen may wish to prolong the summer fishing period as long as possible because, once the lake is drawn down, it may be difficult or impossible to move boats across the exposed mud flats. Moreover, the basin of the lake that is left will probably slope into deep water so gradually that fishing from the bank, once the lake has been drawn down, may be impossible.

The duck enthusiast will insist that the lake must be lowered in sufficient time to absolutely insure a grain crop. The interests of these two groups could be compatible except when the lake bottom is flat and there is too little water left for the fish to survive. In states where spring fishing is permitted, a drawdown in July will have given the fishermen a season of three or four months. They may then well afford to concede to the desires of those who would plant millet or some other duck food crop. Fishermen not only benefit from oxidation of the bottom, but also from the mechanical action of the roots of the grain plants growing in the lake bottom and the lake fertilization resulting from the decay of plant stems and duck excrement in the lake basin.

Lake Fertilization

The fertilization of ponds and lakes for increased production of fish has its origin in antiquity, and for centuries it has been common practice in Europe and parts of Asia to fertilize carp ponds.[79] In the United States the production of fish in ponds for commercial sale is limited. Most ponds and artificial lakes are for sport fishing.

The primary exponents of pond fertilization for the improvement of sport fishing are located in the southeastern United States where soils are often infertile. Swingle and Smith [105, 106] stated that fertilized ponds in Alabama support 4 to 5 times as great a weight of fish as unfertilized ones; and consequently, the former give much better fishing. They recommended the use of 100 pounds of 6-8-4 (N-P-K) and 10 pounds of nitrate of soda per acre of pond for each application, with a seasonal schedule of 8 to 14 treatments, beginning March or April and extending to September or October.

In Alabama such a fertilization program produces a "bloom" of plankton algae that prevents the development of filamentous algae and shades out any rooted submersed aquatic vegetation. It will not control water-lilies, lotus, or spatterdock; but these may be killed by removing the leaves several times during the summer.[106] The first leaf cutting should be made early in June and later ones every three weeks until no new leaves appear.

According to Swingle,[101] the algae produced by inorganic fertilization were largely genera of the Chlorophyceae: *Scenedesmus, Ankistrodesmus, Chlorella, Staurastrum, Pandorina, Cosmarium, Chlamydomonas, Nannochloris, Pediastrum, Coelastrum* and others. Euglenophyceae were also abundant and occasionally dominant. Dinophyceae were often present but usually not in large numbers. The bluegreen algae, *Coelosphaerium* and *Microcystis*, occasionally became abundant for limited periods. Variations in kinds of algae were observed in various types of ponds.

Swingle recognized the competition between plankton algae and filamentous algae for dominance. He stated that either 6-8-4 or cottonseed meal applied in clear ponds in cold weather will stimulate the growth of filamentous algae on the bottom which will rise to the surface and shade out plankton algae. However, if these substances are applied when the water is "warm," plankton algae will be produced. Most organic material encourages the growth of filamentous algae unless it colors the water and thereby shades the bottom.

There is no question but that the application of balanced inorganic fertilizers will increase the production of fish in a pond or lake by increasing the phytoplankton and, in turn, the aquatic animals at various trophic levels between the phytoplankton and fishes.[79]

Not only do potassium, phosphorus, and nitrogen function as fertilizer materials in an aquatic environment, but some other elements such as manganese may produce chemical changes that release inorganic fertilizers from insoluble chemical compounds in the substrate of a pond or lake,[47] giving an end effect similar to that obtained by direct fertilization.

As yet the fertilization of waters is far from an exact science; however, some of the information now available is given below.

Manganese. Hasler and Einsele [43] described the use of manganese to release phosphates from iron. Thus, manganese dioxide (MnO_2), which is not a fertilizer, may release phosphate (PO_4) from an insoluble bond with iron, so that the effect is the same as though phosphate were added.

Lime. Many authors stress the importance of lime in pond fertilization where there is a natural shortage of calcium.[27, 43, 80, 91, 114, 115, 120] In waters containing less than 10 ppm the addition of lime may be followed by a large increase in fish production. Lime is believed to have many effects, particularly on the bottom mud where it changes the colloidal and adsorptive properties and creates an alkaline environment, which is more suitable than an acid environment for bacteria and fungi. Thus, it increases, indirectly, the rate of decay. It is believed to have several possible chemical actions, such as the precipitation of iron compounds, and may counteract the poisonous properties of sodium, potassium, and magnesium ions. The calcium in lime may displace other fertilizing substances from organic colloidal systems, making available K^+, and $-PO_4$.[80, 114] The calcium in stripmine waters may be responsible for the establishment of a strong buffer system that keeps the high sulfate ($-SO_4$) from being toxic to fish and other aquatic organisms. In European fish ponds, enough lime is added to the drained pond basin to give a slight alkaline reaction and a crumbly mud structure. When unslaked lime is used on a drained pond basin, it is believed to have a toxic effect on aquatic organisms and fish parasites.

In soft water, the addition of lime may be followed by an increase in carbon dioxide storage in the form of bicarbonate. Swingle [101] believed that calcium competes with the algae for the free carbon dioxide, but Nielsen [81, 82] demonstrated that aquatic plants used bicarbonate (HCO_3) directly in photosynthesis, up to one half of the amount present. Bicarbonate was used more slowly than free carbon dioxide because the latter diffuses about 8 or 9 times as fast as bicarbonate.

Calcium may be applied in the form of "quick lime" (CaO) or as agricultural limestone. It should never be applied at the same time as phosphate, and "quick lime" should be applied 2-3 weeks before fish are stocked.

Potassium. Ponds with sandy bottom soils are often poor in potassium and respond markedly when this element is added. Usually it is difficult to measure the effects of adding potassium. These effects may be direct if there is a potassium scarcity or indirect if the addition of potassium displaces hydrogen from soil colloids, forming dilute acids in which phosphorus becomes soluble, i.e., potassium may indirectly make phosphorus available. German fish culturists usually mix potassium and phosphate fertilizers and apply them together.[91]

Phosphorus. Phosphorus is the most important fertilizing element in lakes and ponds, but may be easily lost through combination with an excess of calcium to form tricalcium phosphate ($Ca_3(PO_4)_2$).[49] As carbon dioxide increases, the precipitated salt may be converted to the more soluble di- and monocalcium phosphates.[50] As mentioned in connection with manganese above, iron may unite with phosphate to form an insoluble precipitate. Phosphorus also may combine physically with micells of ferric hydroxide or be absorbed directly on organic soil colloids on the pond bottom. For these reasons, phosphorus added to a lake or pond quickly goes out of solution, but still may be available on the pond bottom. It therefore follows that phosphorus applied at one time in some quantity may become available in small but useful amounts over a long period of time. European workers recommend about 17 kilograms per hectare (15.2 lb/acre) of phosphorus (applied as superphosphate) as an optimum dose.[91] Experiments in this country do not seem to substantiate this amount as optimum.

Nitrogen. Nitrogen is more often used in this country than in Europe as a fertilizing material. Some algae are able to fix nitrogen from the atmosphere if phosphorus is available,[26, 36, 90] particularly the bluegreen algae, *Anabaena* and *Nostoc*.[80] However, nitrogen in fertilizers gives a quick source of this element to the algae.

Other Functions of Fertilizers. There are some uses of fertilizer other than those of increasing phytoplankton. Swingle [101] mentions Irwin's work on the use of inorganic fertilizer to cause clay particles to settle out of muddy ponds (see Chapter 3). Ball [3] believed that the addition of fertilizer to the entire shoal area of North Twin Lake (Cheboygan County, Michigan) stimulated the growth of filamentous algae on the bottom which appeared to interfere with the nest building of sunfishes.

Although no controlled experiments have been projected to date, it seems likely that undissolved salts of commercial fertilizers falling into nests of centrarchids containing developing eggs or yolk sac fry would cause the embryos to die. Commercial fertilizer is usually broadcast in shallow water over an area that corresponds roughly with that selected by bluegills and other sunfishes for nesting. If a fertilization schedule called for an application of fertilizer to the shoal waters of a pond at two-week intervals from early spring to September or October, it is probable that many centrarchid embryos would be killed. This might give substantial assistance in keeping the bluegills or other sunfishes from becoming overly abundant.

One of the techniques of pond management often suggested is the systematic destruction of sunfish nests. Less effort would be required to drop a small handful of chemical salts into a nest from a boat than to mechanically destroy the nest, and the former method might be more effective. Jackson [60] used sodium hydroxide pellets for this purpose with good success. If fertilizer should prove useful in poisoning sunfish embryos, pond fertilization would be serving a dual purpose.

Dangers from the Use of Fertilizers. The application of inorganic fertilizers to ponds and lakes for increasing fish production [101, 106] has not been well accepted in parts of the United States outside of the southeast. The objections to pond and lake fertilization are many, and it seems apparent that results have been variable and quite unpredictable.[3, 22, 42, 89]

In the northernmost states, the suffocation of fishes under ice is common during severe winters with heavy snowfall. Fertilization of ponds and lakes in this region increases the danger of winterkill.[17, 107] Ball and Tanner [5] stated that the addition of fertilizer to one of their experimental ponds was the indirect cause of winterkill, because the fertilizer stimulated the algae which later decomposed under the ice.

In all parts of the country there is the ever-present danger of "summerkill" of fishes, where calm hot weather along with an abundance of plankton algae may result in nocturnal oxygen depletion in lakes and ponds.[66] This occurrence is not uncommon in organically rich lakes which are not fertilized. Swingle and Smith [105] advise against applying fertilizer when rooted aquatics are decomposing. They cite an instance when an application of fertilizer was broadcast over decomposing masses of *Najas*, with the result that oxygen was depleted and bass and other fishes died.

In Michigan ponds, the use of fertilizer could not be depended upon to control higher aquatic plants,[4] and produced filamentous algae even if not applied until after the water had warmed in the spring.[4, 85] This agreed with findings in Wisconsin [44] and in the hard water ponds of West Virginia.[100]

The nuisance values of algae stimulated by inorganic fertilizers are stressed by several authors. Ball and Tanner [5] state: "The appearance of the lake and its use for swimming, boating, and other recreational purposes were adversely affected by the fertilizer. The matted green scum formed by the filamentous algae around the shore and festooning the marginal vegetation was very unsightly and was a hindrance to fishermen, both in the use of their boats and by the fouling of their baits. The odor of the decaying algae was very unpleasant." Patriarche and Ball [85] warn about the unsightly condition that occurs when a growth of filamentous algae follows fertilization. Hansen, *et al.*,[42] describe a bloom of *Rhizochlonium sp.* in Lauderdale pond (Illinois) which covered from 25 to 75 per cent of the surface and stopped fishing except where the alga was absent.

There has been a tendency on the part of some aquatic biologists to over-simplify the problem of pond fertilization and to consider results obtained under some conditions to be universally meaningful.[80] Actually the problem of fertilization of waters is so complex that it is difficult to duplicate results from one pond to another, to say nothing of duplicating results from one research station to another.

There are dangers inherent in the fertilization of any eutrophic lake by any means.[58, 107] Hasler and Einsele [43] cite the changes that have taken place in Lake Snake, Vilas County, Wisconsin; Pontiac Lake, Michigan; Lake Okoboji, Iowa; Sylvan Lake, Noble County, Indiana; and Stadlsee near Waldsee in Wüerttemberg, Germany. They also describe the possibility that fertilization may upset an efficient natural food chain for one that is much less efficient. "For example, in a natural lake, a rich growth of *Cyclotella*, a small diatom, fulfills the ideal food requirement of *Daphnia*, but fertilization might encourage previously rare or nonexistent algae which are not adapted at all well as food for *Daphnia*, while the desirable form, *Cyclotella*, is suppressed."

Swingle and Smith [104] demonstrated that by applying inorganic fertilizer to ponds in the proper amount they could increase the standing crop of bluegills from 130 pounds per acre to between 300 and 500 pounds per acre. These results have not been demonstrated in Michigan,[85] in Indiana,[66] in Illinois [42] or in any other part of the United States outside of the southeastern states.

In ponds in some of the least productive soil types in Illinois the addition of recommended amounts of inorganic fertilizer increased the average standing crop of fish by about 1.22 times.[42] The improvement in fishing was such that uninformed fishermen could not tell which ponds were fertilized and which were not; yet in terms of total yield, rate of catch, and average size, the fertilized ponds produced considerably better bluegill fishing than did unfertilized control ponds. In contrast, the controls usually produced a higher yield of bass 10 inches or larger than did the fertilized ponds.

The fertilization of ponds and lakes cannot be recommended as a general fish management technique outside of the southeastern United States, because the results are too variable and uncertain. Once the fertility of small impoundments in productive soils has been built up, this fertility may manifest itself in luxuriant annual crops of filamentous algae, bluegreen algae, or rooted aquatic vegetation. There are already numerous examples of such ponds, most of which are quite productive of fish; but they are problem waters because a treatment to kill rooted vegetation will be followed by obnoxious blooms of algae which in turn may require chemical treatment. These lakes have reduced aesthetic values, and fishing and swimming are limited by plant growths of one type or another.

If fertilization appears desirable in starting new ponds of low natural fertility, the program should be stopped before undesirable plant growths are evident. New gravel-pit ponds, stone-quarry ponds or dug ponds having basins of raw clay are often poor fish-producing waters when first formed. The addition of several hundred pounds per acre of commercial fertilizer during the first year will improve fish production without creating nuisance vegetation problems in later years.

AQUATIC VEGETATION AND CONTROL MEASURES

The vegetation that develops in an aquatic environment is as characteristic and specialized as that associated with any terrestrial habitat. How then may aquatic plants suddenly appear in a new artificial lake, which a few months before was a dry valley supporting only terrestrial grasses and shrubs? Since the valley was flooded, the terrestrial plants have disappeared and have been replaced by widespread floating mats of green "scum" composed of one or several varieties of filamentous algae. In shallow water are a few scattered plants of a fine-leaved pondweed (*Potamogeton sp.*), a higher plant that grows almost entirely below the water surface and which cannot support its own leaves when it is lifted out of water.

How did these plants manage to suddenly appear in a location separated from other standing water by miles of dry land? Undoubtedly, resting cells of various kinds of algae blow about on winds. Seeds of certain higher plants may be transported by special organs which allow them to become airborne (as in the feathered seeds of the cattail). Still other seeds which are covered with a very hard coat are eaten by aquatic birds and pass through their digestive tracts undigested, only to fall to the pond bottom and germinate in the next location visited by the bird. It is conceivable that seeds and parts of plants might become entangled with or stick to the muddy toes of aquatic birds and be carried for short distances in this manner.[92] Some seeds float from one location to another through connecting water courses. Thus, during a flood period a pond located well upstream in a watershed might furnish floating seeds to a downstream impoundment.

Aquatic plants get around in one way or another, and certain species are likely to appear before others. Among the large emergent plants the cattails usually appear first, perhaps because the seed-bearing "fuzz" of the cattail head is so readily carried by the wind.

Of the submersed pondweeds, the fine-leaved varieties usually appear first, later to be followed by coarser-leaved varieties. Why this should be so is unknown, although there is evidence that the new habitat is more suitable for some species than others. This may be demonstrated by artificially introducing a variety of submersed and emergent aquatic plants into a newly-impounded water area. Usually only a few kinds will survive and these are the species that might be expected to move in naturally. Experience has shown that it is often a complete waste of money to purchase aquatic vegetation for plantings in new impoundments, particularly if these species are not common in similar waters.

TYPES OF AQUATIC PLANTS

Aquatic vegetation exclusive of bacteria may be separated into several types:

ALGAE

(1) Plankton algae—free floating cells of single or colonial habit, forming characteristic groups, plates, short strands, or spheres with or without power of movement: *Phacus, Scenedesmus, Microcystis, Pandorina.*

(2) Filamentous algae—usually forming strands or threads of cells which may grow on the pond bottom but often float to the surface forming scums or floating mats of hairlike strands: *Spirogyra, Zygnema.*

(3) Algae that grow upward from the pond bottom in a plant form not unlike that of some of the higher plants: *Nitella, Chara.*

HIGHER PLANTS

(4) Floating aquatic plants—unattached and floating about on the surface: Water hyacinth (*Echhornia*), Watermeal (*Wolffia*), Duckweed (*Lemna*).

(5) Submersed aquatic plants—mostly below the surface and supported by the water: Pondweeds (*Potamogeton*), Coontail (*Ceratophyllum*), Waterweed (*Elodea*), Milfoil (*Myriophyllum*).

(6) Emergent aquatic plants—mostly above the surface and self-supporting: Cattails (*Typha*), Bulrush (*Scirpus*), Arrowheads (*Sagittaria*), Figure 6.11.

(7) Woody plants and trees—not true aquatics but usually associated with water: Button bush (*Cephalanthus*), Cypress (*Taxodium*), Willows (*Salix*).

These plants serve the same functions in an aquatic habitat as in a terrestrial one, i.e., some are sources of food for herbivorous animals, some represent substrata upon which certain animals live, still others serve as cover and a mechanical aid in escape from natural predators.

Aquatic plants compete for space in an aquatic environment much as terrestrial plants do. However, the environment of the former is less stable than the terrestrial environment, and for this reason the plant communities are much less stable. This is particularly true of the algae which are short lived and sensitive to minute changes in the environment and of the submersed aquatic plants which may be shaded out by high levels of turbid water.

Algae as a Basic Food. Certain of the algae are believed to form basic foods for herbivorous animals in the aquatic environment, much as the grasses are basic foods for many of the herbivorous animals in a terrestrial habitat. In this function some species of algae are much more valuable than others just as some grasses and grains on land are more valuable

Figure 6.11. Dense stand of cattails (background) with Arrowhead (*Sagittaria*) in foreground. These are among the more common forms of nuisance emergent aquatic vegetation.

than others as foods. Probably the plankton algae and bottom microflora in shallow water are more readily utilized than the filamentous forms. Actually very little is known of specific aquatic food chains and the relative values of various species of algae.

Plant cells or plant debris serve as foods for certain species of aquatic animals from protozoa to fishes. However, most of the fishes important for angling are not herbivorous, or eat only limited amounts of plant material. This is true for bluegills which feed largely on insect larva and entomostraca but which at certain seasons apparently take algae and the leaves of some submersed aquatic weeds. It has not been determined whether this vegetable matter is a selected food or simply stuffing, taken because other more desirable foods were not readily available.

Dangerous Algae. Several species of bluegreen algae (Cyanophycae) produce toxic substances when they die and decay. These algae have been responsible for mammalian, avian, and fish deaths.[59] The genera involved in these deaths were *Aphanizomenon, Anabaena, Nodularia, Coelosphaerium,* and *Glaeotrichia.* These algae are particularly dangerous when they appear as "blooms" on lakes and ponds and are concentrated by wind action along the downwind lake margin. Domestic stock drinking

Figure 6.12. Floating mats of filamentous algae are a nuisance to boaters and swimmers and make fishing nearly impossible.

this concentration of water and bluegreen algal cells rapidly show signs of acute poisoning. The toxic substance produced by the cells will cause the death of animals when algal cells are themselves excluded, and will survive the equivalent of water treatment using alum coagulation, filtration, and chlorination. However, as far as is known, no human deaths or outbreaks of human gastroenteritis have been positively traced to these algae, although unexplained outbreaks of gastroenteritis have been reported in the same areas where extensive algal blooms were present.[83]

Nuisance Algae. Most filamentous algae are considered nuisance plants because they eventually rise to the water surface and float about as green "slime" or "scum" until they die and disintegrate (Figure 6.12). In this position they are obnoxious to swimmers, and foul motor blades, oars, and lines of boaters and fishermen.

There are several genera of filamentous algae that grow luxuriantly on the pond surface to form a thick blanket that may almost completely cover the pond. Lawrence [70] lists *Pithophora* as a nuisance form for this reason in the southeastern states, and Hansen *el al.*[42] describe a pond in southern Illinois that was nearly always partly covered with a floating layer of *Rhizoclonium*. Hatchery personnel in northern states are sometimes bothered with *Hydrodictyon,* an alga in which the elongated cells are arranged in the form of a net with 6-sided mesh. Small fish become entangled in these algal nets and die because they are unable to escape.

Some algae that grow on rocks and submerged concrete are dangerous to bathers and wading fishermen because they create slippery footing and often cause waders to fall. One type of *Spirogyra* with very coarse filaments is notoriously slippery, and I once saw a bather slip and sit down at the top of a steep, spirogyra-covered lake spillway and slide entirely to the bottom before he could stop. Needless to say, he repeated the act until the algae as well as the seat of his bathing suit was practically gone.

Control of Algae. Algae are very sensitive to copper and for many years crude copper sulfate crystals dissolved in water and sprayed on algae or dragged in a sack behind a boat has been a standard method of algae control. In soft water, 1 ppm or less was toxic to algae, but when used in hard water the copper ions united with carbonate in the water to form an insoluble precipitate that was useless in killing algae. Thus, it was necessary to use a much stronger dosage (5 to 12 ppm) in order to control algae. At dosages higher than about 12 ppm the copper became toxic to fish. Because the hardness of water varies a great deal it is difficult or impossible to define a dosage, and only trials will allow one to discover the amount needed for an effective treatment for a specific water.

Copper citrate is sometimes used in algae control work. This copper compound is much more expensive than copper sulfate, but a dosage of 0.5 to 1 ppm is usually sufficient to kill algae. Copper citrate is also more toxic to fish than is copper sulfate.

CMU [3-(p-chlorophenyl)-1, 1-dimethylurea] has been recommended as a deterrent to algal growth after an established bloom has been killed by other chemicals.[35, 76]

LOSS OF FISH PRODUCTION THROUGH ROOTED VEGETATION

There is some evidence that dense stands of submersed rooted aquatic plants may bind up nutrient materials throughout the growing season,[9] so that they are not available for the production of phytoplankton and the organisms that feed upon phytoplankton. This, in turn, may be reflected upon the fish through an eventual reduction of their food supply.

An apparent relationship between fish yields and increasing stands of *Potamogeton foliosus* and *P. nodosus* is shown in Table 6.4.[9] The area of open water in this pond was reduced to 51.2 per cent of the total surface area by a dense stand of *P. foliosus* and *P. nodosus*. The fish yield was reduced to 58.1 per cent of the yield taken during the year when aquatic vegetation was largely absent, although during the year when the low yield of fish was taken the net fishing intensity was increased 359 per cent and the angling intensity was increased 157 per cent. Swingle [101] investigated a pond that became filled with a heavy growth of naiad, *Najas guadalupensis*. He concluded that the rank plant growths did not reduce the hook-and-line yield. Evidence from the study cited above indicated that the fish were actually supported in this pond at a lower poundage than they had been before the dense stand of vegetation developed.

TABLE 6.4   REDUCED YIELD OF FISH (IN SPITE OF INCREASED FISHING PRESSURE) ASSOCIATED WITH THE SPREAD OF DENSE STANDS OF ROOTED POND-WEEDS, *Potamogeton foliosus* AND *P. nodosus*, IN A POND IN CENTRAL ILLINOIS.[9]

Year	Yield		Area of Open Water Not Filled with Vegetation		Net-Fishing Intensity		Angling Intensity	
	Pounds	Per Cent of 1939 Yield	Acres	Per Cent of 1939 Area	Net-days	Per Cent of 1939 Net Fishing	Man-hours	Per Cent of 1939 Angling
1939	223.4	100.0	1.25	100.0	92	100.0	27.0	100.0
1940	200.2	89.6	0.95	76.0	182	197.8	36.3	134.4
1941	129.9	58.1	0.64	51.2	330	358.8	42.3	156.7

Algae and rooted vegetation are in competition for available plant nutrient materials and space in an aquatic habitat; when algae are abundant they shade rooted aquatic plants and bind up the plant nutrient materials within their cells. Similarly, rooted plants trap nutrients when they become abundant and hold them from use by algae until the higher plants die and decay and the nutrients are again released. Rooted vegetation often is able to suppress the growth of algae and, because it is longer-lived and more stable than the algae, it tends to persist throughout the growing season. This vegetation may die down in the fall when the water becomes cold, but the release of nutrients in cold weather is of little use to the trophic cycles of the lake or pond.

Sudden Plant Die-offs. Occasionally progressive plant "die-offs" occur in ponds and lakes. In two instances of plant die-offs that I have observed, the deaths began at specific locations and spread to include all of the rooted vegetation in a pond. One of these occurred in early August of 1941 at Fork Lake (Illinois).[9] Here the vegetation involved was *P. foliosus*

Table 6.5 Some common kinds of aquatic vegetation, with chemicals and dosages recommended for their control.[51]

Group and Species	Chemical	Rate of Application	Remarks
Emergent	Free Acid Equivalent		
Water willow Dianthera spp.[1]	2,4-D (20%G)[2] 2,4,5-T (L)[2] 2,4,5-TP (L)	1 lb/430 sq ft 1 cup/gal water 1 cup/gal water	spread on water wet foliage thoroughly wet foliage thoroughly
Water primrose, Jussiaea spp.	2,4-D (20%G) 2,4,5-T (L) 2,4,5-TP (L)	1 lb/430 sq ft 1 cup/gal water 1 cup/gal water	spread on water wet foliage thoroughly wet foliage thoroughly
Arrowhead, Sagittaria spp.	2,4-D (20%G) 2,4,5-T (L) 2,4,5-TP (L)	1 lb/430 sq ft 1 cup/gal water 1 cup/gal water	spread on water wet foliage thoroughly wet foliage thoroughly
Cattails, Typha spp.	Dalapon[3] Amino triazole	4 oz/gal water and 3 caps detergent 2 oz/gal water and 3 caps detergent	wet foliage thoroughly wet foliage thoroughly
Submersed Coontail, Ceratophyllum spp.	2,4-D (20%G) 2,4,5-T (L) 2,4,5-TP (L) Endothal (G) Sodium arsenite	3 ppm 3 ppm 3 ppm 5 ppm 5-10 ppm	spread on water apply below water apply below water spread on water apply below water

174

Water milfoil, Myriophyllum spp.	2,4-D (G)	3-4 ppm	spread on water
	2,4,5-TP (L)	2-3 ppm	apply below water
	Endothal (G) [4]	3 ppm	apply below water
	Sodium arsenite	5-10 ppm	apply below water
Submersed Potamogetons			
Sago pondweed, Potamogeton pectinatus	Endothal (G)	1 ppm	spread on water
Curly-leaved pondweed, Potamogeton crispus	Endothal (G)	1 ppm	spread on water
	Sodium arsenite	8-10 ppm	apply below water
Fine-leaved pondweeds, P. spp.	Endothal (G)	1 ppm	spread on water
	Sodium arsenite	5-10 ppm	apply below water
Floating-leaved pondweeds, (Potamogeton spp.)	Endothal (L)	1 cup/gal water	spray leaves on surface

[1] Scientific names are those of Fasset, 1957.
[2] L = liquid form, G = granular form.
[3] Dalapon is the common name for 2,2-dichloropropionic acid.
[4] Sold under the trade name of Aquathol.

Free-floating algae (filamentous) can be controlled by spraying a saturated solution of copper sulphate (blue vitriol) or sprinkling fine crystals on the floating masses. There is no known chemical control for duckweed (Lemna spp.); it must be removed mechanically. Sodium arsenite is widely used to control many kinds of submersed aquatic weeds, but it will not control sago pondweed.

which began to die in a small area of shallow water at the upper end of the pond and spread until all of the vegetation had died and disintegrated, and an algal bloom of *Aphanizomenon flos-aquae* had developed. A second example of vegetation die-offs occurred in Ridge Lake (Illinois) in 1946 when Mr. W. W. Fleming was studying plant-invertebrate relationships in dense stands of the pond weeds, *P. foliosus, P. nodosus, P. pectinatus, Najas flexilis,* and *Elodea canadensis.*[11] In 1948, this die-off began about July 8 and gradually eliminated the rooted vegetation until on July 23 nothing but open water could be found at his selected sampling stations which were previously in dense stands of rooted pond weeds.

This die-off at Ridge Lake has occurred during most summers since 1946; usually when the last of the early summer vegetation is dying, a new second crop is developing in areas where the old crop died first. By early September, there is almost a complete replacement of vegetation in areas where it was present before the die-off, but the stand is somewhat less dense than it was in the original stand that grew in late spring and early summer. It seems possible that this die-off is caused by some disease or parasite, but no causative organism has been isolated.

ROLE OF AQUATIC VEGETATION IN MANAGEMENT

Originally, aquatic biologists held the belief that beds of higher aquatic plants were an essential part of the aquatic environment, presumably because they were almost always present in lakes and ponds. This concept was entirely discarded by Swingle and Smith [106] who recommended the use of inorganic fertilizers in ponds to stimulate the growth of "blooms" of phytoplankton to shade rooted aquatics and thereby cause them to die. These investigators demonstrated that the phytoplankton blooms stimulated a higher production of zooplankton which, in turn, raised the level of food for such omnivorous feeders as bluegills, and thereby increased the total fish production.

At present, excessive amounts of either rooted aquatic vegetation or algae are considered undesirable in ponds and lakes used for fishing, boating, and bathing. Where there is no history of intentional fertilization, excessive vegetation may be indicative of mild or severe organic pollution from barn lots or septic tanks. One of the drawbacks to locating housing developments around small artificial lakes is that such developments often are not connected with sewage disposal systems; rather, each house is supplied with its own septic tank and tile field. If the house is close enough to the lake to benefit aesthetically from it, the tile field must of necessity be laid in land sloping toward the lake. Eventually effluents from these tile fields enter the lake and, because they carry phosphates and nitrates, they act as fertilizers which stimulate aquatic vegetation and create nuisance problems. Prospective home owners who contemplate the purchase of lots for permanent homes on small lakes should insist on a sewage system which will carry all effluents away from the lake.

Dense stands of vegetation, besides being a nuisance, offer too much protection to small fishes, and are sometimes directly responsible for overpopulation and stunting. This is true not only for submersed vegetation, but also for emergent forms such as cattails, bulrushes, arrowheads, water willow and pond lilies. For these reasons, where economically justifiable, excessive aquatic vegetation should be controlled.

CONTROL OF HIGHER AQUATIC VEGETATION

For more than 30 years, sodium arsenite was used for the control of submersed rooted aquatic vegetation, often with good results.[99] The main objections to its use are that (1) it is a poison which may accumulate in a pond or lake; (2) it is dangerous to handle and apply; (3) it is not very effective in the control of certain water weeds, such as sago pondweed, *Potamogeton pectinatus*, and curly-leaved pondweed, *P. crispus*.

Recently many terrestrial herbicides have been tested for their potential usefulness in aquatic weed control.[94] Not only must these herbicides kill aquatic plants, but they must also show low toxicity to fish and aquatic invertebrates. For example, CMU [3-(p-chlorophenyl)-1,1-dimethylurea], a terrestrial soil sterilant was found to control *Najas* in ponds when applied at a rate of 15 pounds per acre.[13] This material was nontoxic to fish and most aquatic organisms.

Some of the more promising herbicides are given in Table 6.5.[51] However, progress in this field is so rapid that it is probable that new and more efficient herbicides will soon replace some of these listed in Table 6.5.

LITERATURE

1. Anon., *Jour. Wildlf. Mgt.*, **14**(1), 85-88 (1950).
2. Applegate, V. C., Howell, J. H., Hall, A. E., Jr., and Smith, M. A., *U. S. Dept. of Int., Fish & Wildl. Serv. Special Scientific Report*, **207**, 157 pp., (1957).
3. Ball, R. C., *Am. Fish. Soc. Trans.*, **78**, 146-155 (1950).
4. Ball, R. C., *Jour. Wildlf. Mgt.*, **16**(3), 266-269 (1952).
5. Ball, R. C., and Tanner, H. A., *Mich. St. Coll. Tech. Bull.*, **223**, 1-32 (1951).
6. Beall, H. B., and Wahl, R. W., *Prog. Fish-Cult.*, **21**(3), 138-142 (1959).
7. Beckman, W. C., *Am. Fish. Soc. Trans.*, **70**, 143-148 (1941).
8. Bennett, G. W., *Ill. Nat. Hist. Surv. Bull.*, **22**(3), 357-376 (1943).
9. Bennett, G. W., *Ill. Nat. Hist. Surv. Bull.*, **24**(3), 377-412 (1948).
10. Bennett, G. W., *North Am. Wildlife Conf. Trans.*, **19**, 259-270 (1954a).
11. Bennett, G. W., *Ill. Nat. Hist. Surv. Bull.*, **26**(2), 217-276 (1954b).
12. Bennett, G. W., and Childers, W. F., *Jour. Wildlf. Mgt.*, **21**(4), 414-424 (1957).

13. Benson, N. G., and Conner, J. T., *Prog. Fish-Cult.*, 18(2), 78-80 (1956).
14. Bowers, C. C., *Prog. Fish-Cult.*, 17(3), 134-135 (1955).
15. Bridges, W. R., *U.S.F.W.S. Spec. Sci. Rept*, 253, 1-11 (1958).
16. Brown, C. J. D., and Ball, R C., *Am. Fish. Soc. Trans.*, 72, 268-284 (1943).
17. Brown, C. J. D., and Thoreson, N. A., *Jour. Wildlf. Mgt.*, 16(3), 275-278 (1952).
18. Buck, D. H., and Whitacre, M., *Prog. Fish-Cult.*, 22(3), 141-143 (1960).
19. Burdick, G. E., Dean, H. J., and Harris, E. J., *N. Y. Fish & Game Jour.*, 2(1), 36-67 (1955).
20. Burnet, A. M. R., *New Zealand Jour. of Sci.*, 2(1), 46-56 (1959).
21. Carlander, K. D., and Moorman, R. B., *Prog. Fish-Cult.*, 19(2), 92-94 (1957).
22. Clark, Minor, *Jour. Wildlf. Mgt.*, 16(3), 262-266 (1952).
23. Cobb, E. S., *Jour. of Tenn. Acad. of Sci.*, 29(1), 45-54 (1954).
24. Cushing, C. E., Jr., and Olive, J. R., *Am. Fish. Soc. Trans.*, 86, 294-301 (1957).
25. Davis, H. S., *Prog. Fish-Cult.*, 50, 1-13 (1940).
26. De, P. K., Proc. Roy. Soc. London B, 127, 121-138 (1939).
27. Demoll, R., *Handb. der Binnenfischerei Mitteleuropas*, 4, 53-160 (1925).
28. Erickson, A. B., *Publ. Health Repts.*, 62, 1254-1262 (1947).
29. Eschmeyer, R. W., *Pap. Mich. Acad. Sci. Arts & Letts.*, 22, 613-628 (1937).
30. Eschmeyer, R. W., *Jour. Tenn. Acad. Sci.*, 17(1), 90-115 (1942).
31. Eschmeyer, R. W., and Jones A. M., *N. A. Wildlf. Conf. Trans.*, 6, 222-240 (1941).
32. Eschmeyer, R. W., Manges, D. E., and Haslbauer, O. F., *Jour. Tenn. Acad. Sci.*, 22(1), 45-56 (1947).
33. Eschmeyer, R. W., Stroud, R. H., and Jones, A. M., *Jour Tenn. Acad. Sci.*, 19(1), 70-122 (1944).
34. Fassett, N. C., "A Manual of Aquatic Plants," pp. 1-405, with revision appendix by E. C. Ogden, Univ. of Wisc. Press, Madison, Wis., 1957.
35. Fitzgerald, G. P., *Trans. Wis. Acad. Sci., Arts & Letts.*, 46, 281-294 (1957).
36. Fogg, G. E., *Brit. Jour. Exp. Biol.*, 19, 78-87 (1942).
37. Forbes, S. A., *Bienn. Rpt. Ill. Sta. Fish Comm.*, 1892-1894, 35-52 (1895).
38. Hall, J. F., *Ky. Acad. Sci. Trans.*, 17(3-4), 140-147 (1956).
39. Hansen, D. F., *Ill. Acad. Sci. Trans.*, 37, 115-122 (1944).
40. Hansen, D. F., *Ill. Nat. Hist. Surv. Bull.*, 25(4), 211-265 (1951).
41. Hansen, D. F., *Ill. Acad. Sci. Trans.*, 46, 216-226 (1953).
42. Hansen, D. F., Bennett, G. W., Webb, R. J., and Lewis, J. M., *Ill. Nat. Hist. Surv. Bull.*, 27(5), 345-390 (1960).
43. Hasler, A. D., and Einsele, W. G., *N. A. Wildlf. Conf. Trans.*, 13, 527-555 (1948).
44. Hasler, A. D., and Jones, E., *Ecology*, 30(3), 359-364 (1949).
45. Hayes, F. R., and Livingstone, D. A., *Jour. Fish. Res. Bd. Can.*, 12(4), 618-635 (1955).
46. Hemphill, J. E., *Prog. Fish-Cult.*, 16(1), 41-42 (1954).
47. Henderson, C., *Prog. Fish-Cult.*, 11(3), 157-159 (1949).
48. Henderson, C., Pickering, Q. H., and Tarzwell, C. M., *Am. Fish. Soc. Trans.*, 88(1), 23-32 (1959).

49. Hepher, B., *Bamidgeh,* **10**(1), 3 (1958a).
50. Hepher, B., *Bamidgeh,* **10**(1), 4-18 (1958b).
51. Hiltibran, R. C., *Ill. Nat. Hist. Surv. Mimeo Series,* **A-5**, 1-18 (1961).
52. Hoffman, C. H., and Surber, E. W., *Am. Fish. Soc. Trans.,* **75**, 48-58 (1948).
53. Hoffman, C. H., and Surber, E. W., *Prog. Fish-Cult.,* **11**(4), 203-211 (1949).
54. Hoffman, C. H., and Linduska, J. P., *Sci. Monthly,* **69**, 104-114, (1949).
55. Hooper, F. F., *Trans. 2nd Sem. on Water Poll., U.S.P.H.S.,* 7 pp. (1959).
56. Hooper, F. F., and Grzenda, A. R., *Am. Fish. Soc. Trans.,* **85**, 180-190 (1957).
57. Huish, M. T., *Proceed. Ann. Conf., S. Eastern Assn. Game & Fish Commrs.,* **11**, 66-70 (1958).
58. Hynes, H. B. N., "The Biology of Polluted Waters," pp. 255, University Press of Liverpool, Liverpool, England, 1960.
59. Ingram, W. M., and Prescott, G. W., *Am. Midland Naturalist,* **52**(1), 75-87 (1954).
60. Jackson, C. F., *N. H. Fish and Game Dept. Tech. Circ.,* **12**, 1-16 (1956).
61. Jackson, C. F., *N. H. Fish and Game Dept. Tech. Circ.,* **14**, 1-28 (1957).
62. Jenkins, R. M., *Okla. Acad. Sci. Proc.,* **37**, 164-173 (1959).
63. King, J. E., *Okla. Acad. of Sci. Proc.,* **35**, 21-24 (1954).
64. Kiyoshi, G. F., and Hooper, F. F., *Prog. Fish-Cult.,* **20**(4), 189-190 (1958).
65. Krumholz, L. A., *Jour. Wildlf. Mgt.,* **12**(3), 305-317 (1948).
66. Krumholz, L. A., *Jour. Wildlf. Mgt.,* **16**(3), 254-257 (1952).
67. Lambou, V. W., *Prog. Fish-Cult.,* **21**(3), 143-144 (1959).
68. Larimore, R. W., *Ill. Nat. Hist. Surv. Bull.,* **27**(1), 1-83 (1957).
69. Larimore, R. W., Durham, L., and Bennett, G. W., *Jour. Wildlf. Mgt.,* **14**(3), 320-323 (1950).
70. Lawrence, J. M., *Prog. Fish-Cult.,* **16**(2), 83-86 (1954).
71. Lawrence, J. M., *Prog. Fish-Cult.,* **18**(1), 15-21 (1956).
72. Leonard, J. W., *Am. Fish. Soc. Trans.,* **68**, 269-280 (1939).
73. Lindgren, P. E., *Fish. Bd. of Sweden, Ins. of Freshwater Res.,* **41**, 172-184 (1960).
74. Linduska, J. P., and Surber, E. W., *U. S. Fish and Wildlf. Serv. Circ.,* **15**, 1-19 (1948).
75. Loeb, H. A., *N. Y. Fish & Game Jour.,* **4**(1), 109-118 (1957).
76. Maloney, T. E., *Am. Wat. Wks. Assn.,* **50**, 416-422 (1958).
77. Mayhew, J., *Proc. of Iowa Acad. of Sci.,* **66**, 513-517 (1959).
78. Moody, H. L., *Proc. Ann. Conf., S. Eastern Assn. Game & Fish Commrs.,* **11**, 89-91 (1958).
79. Mortimer, C. H., and Hickling, C. F., *Colonial Office Fishery Pub.,* **5**, 1-155 (1954).
80. Neess, J. C., *Am. Fish. Soc. Trans.,* **76**, 335-358 (1949).
81. Nielsen, E. S., *Dansk Botanisk Ark.,* **11**(8), 1-25 (1944).
82. Nielsen, E. S., *Dansk Botanisk Ark.,* **12**(8), 1-71 (1947).
83. Palmer, C. M., *U. S. Pub. Health Serv.,* **657**, 61 (1959).
84. Parker, R. A., *Ecology,* **39**, 304-317 (1958).
85. Patriarche, M. H., and Ball, R. C., *Mich. St. Coll. Ag. Exp. Sta. Tech. Bull.,* **207**, 1-35 (1949).
86. Post, G., *Prog. Fish-Cult.,* **17**(4), 190-191 (1955).

87. Prevost, G., *Canadian Fish-Cult.*, **28**, 13-35 (1960).
88. Prevost, G., Lanouette, C., and Grenier, F., *Jour. Wildlf. Mgt.*, **12**(3), 241-250 (1948).
89. Saila, S. B., *Jour. Wildlf. Mgt.*, **16**(3), 279-282 (1952).
90. Sawyer, C. N., *Sewage and Indust. Wastes*, **24**(6), 768-775 (1952).
91. Schäeperclaus, W., "Lehrbuch der Teichwirtschaft," pp. 1-289, Book Pub. House Paul Parney, Berlin, 1933.
92. Schlichting, H. E., Jr., *Am. Microsc. Soc. Trans.*, **79**, 160-166 (1960).
93. Smith, L. L., Jr., Franklin, D. R., and Kramer, R. H., *Am. Fish. Soc. Trans.*, **88**(2), 141-146 (1959).
94. Snow, J. R., *Proc. Ann. Conf., S. Eastern Assn. Game & Fish Commrs.*, **11**, 125-132 (1958).
95. Starrett, W. C., and McNeil, P. L., Jr., *Ill. Nat. Hist. Surv. Biol. Notes*, **30**, 1-31 (1952).
96. Starrett, W. C., and Barnickol, P. G. *Ill. Nat. Hist. Surv. Bull.*, **26**(4), 325-366 (1955).
97. Stringer, G. E., and McMynn, R. G., *Canadian Fish-Cult.*, **23**, 39-47 (1958).
98. Stringer, G. E., and McMynn, R. G., *Canadian Fish-Cult.*, **28**, 37-44 (1960).
99. Surber, E. W., *Am. Fish. Soc. Trans.*, **61**, 143-147 (1931).
100. Surber, E. W., *Am. Fish. Soc. Trans.*, **73**, 377-393 (1945).
101. Swingle, H. S., *Ala. Poly. Inst. Ag. Exp. Sta. Bull.*, **264**, 1-34 (1947).
102. Swingle, H. S., *N. A. Wildlf. Conf. Trans.*, **21**, 298-322 (1957).
103. Swingle, H. S., Prather, E. E., and Lawrence, J. M., *Ala. Poly. Inst. Ag. Exp. Sta.*, **113**, 1-15 (1953).
104. Swingle, H. S., and Smith, E. V., *Am. Fish. Soc. Trans.*, **68**, 126-135 (1939).
105. Swingle, H. S., and Smith, E. V., *Ala. Ag. Exp. Sta. Bull.*, **254**, 1-23 (1942).
106. Swingle, H. S., and Smith, E. V., *Ala. Poly. Inst. Ag. Exp. Sta. Bull.*, **254**, 1-30, revised (1947).
107. Tanner, H. A., *Am. Fish. Soc. Trans.*, **89**, 198-205 (1960).
108. Tarzwell, C. M., *Publ. Health Repts.*, **62**(15), 525-554 (1947).
109. Tarzwell, C. M., *Publ. Health Repts.*, **65**(8), 231-255 (1950).
110. Thompkins, W. A., and Bridges, C., *Prog. Fish-Cult.*, **20**(1), 16-20 (1958).
111. Thompkins, W. A., and Mullan, J. W., *Prog. Fish-Cult.*, **20**(3), 117-123 (1958).
112. Therinen, C. W., *Prog. Fish-Cult.*, **18**(2), 81-87 (1956).
113. Viosca, P., Jr., *Am. Fish. Soc. Trans.*, **73**, 274-283 (1945).
114. Waters, T. F., *Am. Fish. Soc. Trans.*, **86**, 329-344 (1957).
115. Waters, T. F., and Ball, R. C., *Jour. Wildlf. Mgt.*, **21**(4), 385-391 (1957).
116. Westman, J. R., and Hunter, J. V., *Prog. Fish-Cult.*, **18**(3), 126-130 (1956).
117. Wolf, P., *Am. Fish. Soc. Trans.*, **80**, 41-45 (1951).
118. Wood, R., *Jour. Tenn. Acad. Sci.*, **26**(3), 214-235 (1951).
119. Wood, R., and Pfitzer, D. W., *Inter. Union Cons. Nature and Nat. Res.*, mimeo, **7**, 1-29 (1958).
120. Wunder, W., "Fortschrittliche Karpfenteichwirtschaft," pp. 1-386, E. Schweitzerbart'sche Verlagsbuchhandlung, Erwin Nagele, Stuttgart, 1949.

7 $\approx\approx\approx$

Fishing and Natural Mortality

POPULATION ESTIMATION

The direct counting of the fishes in a lake population requires drastic methods such as draining or poisoning. However, in large lakes the performing of these operations is impossible or impractical.

The disadvantages involved in direct counting have stimulated mathematicians to develop techniques for indirect enumeration. As a result, the number of animals in a specific habitat can now be calculated on the basis of recaptures of previously-marked individuals.

In the case of fishes, marking can be accomplished by the removal of all or part of a fin or by the application of a tag. The fishes must be taken by one or a combination of methods that reduce selection for certain kinds or sizes of individuals.

The principle of indirect enumeration is as follows: In a random sample of individuals, each one is marked, and released alive, and within a short period of time another random sample is taken. In this second sample appear some marked individuals from the first one. The proportion of recaptures to the total number of fishes taken in the second sample, should be the same as the proportion initially marked to the total population.[26]

$$\text{Total Population} = \frac{\text{total marked} \times \text{total caught when recapturing}}{\text{recaptures}}$$

If the calculation is to approach a reasonable degree of accuracy, no individuals must be any more likely than others to appear in the catches on the day of recapture. From what is known of the selectivity of fishing gear and the nonrandom distribution of fishes, it becomes obvious that this poses a real problem in fish population estimation, unless the method is used in a very restricted sense, as fish behavior (and catchability) is modified by species, size, sex, season, environment, and many other factors.

It is important that the date of recapture be close to the date of marking, so that there is a minimum of replacement of marked individuals through death and recruitment; however, in some situations replacements may occur at a fairly constant rate in relation to time, and adjustments can be made to compensate for them. The ramifications of this population estimation method are not given here; however, References 1, 14, 17, 18, 21, 23, 26, 29, 40, 43, 44, 45, 46, 49, 50, 51, 52, 54, 56, and 58 provide an adequate introduction to the subject.

Another method of population estimation [20, 70] is based on changes in the effort-catch relationship as a population is reduced by the removal of individuals. Here, the precision of an estimate is primarily dependent upon the capture and removal of a sizeable proportion of the population.

FORCES ACTING UPON A FISH POPULATION

Each year in every pond and lake containing fish thousands of their eggs hatch; some of these small fishes die from predation, accidents, and disease before becoming free-swimming fry; more of them expire between fry and fingerling stages. It has been estimated that in one lake the loss of bluegills between these two stages was about 86 per cent.[33] Fingerling-sized fishes are not only subject to death by accidents and disease but also they are still decimated by predation. However, a few survive and grow to sexual maturity and old age, eventually succumbing to disease or senile degeneration. Whether an individual fish reaches maturity and produces progeny is unimportant as long as total recruitment and growth in a population equal total losses from various causes. If such is the case, the population will continue to be numerically healthy. A simplified discussion of the interaction of these factors is given by Russell,[53] although he was describing the dynamics of a population exploited through commercial rather than sport fishing.

If we apply Russell's reasoning to a sport fishery, all fish that reach a "catchable" size in any given year are liable to capture. Thus, the total stock may be divided into the catchable and the noncatchable. Of the catchable stock, individuals will either (1) survive to the end of the year, having grown in the interval, or (2) be caught with a growth increment proportionate to the length of time they have survived or (3) die in some other way by natural causes. The catchable stock will receive additions through growth among noncatchable individuals which, once they are of catchable size, are subject to the same forces of fishing and natural mortality that affect the others.

The weight of all stocks at the beginning of the year (S_1) may or may not equal those at the end of the year (S_2).[53]

Factors involved in this situation are:

A = weight of new recruits reaching catchable size,

G = total weight of all flesh added to catchable fish during the year,

C = weight of fish captured and removed, and

M = weight of fish that die of natural causes.

In any case,

$$S_2 = S_1 + (A + G) - (C + M)$$

Thus, if the catch of fish (C) is low and many new recruits (A) are added, S_2 may so nearly approach the maximum poundage of fish supported by the water, that the addition of flesh (G) may be very small, particularly if the fish population at the beginning of the season (S_1) was already comparatively large. In contrast, if S_1 were very small, growth (addition of flesh, G) might be large in spite of a low catch (C) and high recruitment (A).

Natural mortality (M), the other decimating factor operating with catch, can be a constant or can vary considerably with the various age components of a population or from season to season. For this reason natural mortality is difficult to evaluate except by direct methods.

In this chapter we are primarily interested in forces which cause losses of fish, i.e., the catch, in total amount and rate, and the natural death rate to the extent that it may be determined.

FISHING MORTALITY

The average angler does not think of himself as a mortality factor for fish. What he takes he assumes is justifiable, particularly if he is operating within the law. Such an attitude may be reasonable because in many situations he is simply substituting himself for other mortality factors that might remove the same or greater quantities of fish.

As discussed in Chapter 5, fish have been subjected to high mortality rates for almost as long as they have existed on the earth's surface, and it must be assumed that high mortality rates are normal and beneficial.

ANGLING COMPARED TO NATURAL PREDATION

Most methods of angling are not only very inefficient for taking warm-water fishes, but are also highly selective for certain species and sizes. Unless many natural predators are present, this inefficiency and selectivity create a problem in the management of small artificial lakes because pole-and-line fishing permits the survival of too many small fish.[7]

Under a system of population control through natural predation, fish populations are cropped in relation to the relative abundance of the component species of fishes. This type of cropping tends to hold down the numbers of all species. Also, since there are more predators of small fish than of large ones, a severe culling of small fish is continuously taking place.

Man has yet to devise a cropping system comparable to a natural system of population control. His nearest approach in artificial waters has come from stocking predatory fishes in sufficient numbers to dominate, momentarily, the aquatic environment.

YIELDS AND STANDING CROP

It is logical to assume that a yield of fish, if it has been sustained over a period of years, must bear some definite relationship to the population of these fish (poundage) that the body of water supports and to the rate of their replacement. As the crop is taken, increased food resources become available for the potential replacement of fish flesh removed, and this replacement must depend upon (1) the efficiency of food gathering, (2) the replacement time available, and (3) the ability of the number of digestive tracts uncaptured and those added through new recruitment to convert the food into proteins, to replace those taken.

Usually when one speaks of a sustained yield, he is talking about a yield level repeated in each successive season for a period of years. He probably is not speaking of the *maximum* poundage of fish that may be replaced in each growing season. Rather, he may be thinking of some poundage below the absolute maximum, that may be taken by a reasonable amount of effort on the part of the fishermen. Thus, there are many levels of so-called sustained yields, none of which is, in reality, the maximum.

In small lakes and ponds containing a limited number of kinds of fishes, it is sometimes possible to demonstrate competition between species and individuals for food and space. One may suspect that the same factors are active in larger waters with a greater variety of species; but direct observation is difficult or impossible and changes are measured largely on the basis of variations in the commercial catch of species valuable for human consumption.

In the Great Lakes, for example, yields were higher before 1920 than they have been since. According to Van Oosten [67] the annual yield of fish before 1920 varied around 100 million pounds; from 1920 to 1947 it ranged around 78.5 million pounds, a reduction of 22 per cent. Van Oosten believed that factors leading to the decline of this fishery were (1) increased fishing pressure, (2 improvement in fishing methods, (3) extension of fishing grounds, (4) replacement of better classes of fishes with poorer types and (5) (a variation of 4) the introduction of the smelt.

In considering the factors that reduced the standing crop of the more desirable fishes, Van Oosten hesitated to place major importance either on interspecific competition as such or on partial loss of competitive ability due to selective cropping, but looked for causes in pollution, change in the habitat, and disease. However, the fact that in Lake Michigan a big increase in the 1945-47 yield of ciscoes followed the almost complete disappearance of smelt in 1943, suggests that changes in the population might be due to interspecific competition, even in waters as large as the Great Lakes. Within the 1947-1960 period the sea lamprey has greatly reduced the yields of certain Great Lakes fishes.

In small lakes direct competition plays an important role in the size of the standing crop of catchable fishes. However, larger waters are not as easy to evaluate. For example, the spawning site of a species may be far removed from its feeding grounds; also, competition on the spawning grounds might be intensive with little competition on the feeding grounds. Competition for spawning space might result in a smaller number of individuals of a desirable species and, if food gathering could not be accelerated in proportion to this decrease in the number of individuals, the fish would show no growth compensation.

Several authors have attempted to predict a sustained yield in relation to the standing crop of fish. Swingle [65] estimated that 50 per cent of the total weight of fish in a pond could be removed each year by angling. At this point, the number had been reduced sufficiently so that those remaining found plenty of natural foods and consequently did not bite well. This approach is somewhat theoretical, as the hypothesis is not supported by statistics on yields with related statistics on the total populations of fish that produced them.

MAXIMUM YIELDS AND LENGTH OF GROWING SEASON

Thompson,[66] on the basis of digestive rates of fish at different temperatures and on the lengths of warm seasons at various latitudes in North America, calculated the maximum annual yields (based on theoretical replacement of protein) that could be taken at latitudes from 46° N to 30° N. These ranged from 21 per cent of the carrying capacity in northern Wisconsin to 118 per cent in southern Louisiana. Thompson's figure for central Illinois was 50 per cent of the carrying capacity. Cropping tests at Fork Lake (central Illinois), a small pond of 1.38 acres, appear to substantiate a 50 per cent yield potential.[11] Here the 1939 catch of bass and bluegills was equivalent to 934 fishes, or 162 pounds per acre, a yield of "about half of the theoretical carrying capacity of the lake for hook-and-line fish." These fishes were taken in 1-inch mesh wing nets and by hook-and-line, and all were removed from the lake regardless of size. In 1940 and 1941 the yield was reduced in spite of more intensive net fishing,[8] but the reduction in fish was attributed to the trapping of nutrient materials by dense stands of submersed rooted vegetation.

However, a later investigation, involving the cropping of smallmouth bass from another central Illinois pond, did not bear out Thompson's estimate of maximum production.[10] In this pond of 1.42 acres, the annual yields of smallmouth bass for four successive years were 78.0, 119.0, 123.0, and 81.3 pounds per acre. In June of the fifth year the pond was treated with rotenone and a census was made of the remaining smallmouth bass. The total bass population, exclusive of the 0 age class (1 to 1.5 inches total length) amounted to 52.3 pounds per acre. Previous to this census (from April 11 to June 6) fishermen had taken 48 pounds of bass per acre. Together, the census and the pre-census catch amounted to 100.3 pounds of smallmouths per acre, a figure that must include the flesh added to individuals of the population that were alive during April and May. On the basis of this experiment, the replacement potential for fish flesh at the latitude of central Illinois may approach 100 per cent during a single growing season. While this high level of cropping must be considered a sustained yield, the future yield status of this population of smallmouths was precarious in that a reproduction failure for a given season probably would have seriously curtailed the yield for the fishing season two years hence. Since individuals in this population were converting food into flesh with some efficiency, any severe reduction in the number of digestive tracts would be followed by a reduction in food conversion.

Certain species of warm-water fishes cannot be depended upon for a sustained yield because they do not produce new year classes every year. This production of intermittent year classes may prevent the entrance of new recruits into the fishable population as older fish are taken, until the latter become scarce and the yield is forced downward. Failure to produce annual year classes may be associated with environmental conditions or with the collection of metabolic products (see Chapter 5). Yields including several species of fishes usually are more constant, because failure of a year class in one species may be compensated for by high production in other species.

In Chapter 5, I expressed certain relationships between carrying capacity, productivity, and growth. In populations of fishes composed of one, two, or several kinds, a substantial sustained removal of one species should result in (1) increased growth rate and improved reproduction success of uncaptured individuals of that species and/or (2) the expansion of the population of some other species to fill the space created by the removal of the first species, with the final result that the population of the first species might level off at a much lower point than formerly. This may be what happened to many of the more desirable fishes inhabiting the Great Lakes prior to 1947 before the sea lamprey became numerous.

UNDERFISHING

In artificial ponds and lakes where natural predators are limited, severe competition among fishes may take place because of a scarcity of adequate mortality factors (Figure 7.1). This competition results in poor growth and eventual stunting and often causes a gradual change in population composition.

Most artificial impoundments, large or small, are underfished, i.e., usually hook-and-line fishing is not intensive or diversified enough to replace the normal system of natural predation which is usual for "wild" waters beyond the influence of human populations. Also, some individuals of certain species apparently become wary of baited hooks or artificial lures.

Fishing pressures and the degree of stunting caused from overpopulation may vary from one body of water to another. The advent of stunting is purely arbitrary, and has been defined on the basis (and perhaps falsely) of average growth rates of a selected species taken from specific waters in a limited region. One might determine that the average rate of growth of largemouth bass in northern Illinois and southern Wisconsin produced fish that were 4.0 inches the first year, 8.3 inches the second, 10.6 inches the third, and 12.0 inches the fourth. These averages might not be at all representative of bass growth in this region if the populations of bass inhabiting the lakes from which samples were taken were unusually fast-growing. Yet, it would seem logical to assume that fish that grew faster than these averages were living in a very satisfactory environment and those that grew more slowly were stunted.

Underfishing can be defined as *all levels of fishing pressure that, when operating with the forces of natural mortality, cause insufficient total mortality to prevent excessive survival of juveniles and moderate to severe food competition among adults.* It becomes obvious that fishing mortality and natural mortality combine to define total mortality, and, where natural mortality is high or variable, underfishing cannot be defined in specific terms. For example, the seasonal fishing pressure exerted by resident Indians on a Canadian lake might be no more than 2 man-hours per acre, while that of farm families on an Ozark hill pond was 30 man-hours per acre. In spite of the fact that the Ozark pond received 15 times the fishing pressure of the Canadian lake, the former could be underfished while the latter was not. This can be explained only through a consideration of all mortality factors. In the Canadian situation, Indians might be a mortality factor of minor importance compared to predatory fish and fish-eating birds. On the Ozark pond, perhaps fish predation was limited largely to humans engaged in fishing.

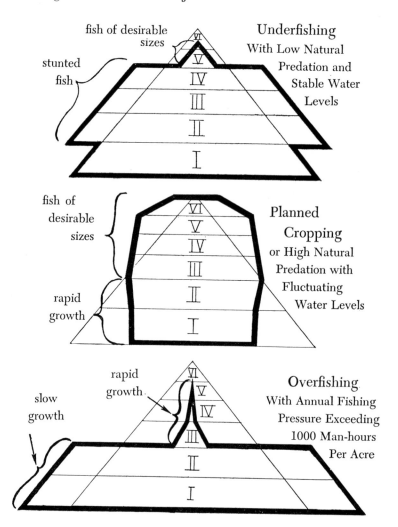

Figure 7.1. Diagrams representing theoretical fish populations superimposed on segmented triangles proposing the first six year classes of fish populations reduced (space) on a 50 per cent mortality rate. *Underfished population* is characterized by high survival of all year classes and stunting, with few fish attaining desirable sizes. *Planned cropping* and/or high natural predation with fluctuating water levels produces a population, the members of which grow rapidly to large average sizes. Overpopulation is prevented, and, therefore, an abundance of food is usually available. *Overfished population* is characterized by over abundant year classes of very young fish showing slow growth until they reach sizes large enough to interest anglers. At this point, many are taken and the few that escape grow rapidly to large average sizes.

The fact that fish can live indefinitely on a maintenance diet practically eliminates mass mortality through starvation; barring some catastrophe, such as the drying up of a pond or the freezing of the water to the bottom, stunted populations of fishes remain so indefinitely. These populations are rather easily identified, because individuals usually are thin and their eyes are disproportionately large for the size of the body. Apparently the eyes of a fish continue to grow even when the body stops growing.

OVERFISHING

When more pounds of fish are removed from a body of water in a single season than can be replaced through food gathering, assimilation, growth, and recruitment, the body of water is said to be overfished (Figure 7.1). According to James, Meehan, and Douglass,[27] waters located near centers of population frequently are overfished, but their concept of overfishing may deal with selected species rather than the complex of all species present in a body of water.

Fish populations show considerable resistance to intensive angling and are not easily decimated. This point was made by Viosca [68] who stated: "... when a body of water is said to have been fished out by angling, only a relatively small percentage of the fish have actually been removed. ... Apparently, the majority of fish in a body of water cannot be taken by angling because of the automatic increase in their prey resulting from the removal of part of the stock by the very act of angling." Swingle and Smith [65] made essentially the same statement. Through fishing experiments using largemouth bass populations of known numbers per acre, Lagler and DeRoth [32] concluded that fishermen angling in experimental ponds could scarcely be induced to fish for this species when it was represented by a population density as low as 6 legal bass per acre (because the rate of catch was only 0.04 legal fish per man-hour); the interest in fishing had waned completely among cooperating fishermen and the impression was general that the ponds had been "fished out."

One of the first comprehensive studies of the overfishing of warm-water fishes in ponds became possible because of a complex of several favorable circumstances. A conscientious custodian at the Owens-Illinois Glass Company recreation area collected information on the fish yield of Onized Lake (Illinois), a two-acre pond that was overfished, largely because picnicking and fishing could be combined.[5] Here family groups came for picnics, but brough fishing equipment and baits, too, because it was possible to watch a bobbing cork while otherwise occupied at the picnic table. With these "double" recreation facilities, many man-hours of fishing were logged because, with the stimulus of the hamburger and hot dog, the low catch rate lost its importance as a fishing deterrent. The result was that during two successive years the fishing pressure on Onized Lake exceeded 1400 man-hours per acre; the catch amounted to 350 pounds per acre for the first year and then dropped to 142 pounds per acre the second. This drop in yield suggested overfishing. When the pond was completely censused in June of the third year (after a spring catch of 71 pounds per acre had been taken by a fishing pressure of 634 man-hours per acre), it contained 9171 fish (exclusive of the young of the year which were largely lost or eaten by larger fish), but only 481 of the larger fishes were of desirable * sizes. The lake contained largemouth bass, black crappies, bluegills, green sunfish, yellow bass, black and yellow bullheads, golden shiners, and a few fishes of several other kinds. Of the important fishes in the hook-and-line catch for the preceding two years, the black crappies had been reduced to 22 fish, the yellow bass to 4, and the black bullheads to 2 fish. There were 275 bass, of which 12 fish ranged from 3 to 6 pounds each. At the time of the census there were 23 bass of at least 10 inches in length per acre. Bluegills were represented by 6545 fish, warmouths by 1638, green sunfish by 245, yellow bullheads by 347, and golden shiners by 90. Fishes grew at moderately slow rates until they reached desirable sizes and then, very rapidly because of population thinning through angling. If fishing had been continued at this rate for another season, the populations of black crappies, yellow bass, and black bullheads might have disappeared entirely. However, the census gave evidence that largemouth bass, bluegills, warmouths, green sunfish, yellow bullheads, and golden shiners might be able to maintain populations indefinitely, either because of high reproductive success with high survival of young or because of increased resistance to capture, or for both of these reasons. One season with reduced fishing pressure would have allowed the population to expand to approach the carrying capacity of the pond and obscure all evidence of overfishing.

FISHING PRESSURE VERSUS YIELD

In 1950 and 1951, Barnickol and Campbell [4] studied the fish yields of many small impoundments located on the August A. Busch Memorial Wildlife Area near St. Louis, Missouri. These ponds were fished at rates ranging from about 300 to 4000 man-hours per acre per season, and yields varied from as low as 20 to as high as about 300 pounds of fish per acre. In 1959, Gilbert F. Weiss, Fishery Biologist for Missouri, furnished additional data on fishing pressures and yields from the Busch ponds as well as from several other Missouri lakes that were fished less heavily.

The 26 impoundments of one to 20 acres on the Busch Memorial Wildlife Area were not all in use during all years between 1949 and 1959, but

---

* Desirable sizes were arbitrarily set as follows: at least 10 inches for largemouth bass (legal limit); 8 inches for crappies; 7 inches for yellow bass, bullheads, and golden shiners; and 6 inches for bluegills, warmouths, and green sunfish.

sufficient records were available to furnish data on more than 100 pond-seasons.* Some stocking of ponds was done during the period but the numbers of fishes released were usually insignificant in relation to the fishing pressures and yields and no measurable effect of stocking could be demonstrated in the rate of catch.

Data on rates of catch for various fishing pressures on the Busch ponds and several other Missouri impoundments were combined with similar information from some lakes and ponds in central and southern Illinois.[9, 25] All of the ponds contained largemouth bass and bluegills and sometimes, in addition, red-ear sunfish, green sunfish, bullheads, and channel catfish. These pond-season records were plotted in Figure 7.2 [12] as symbols and a line drawn by inspection, representing the average relationship between man-hours of fishing per acre and rate of catch in pounds of fish per man-hour.

Figure 7.2 shows that the seasonal rates of catch from 4000 man-hours per acre to about 300 man-hours per acre were averaging about 0.10 pound per hour of fishing, and that within this range of pressures there was no change with increasing man-hours per acre. Very few fishermen will continue to fish if their catch rate does not exceed 0.10 pound per hour unless a fishing trip is combined with picnicking or escape from an unfavorable environment, such as might be produced by the heat and noise of a big city.

With decreasing fishing pressures from 300 down to 130 man-hours per acre the rate of catch increased gradually and at a rather slow rate, i.e., from 0.10 to 0.23 or 0.24 pound per man-hour. Below a seasonal pressure of 130 man-hours per acre the rate of catch increased very rapidly until in the best ponds at fishing pressures of 40 to 60 man-hours per acre the rate of catch averaged 1.0 to 1.5 pounds per hour. These very high rates of catch were attained only where populations contained a high percentage of fish of useful sizes.

If it is assumed that the curve in Figure 7.2 represents a reasonably accurate relationship between a building-up of fishing pressure and a depreciating rate of catch for largemouth bass and bluegills (or other sunfish), the curve can be used to estimate the hours of productive fishing that a lake of a given surface area may furnish each season. Also, an owner of a private lake might employ it in maintaining the proper level of fishing pressure for a high catch rate. In reverse, it could be used to figure the size of artificial impoundment needed to satisfy the fishing pressure level of a fishing club of predetermined membership.

For example, if the estimated total annual fishing pressure for the members of a club approximated 8000 man-hours and they wished to

---

* A pond-season is one pond fished for one season.

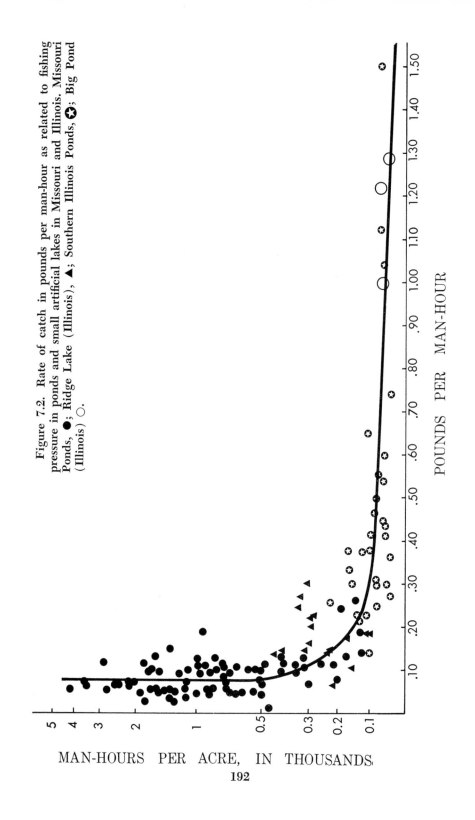

Figure 7.2. Rate of catch in pounds per man-hour as related to fishing pressure in ponds and small artificial lakes in Missouri and Illinois. Missouri Ponds, ●; Ridge Lake (Illinois), ▲; Southern Illinois Ponds, ✪; Big Pond (Illinois) ○.

POUNDS PER MAN-HOUR

MAN-HOURS PER ACRE, IN THOUSANDS

192

maintain a catch rate of 0.50 pound per hour they would need to construct a lake of about 107 acres:

(1) Figure 7.2: For an average catch rate of 0.50 pound per hour the fishing pressure should be about 75 man-hours per acre per season.

(2) $8000 \div 75 = 106.6$ acres. A lake of this size might cost $1000 to $1500 per acre or $110,000 to $160,000.

TYPES OF FISHING PRESSURE

The total hours of fishing and the fishing schedule vary greatly from lake to lake. For example, a lake open to the public may be fished at a high rate during May and June and then chiefly on weekends during July, August, and early September. Where both boat and bank fishing are permitted, the daily pressure may be very high—as much as 50 man-hours per acre per day if the fishing is good. But at this level of fishing, the rate of catch will drop off very markedly in 4 days or less.

At Ridge Lake (Illinois) where bank fishing was not permitted and only 7 boats were available on 18 acres of water, the approximate rate of accumulation of fishing hours was 9 or 10 per acre per day. As the lake was open 5 days per week, we can estimate a fishing pressure of about 25 to 50 man-hours per week during the first week; later in the season the pressure was less.[9]

Many private lakes and farm ponds are fished in a leisurely manner: On one day three fishermen fish for a total of 12 hours, but the pond is not visited by fishermen again for several days or weeks. The accumulation of fishing hours is so slow that only 50 hours per acre are logged for an entire season. The same may be true for large reservoirs but for a different reason: some artificial reservoirs are so large that the fishing pressure of all available fishermen builds up a seasonal pressure of only a few dozen hours per acre.

As fishes react in different ways to various levels of fishing, the schedule and intensity of fishing affects the yield. The bass in Ridge Lake showed a much reduced catch rate after the morning fishing period of the opening day (Figure 7.3), and by the end of the third day, the rate had nearly reached a low point for the summer—after only about 25 hours of fishing pressure per acre.[9] Creel censuses on three Kentucky lakes demonstrated that 70 per cent of all largemouth bass caught during the first week were taken in the first 30 hours of fishing.[13]

Records of the largemouth bass catches from relatively infertile unmanaged waters in Virginia indicated that about 19 trips per acre removed the "harvestable surplus" of these fish amounting to 3.6 bass per acre averaging approximately a pound each.[36] According to Martin [36] there is an easily harvested segment of any bass population which can be readily taken at a high rate of catch by light fishing pressure. After these fish have been removed, additional fishing pressure has little effect upon further harvest and the rate of catch declines rapidly.

Several common warm-water fishes are rather seasonal in their biting habits and fishermen increase fishing pressure at these times because they know that their chances of catching fish are improved. For example, both white and black crappies bite best in the early spring before the lakes

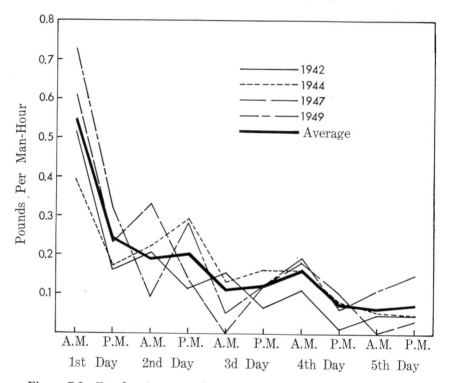

Figure 7.3. **Decelerating rate of catch of largemouth bass at Ridge Lake** (Illinois) during the first week of public fishing in each of the named years, and the average rate of catch for all of these years. The first 5 days of fishing usually showed an accumulated fishing pressure of less than 40 man-hours per acre. [From Bennett, G. W., *Ill. Nat. Hist. Surv. Bull.*, 26 (2) (1954)]

warm to temperatures in the 70°F range. Warmouths bite much better in late spring and early summer than in late summer.

Also, some fish bite well under the ice in winter, while other common species are scarcely ever caught through ice fishing. The fishing intensity of ice fishermen in sections of northern United States where the ice is thick enough to support them may nearly equal that of the summer anglers, and exceeds the summer fishing in certain localized areas.

Fishing intensity for certain species may be increased with changes in weather conditions because fishermen know that rising waters, for example, stimulate certain species of fish to move about and feed. Most sight-feeding fishes become inactivated by rising waters because increased turbidity limits their vision.

Returns from angling effort directed toward species of warm-water fishes other than largemouth bass indicate that intensive fishing pressure also depresses the rate of catch but not so rapidly as with the largemouth. Thus it is safe to state that a leisurely pattern of angling over a season is more conducive to satisfactory fishing than is an alternation of relatively intensive angling with periods of complete rest.

FACTORS RELATED TO RATE OF CATCH

The exact relationship between the number of fish per acre or per acre-foot of water and the rate of catch is usually obscured by one or more factors, some of which have been discussed previously. Quite obviously there must be some relationship between numbers of fish available and catch rate, but often the relationship is clear only when numbers of fish are reduced to a very low figure.[32]

Stroud [63] studied the recovery of marked "salvaged" fishes released in Massachusetts lakes and ponds to gain information on the relationship between available fishes and angling returns. He could only estimate roughly the population density of the various marked species recovered. Thus, he calculated an over-all harvest of 9 per cent (from 10 ponds) for marked largemouth bass, with a somewhat higher return for smallmouth bass; whereas marked chain pickerel ranged from 15 per cent to 59 per cent. Recaptures of other warm-water pond fishes were usually between those for bass and pickerel, although in some instances a large per cent of the salvaged fishes did not survive.

The presence of more pan fishes, such as bluegills, crappies, yellow perch or bullheads, per unit of water, could conceivably mean better fishing. One reason for poor fishing in unfertilized Alabama ponds given by Swingle and Smith [65] is that the "water is too poor to support many legal-sized fish." However, Hansen et al.[25] were unable to show that the rate of catch in fertilized ponds (which contained somewhat higher poundages of fish than the control ponds) was consistently better than in the control ponds.

Lux and Smith [35] attempted to discover which of a number of physical, chemical, and biological factors bore a relationship to seasonal changes in the angler's catch in a Minnesota lake. They concluded that as the available food supply increased after the middle of June, the fishing became progressively poorer. This may explain a seasonal cycle, but cannot be used to explain trends extending over several seasons.

Evidence shows that rate of growth of fishes and rate of biting are often in direct relationship. In fact, anyone fishing a new impoundment will probably discover the excellent fishing typical of an expanding population.[69] Fishing during the early years of impoundment in most water-supply reservoirs is better than in later years, and most of these reservoirs go through a predictable cycle.[6, 69] Exceptions seems to be those reservoirs having large annual water-level fluctuations which prevent the development of "climax" fish populations. One possible explanation for the excellent fishing in new reservoirs is that the fish have an abundance of available food and are growing rapidly. They have the habit of feeding for long periods each day, and bite readily at almost any time.

This situation may be contrasted with one where inter- and intraspecific competitions are moderately keen and food is more readily available at certain periods of the day than at others. Growth is slower and fish no longer have the opportunity of gorging themselves; instead they have developed feeding cycles related to periods of the day when certain foods are more readily available than at other times. During these periods the fish are caught quite readily by anglers, but the catch may show little relationship to the relative abundance of the fish.

When fish are crowded and inter- and intraspecific competitions are very severe, the fish are thin and stunted and their growth may have practically stopped. Under these conditions, they bite very poorly[64] and give the impression that few or no fish are present. One explanation for this behavior pattern is that these fish are living on a subsistence diet of small aquatic organisms and are not conditioned to utilize foods as large as most live or artificial baits.

In summary, the evidence seems to favor the assumption that, within limits, there is a positive relationship between good fishing and rapid growth and an expanding population of fish and a negative relationship between good fishing and population density, although these relationships are not always clear.

ROLE OF COMMERCIAL FISHING IN SPORT-FISH MANAGEMENT

When angling becomes temporarily or permanently poor in waters where commercial fishermen are operating nets, the commercial operators are usually blamed for the poor angling, even though they are not taking the same species fished for by the anglers.

Although commercial fishermen compete with anglers for such fishes as walleyes and lake trout in low-producing northern lakes, no valid evidence exists that commercial fishing in shallow warm-water lakes provides competition for the angler,[30, 31] even when commercial fishermen are permitted to take all sizes and kinds of fish.

An experiment involving the use of illegal-meshed commercial gear in a small pond clearly demonstrated the effects of intensive fishing with fyke or wing nets for largemouth bass and bluegills.[8] Six 1-inch-mesh wing nets with leads were set across a 1.38-acre pond in two gangs so as to completely block the pond at two points (Figure 7.4). These nets were fished for 96 to 149 hours each month, from March to November of each year for two and one-half years, and all fishes captured were removed, regardless of size or species. These nets held bass as small as 9 inches and bluegills as small as 5 inches. The catch consisted largely of bluegills, as the bass soon avoided the nets. Supplementary cropping was done by hook-and-line. At the end of the study period the bluegill population

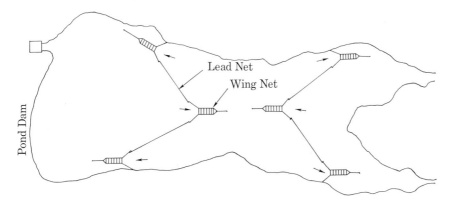

Figure 7.4. Outline map of Fork Lake (Illinois) showing the customary arrangement of wing nets and lead nets for cropping studies. No fish could swim for any great distance in this 1.38-acre pond without running into a lead net or wing net. Arrows mark openings of wing nets. [From Bennett, G. W., *Ill. Nat. Hist. Bull.*, 24(3) (1948)]

amounted to about 67 pounds per acre and the bass to over 120 pounds per acre. The netting operation unquestionably was a major influence in the buildup of a very large population of bass.

In some states commercial fishermen have been forced out of business except on the major rivers, and the state fisheries departments have had to assume the task of controlling rough fish. This is an expensive never-ending job, and when commercial fishing is outlawed, rough-fish removal must be paid for by the sport fishermen. However, in states where commercial fishing is legal, rough-fish removal is self-sustaining and the commercial man operates at a profit.

Many studies show that removing large crops of coarse fish with commercial gear is beneficial or at least not harmful to sport fishing. This is universally true in large shallow lakes and reservoirs containing substantial numbers of coarse fish which, because of low fishing pressure, are not cropped by hook-and-line.[62] Here commercial fishing is about the only means (except through natural predators) of reducing competition among species.

Originally the scope of operation of the angler and commercial fisherman overlapped: They both took any and all species on the basis of relative abundance and their ability to capture them. However, gradually the angler was able to restrict the commercial fisherman to "rough" species (carp, buffalos and catfish), while reserving for himself all of the "fine" fish (crappies, bluegills, white bass, etc.) and game fish (largemouth bass, northern pike, pickerel and often walleye). These restrictions on the commercial fisherman did not benefit the angler, for the quality of the fishing became worse.

In the 1930's an interesting relationship existed between anglers, commercial fishermen, and natural fish predators at Reelfoot Lake (14,500 acres, Tennessee). Here anglers made an average catch of 0.89 pound of fish per hour. Largemouth bass averaged 1.91 pound each, crappies 0.70 pound, sunfish 0.37 pound, and catfish 2.39 pounds.[30] The total anglers' yield in 1936 was 22,124 pounds. At the same time, commercial fishermen were taking 529,093 pounds plus an additional estimated 95,000 pounds of small fish killed in netting operations.[31] Commercial fishermen were not restricted to any species, i.e., they were taking the same kinds of fishes as the sport fishermen. More obvious fish predators on Reelfoot Lake were 4000 egrets, 1500 cormorants, and 500 Ward's herons, plus smaller numbers of 7 other species of fish-eating birds. These birds were taking more than 400,000 pounds of fish of kinds and sizes related to their availability. The total of fish taken by birds, commercial fishermen, and anglers in 1937 was 1,046,133 pounds or about 72 pounds per acre. On the basis of rate of catch for angling and sizes of fish taken, the fishing in 1937 was excellent.

However, soon after this, Tennessee began restricting commercial fishing. First, the state prohibited the commercial fishing of largemouth bass, then regulations on other species became increasingly restrictive until in 1955 commercial fishing was abolished.[57]

During the period 1937 to 1958, as small fish were given more protection in Tennessee, the growth rate for bluegills and other centrarchids at Reelfoot Lake decreased. By 1953, anglers had increased almost 100-fold, yet they were catching only about 21 pounds of fish per acre.[16] However, had they been taking as many pounds per fisherman as in 1937, their catch would have approached 153 pounds per acre. The commercial fishing yield in 1953 was 21 pounds per acre instead of the 1937 yield of about 36.5 pounds per acre. No report is available on numbers of fish-eating birds on the lake in 1953, but since the number of fishermen increased 100-fold, it is doubtful that cormorants, egrets, and herons were as abundant as in 1937. It seems probable that the total yield of fish in 1953 was considerably less than in 1937 but more selective for larger fish.

From the standpoint of the angler the relationship in 1937 between anglers, commercial fishermen, and fish-eating birds was near optimum, and the combined action of these cropping agencies was taking a reasonable annual fish crop. Thus the benefits of an expanding population were evident: fish had food and space to grow. Because the total annual mortality of fish in this lake was nearly optimum (72 plus pounds per acre), fishing remained good. Without the help of the commercial fishermen, the fish-eating birds and other natural predators available in 1937 could not have kept up with the reproductive potential of the fishes. What happened to the population is fairly evident, for the number of fish caught per fisherman in 1953 remained about the same as in 1937,[16] yet the weight of fish taken was less than one-third that of the earlier year.

NATURAL MORTALITY

Natural mortality includes all causes of death of fish exclusive of pollution, angling, and commercial fishing. Deaths may result from predation, injuries received through unsuccessful attempts at predation, competition for food and space resulting in fatal injury or starvation, disease or excessively heavy infestations of parasites, catastrophes such as adverse weather conditions, floods, etc., as well as from senile degeneration or a combination of several of these factors.

Causes of Natural Death

Important causes for the deaths of fish change with a fish's age and size as related to its normal life span. In the embryo and early free-swimming stages when fish are very small, high mortality rates are probably caused by predation from aquatic insects and larger fish.[33]

The approximate numbers of largemouth bass fry in enumerated schools at Ridge Lake (Illinois) were compared with the bass taken by lake draining at the end of the second succeeding growing season. It was estimated that the survival rate of schooling bass fry ranged from 1 in 29 to 1 in 195.[9] These bass fry were exposed to very favorable conditions because many potential predators in the form of small bluegills, large predaceous aquatic insects, and crayfish had been removed from the lake prior to the bass spawning season. A survival ratio of schooling bass fry to yearlings of at least 15 to 1 was attained by the first year class of bass spawned in Ridge Lake after water was first impounded. Predation rates on embryos and fry of other nest-building centrarchids may be higher than those of largemouth bass because the former produce larger numbers of eggs and probably offer less protection to their young.

If the young fishes of the larger species escape predation and can find sufficient food, they may survive the first growing season and be well on their way to adulthood. Many of the smaller species reach sexual maturity and spawn during the early part of the second summer of life. Most of these yearlings are small enough to be preyed upon by some kinds of fishes and nearly all of the predaceous amphibians, reptiles, birds, and mammals; however, they are beyond the size for predation by most aquatic insects. By the end of the second growing season, direct predation may become a minor cause of death and other mortality causes may take over.

Ricker [47] investigating the natural mortality rate among the fishes of several Indiana lakes concluded that once the fish reached sizes larger than 5 inches, senility must account for most of the natural mortality. Ricker believed that senility in fish was active over a wide range of ages, relatively much wider than that of domestic animals and man. He based this assumption on his discovery that natural mortality in the bluegill was rather constant in fish from three to six or seven years, the approximate maximum age of this species.

Once a fish reaches a size beyond that of "easy" predation its death may result from a combination of several factors. A 5-inch green sunfish may fall prey to a 16-inch bass because a bacterial infection of the sunfish's fins has caused it to swim in such an abnormal manner as to attract attention. The internal parasites of a minnow may reduce its swimming activity so greatly that it cannot avoid being captured by a crappie or a heron. Even senility may be followed by predation before the individual fish has time to die from organic degeneration.[37]

When Do Fish Die?

Fish may die at any time of year but it is probable that most of them expire during spring, summer, and fall (one must discount deaths caused by suffocation under ice resulting from unusual circumstances). However, Snieszko [60] believes that winter conditions are responsible for reducing the resistance of fish to bacterial diseases in the spring and that reported deaths associated with rising water temperatures are due to a deficiency of antimicrobial components in the fish's blood; the studies of carp blood by Schäeperclaus [55] and Plančić [42] substantiate this hypothesis. There is little question that many fish die in the spring, a large number of which appear to be diseased or infested with aquatic fungi (Saproligniales). In the case of fungus infestations, it is believed that injuries acquired by fish might heal during other times of the year. In the spring, however, conditions are optimum for the growth of aquatic fungi, and they readily gain entrance through skin abrasions and produce a toxin that causes the death of the fish. *Achlya sp.*, one of these fungi, is reported to attack healthy fish without breaks in the skin.

Biologists active in state fisheries departments learn to anticipate a spring period each year when many phone calls and letters report deaths of fish in various state and private waters. Part of these originate directly from winterkill: the fish that have died over the winter decompose and float to the surface in spring soon after the ice goes out. Other spring reports of dead or dying fish can be assigned to disease or fungus infestations. Usually, nothing can be done to stop the fish from dying and the situation must be left to run its course. In no case that I know of has a partial loss of fish had serious consequences, unless severe winterkill was the cause of death. When fish suffocate under the ice, a partial kill may have serious consequences to later fishing (see Chapter 3).

Many fish die during the summer and fall. Usually these never appear at the surface or else float up in numbers too small to receive attention. The complete disappearance of a year class of crappies during summer is not unusual. In one instance where 1-inch mesh wing nets with leads were used at 30- to 40-day intervals over a period of years for catching crappies, a year class was followed from the time its members were first large enough to be caught until they suddenly and permanently disappeared, indicating a complete mortality for that year class.[24] Angling returns of marked crappies in Lake Chautauqua (Illinois) showed that fishermen were taking less than 5 per cent of the available large fish; thus, about 95 per cent of the large crappies were dying from old age. Most of these deaths apparently occurred during the warm months.[61]

SCAVENGERS

As a result of pollution, many fish die at about the same time, making available a large amount of carrion for such scavengers as survive in the lake. However, these remaining scavengers are unable to assimilate such an abundance of protein. As a result, the fish decay and float to the surface where they may be consumed by terrestrial scavengers and blowfly larvae.

Underwater scavengers are probably not so efficient as terrestrial carrion feeders. However, they do well enough to consume a seasonal quantity of carrion of as much as 100 pounds per acre in some waters, without allowing any of these fish to appear on the surface. Crayfish are important as underwater scavengers and will attack injured or disabled fish before they are dead.[37] Certain kinds of turtles also act as scavengers.

LENGTH OF LIFE OF FISHES

Growth studies based on scale analyses furnish valuable information on the length of life of fishes. Most species do not live as long as is popularly believed, but those inhabiting the cooler northern sections of the country live longer than the same ones in the warmer southern and central sections: Largemouth bass in northern Wisconsin may reach ages of 14 to 15 years; in central Illinois, 500 miles south, these fish seldom live longer than 10 to 11 years.

As a rule, the species that attain the largest sizes live the longest, although in any single species, individuals that grow rapidly and gain exceptional sizes are usually short lived for their species. For example, when I was investigating the ages and growth rates of largemouth and smallmouth bass in Wisconsin, I found that bass of 5 pounds or larger were often not more than 5 to 7 years old. In contrast, the bass that showed 14 or 15 annuli on their scales (14+ to 15+ years) seldom exceeded 4 to 4.5 pounds in weight; none of the fishes of exceptional sizes for these species were slow-growing individuals. It was as if a fish were "wound up" like a mechanical toy when small, with the potential to run down rapidly or slowly depending upon its individual genetic make-up, the available food, and the forms of competition encountered.

Table 7.1 gives approximate ages for some common fishes of interest to anglers. Probably most of the ones that reach ages within the range shown in Table 7.1 die of senility.

TABLE 7.1 APPROXIMATE LIFE SPANS OF SOME SPORT FISHES.

Kind of Fish	Regions	Life Span in Years
Largemouth Bass	North, Central, and South	14 to 16 9 to 12
Smallmouth Bass		Same as largemouth
Walleye	North South	15 to 16 10 to 12
Northern Pike	North	16 to 17
Muskellunge	North	16 to 17
Crappie		4 to 7
Bluegill		5 to 8
White Bass		2 to 5

PROBLEMS OF MEASURING NATURAL MORTALITY

It is usually quite impossible to observe much more than casual activities of the larger aquatic animals in the smallest and clearest ponds; therefore, direct observation is presently of little importance for obtaining information on numerical changes in a fish population. This does not minimize the value of underwater observations for many other purposes.

A comprehensive measurement of fish mortality, however, requires either a complete inventory of a fish population at specific intervals (which is usually impossible) or a mathematical approach, either where returns from marked fishes over several seasons are employed to estimate natural losses for the entire population during that time, or where numbers of fish caught (separated into age classes) are used with data on effective effort, to estimate natural mortalities.[41] A dependable creel census is essential for furnishing information on fishing mortality.

If successive annual broods of young of a given kind of fish were nearly the same size, a comparison of the numerical sizes of all of the year classes present in a lake in any year would give accurate information on total annual mortality over the life span of that species. Thus a consideration of the relative abundance of successive year classes of a species in any mixed population may show total mortality, although it may show little more than length of life of that species in the lake in question.

If fish could be marked in sufficient numbers, a measure of the returns from fishing for these marked fish over a period of several years would give an estimate of natural mortality. This method was developed by Ricker[48] who investigated the mortality rates of bluegills in several Indiana lakes, by fin marking these fish prior to the opening of the fishing season (June 16) in two or more successive years. Catch records of marked fish over a period of two or more years furnished data on rate of exploitation. The relationship between the number of fish captured and marked the first year, and recaptured in the first and second years, allowed calculations of total mortality from which angling mortality could be subtracted to give natural mortality. Ricker also discussed the "indirect" method of determining total mortality through a consideration of the relative numerical abundance of successive year classes, and he describes the weaknesses of such a system.

His estimates of total mortality for bluegills in three Indiana lakes ranged from 60 to 77 per cent per year. Of this range, fishing accounted for 19 to 36 per cent, leaving 40 per cent to about 50 per cent for natural mortality. Ricker's calculations for total annual mortality, rate of exploitation, and natural mortality (two methods of calculation) are shown in Table 7.2.

It is perhaps presumptuous to separate fishing mortality and natural mortality. Certainly, some of the fish that fall prey to anglers might die during the same period from natural causes, and fish might be caught by anglers if they had not previously died from natural causes. The mortality rate could be as high with no fishing as with the exploitation rates shown in Table 7.2. However, it probably would not be so high because fish populations that are not fished tend to become numerically overabundant sooner than those subjected to a substantial annual cropping.

The fish population of Sugarloaf Lake (Michigan), which was studied intensively from 1948 through 1952,[18, 19] was found to remain quite constant for 5 consecutive years; this meant that recruitment and total mortality were nearly equal during those years.

TABLE 7.2 CALCULATIONS OF RATES OF TOTAL ANNUAL MORTALITY, EXPLOITATION, AND NATURAL MORTALITY FOR BLUEGILLS IN MUSKELLUNGE, SHOE, AND WAWASEE LAKES (INDIANA), RICKER.[48]

Lake and Year (beginning June 16)	Total Annual Mortality a	Rate of Exploitation μ	Natural Mortality Rate First Method n_1	Natural Mortality Rate Second Method n_2
Muskellunge 1942-43	0.60	0.19	0.51	0.47
Shoe 1941-42	0.76	0.36	0.62	0.52
Shoe 1942-43	0.71	0.24	0.62	0.56
Wawasee 1939-43	0.77	0.20 *	0.71 *	0.66 *

* Based on an estimated rate of exploitation of 20 per cent.

Under these conditions the assumption was made [19] that survival could be expressed by the ratio of the number of fish in a particular age group divided by the number in the next younger age group, thus:

$$S \text{ (Survival)} = \frac{\text{II} + \text{III} + \text{IV} + \ldots}{\text{I} + \text{II} + \text{III} + \ldots}$$

From the rate of survival, it was possible to figure total mortality and, from fishing mortality, natural mortality. These investigators calculated that the total mortality for bluegills was 66 per cent. As the annual fishing mortality was 21 per cent, the natural mortality rate was 45 per cent. This was a little less than Ricker calculated for Indiana lakes, but still in the same general range.

Statistics on the catches of marked largemouth bass at Ridge Lake (Illinois) and the survival of marked fish from one draining census to another (usually 2 years) gave information on fishing mortality and total mortality of the 1941 year class from 1943 to 1951.[9] Similar (but previously unpublished) data on the 1947 and 1949 year classes of bass are included with data for the 1941 year class first in Table 7.3. In this table the number of fish shown opposite each period listing was the number put back following the census at the beginning of the period. The fishing mortality rate (exploitation rate) for the first year was the fraction put back after the March census that were caught during the fishing season (June, July, and August) of that year.

Thus,

(1) Exploitation rate, 1st year $= \dfrac{C_1}{N_1}$

$C_1 =$ no. of marked fish caught during summer of census year,
$N_1 =$ no. of marked fish returned following census.

Some fish might be expected to die of natural causes during this period.

The fishing mortality rate (exploitation rate) for the second year was figured in the same way except that the calculation of available fish was based on the number of fish returned following the census of March of the first year, minus the fish caught during the first year, minus one half of the fish that disappeared between censuses (natural mortality):

(2) Exploitation rate, 2nd yr. $=$

$$\dfrac{C_2}{(N_1 - C_1) - \left[\dfrac{N_1 - C_1 - C_2 - N_2}{2}\right]}$$

Where, $C_2 =$ no. of marked fish caught during the 2nd summer
$N_2 =$ no. of marked fish in census following 2nd summer

The total mortality for any 2-year period was the difference between the number of marked fish restocked after a draining census and the number bearing the same mark that were captured in the next succeeding census. These ranged from 60 to a little more than 90 per cent (Table 7.3) for two years, averaging around 35 per cent for a single year. When the fishing mortality of 25 to 30 per cent per year was subtracted from total mortality, the remainder, natural mortality, averaged from 5 to 11 per cent. This 11 per cent calculation was the average of four 2-year periods, all part of the life span of the 1941 year class. Table 7.3 shows that the average weight of the bass at the beginning of this period was 0.17 pound (7.6 inches) and their natural mortality rate for the two years was 33 per cent. These fish were still vulnerable to predation. The natural mortality rate for this group as old fish in the 1949-1951 period was 34.4 per cent. Here we were dealing with fish nine to eleven years old and they were beginning to die of senile degeneration. If these two groups, the small (young) and the old, are omitted, the annual natural mortality rate for 1941 brood fish was 6 per cent or about the same as that for the 1947 and 1949 broods (5.5 and 6.3 per cent, respectively).

Table 7.4 shows annual mortality rates of bluegills and largemouth bass described above, with those of largemouths, smallmouths, walleyes, and

TABLE 7.3 EXPLOITATION RATES AND MORTALITY RATES FOR LARGEMOUTH BASS IN RIDGE LAKE.

Mark and Period	Number of Fish	Rate of Exploitation			Losses for 2-, or 3-year Period			Av. Annual Natural Mortality Rate	Av. Weight at Beginning of Period, Pounds
		1st Year	2nd Year	3rd Year	Total Mort. Rate	Fishing Mort. Rate	Natural Mort. Rate		
LP. and RP., 1941 year class									
1943-45	1500	—*	.370	—	.638	.309	.329	.164	0.17
1945-47	638	.628	.431	—	.870	.776	.104	.052	0.77
1947-49	81	.259	.227	—	.605	.469	.136	.068	2.44
1949-51	32	.469	—	—	.813	.469	.344	.172	3.96
Av. per year		.452	.342		.366	.253	.114		
Dorsal, 1947 year class									
1949-51	917	.482	.372	—	.811	.643	.168	.084	0.51
1951-53	170	.688	.046	—	.818	.700	.118	.059	1.97
1953-56	31	.387	.389	0.100	.742†	.645†	.097†	.032	3.16
Av. per year		.519	.269		.339	.284	.055		
L Pect., 1949 year class									
1951-53	619	.590	.596	—	.929	.794	.135	.067	0.59
1953-56	44	.477	.600	.000	.932†	.750†	.182†	.061	1.98
Av. per year		.534	.598		.372	.309	.063		

* Lake not opened to fishing.
† 3 years combined in these figures instead of 2 years.

several kinds of pan fishes of other investigators. There is some evidence that annual mortality rates for longer-lived species are usually lower than for bluegill and other pan fishes which are relatively short-lived.

TABLE 7.4 ANNUAL MORTALITY RATES FOR SOME COMMON HOOK-AND-LINE FISHES.

Kind of Fish	Total Mortality Per Cent	Fishing Mortality Per Cent	Natural Mortality Per Cent	Location	Source
Bluegills	60 to 77	19 to 36	40 to 54	Indiana Lakes	Ricker [48]
Bluegills	66	21	45	Sugarloaf L., Michigan	Cooper and Latta [19]
Largemouth Bass	35 to 40	25 to 30	5 to 11	Ridge L., Ill.	Bennett [9]
Largemouth Bass	56	20	36	Clear L., California	Kimsey [28]
Largemouth Bass	70	26	44	Sugarloaf L., Michigan	Cooper and Latta [19]
Smallmouth Bass	58	22	36	Lake Michigan, Michigan	Latta [34]
Walleye	31	27	4	Many Point L., Minnesota	Olson [39]
Rock Bass	85	15	70	Sugarloaf L.	Cooper and Latta [19]
Pumpkinseed	81	21	60	Sugarloaf L.	Cooper and Latta [19]
Warmouth	70	5	65	Sugarloaf L.	Cooper and Latta [19]
Black Crappie	81	20	61	Sugarloaf L.	Cooper and Latta [19]

FISHING MORTALITY, NATURAL MORTALITY, AND RECRUITMENT

Among warm-water fishes there is little evidence that a high mortality rate either from natural mortality or fishing mortality or both, will seriously reduce the angling potential of a fish population. This is because the number of embryos produced during each spawning period is so large, and the number that can find room to grow is so small, that a large reserve is always available for a population to recoup its most severe losses. Our information on warm-water fishes fails to demonstrate a relationship between the number of spawners and the number of embryos surviving to reach the catchable stock.

Many common warm-water species have short lives and high natural mortality rates. Broods of such fishes as crappies and the sunfishes, the white and yellow basses, and the several kinds of bullheads live but a few years and are replaced. These fishes are subject to wide fluctuations in abundance and in growth rates, and should be cropped when they are available. With some exceptions, short-lived species are responsible for many of the problems of fish management.

Angling mortality is probably far less important in the dynamics of sport fish populations than most fishermen are led to believe.

Restrictions and Mortality

The history of the fisheries resources of North America follows the pattern of man's use of other renewable natural resources. At first there is unrestricted use, followed by a gradual increase in restrictions until a maximum number has been imposed. Then as more information becomes available on the correct management of a resource, unnecessary or useless restrictions are gradually removed.

A maximum of restrictions were imposed upon the warm-water fisheries resources by about 1935; since then, a gradual understanding of fish population dynamics has resulted in an almost complete reversal, once it became appreciated that fish would hatch, spawn, and die in spite of how man restricted himself.

Under conditions of rapid "turnover," it is of some interest to consider size limits, bag limits, seasons, and other restrictions which man has developed to control himself.

Size Limits. There are several assumptions upon which the idea of a minimum size limit is based. One of the most common is that each fish should have an opportunity to reproduce before it is caught. This assumption might be valid if one could demonstrate a shortage of spawn or show a relationship between abundance of spawn and number of spawners. When growth rate shows an inverse relationship to population numbers, a size-limit restriction on a short-lived species may make certain that most of a crowded population of these fish will die of senility before they are large enough to be taken legally. For example, an 8-inch minimum limit governing the take of crappies would allow from 50 to 90 per cent of them to die unused.

When Escanaba Lake (northeastern Wisconsin) was opened to unrestricted hook-and-line fishing, 1946 to 1956, there was no evidence of depletion after 10 years.[15] More than 50 per cent of the fishes taken from this lake by anglers during the test were illegal elsewhere in Wisconsin because of their size. Eighty per cent of the catch consisted of walleyes and perch.

In contrast to the uselessness of size limits in the management of most warm-water lake fishes, Allen[2] cites the catch of marked hatchery-reared trout liberated just before the angling season in American trout streams where the return may be 80 per cent or more in the current season. Shetter, Whalls, and Corbett[59] were able to demonstrate that protection of brook trout in a part of the Au Sable River (Michigan) by a length limit that allowed them to spawn at least once was followed by an increase in fingerlings present. This protection, plus a "flies only" regulation, allowed a buildup of the brook-trout population. If warm-water species were as low in reproductive potential and as vulnerable to angling as are trout, size restrictions would certainly be reasonable.

Prior to 1940 most state fish and game codes specified minimum legal length limits for all important species. Fifteen years later many states had eliminated minimum legal lengths on most species except a few long-lived ones of limited abundance.

Creel Limits. The purposes of a bag or creel limit may be to conserve breeding stock where fish are highly vulnerable to angling. Usually, however, justification for a creel limit is based on the assumption that the limit will reduce the creels of the more successful anglers and thereby make more fish available for the less successful anglers. Also, a creel limit may prevent an individual from taking more fish than he can use.

Where creel limits are a proven necessity, permission to change these limits should not be vested in a legislative branch of government—otherwise adjustments cannot be made to deal with fluctuations in the stock.[3]

Many states retain daily creel limits on important game fish species. In some cases this is to conserve the breeding stocks but more often its purpose is to "spread the fish around" among a theoretical maximum number of anglers. Often the skilled fisherman still catches more than his share of fish but with a daily limit it takes him a longer time.

Closed Seasons. For many years closed seasons were the rule for most species of sport fishes during their spawning season until studies began to indicate that fishing had little or no effect upon the production of young.[5, 22, 38] Murphy [38] set up two areas along the shore of Clear Lake, Lake County, California, one of which was opened to fishing and the other closed, and studied the production of bass fingerlings in these areas. There was no greater fingerling production in the closed area than in the area open to fishing. In later years when both areas were opened to fishing, more bass fingerlings were produced in each than in the year of the test. Murphy felt that the only times a closed season might be useful were (1) when the fishing pressure was extremely high, (2) when a lake had low productivity due to low average annual temperatures, (3) to balance excessive fishing of a highly-prized species, and (4) when nongame fish were crowding out game fish. In every case, he was in doubt that the closed season would accomplish the desired results.

Sometimes closed seasons were set at the wrong time to give protection. From 1939 to 1949 the closed season on bass for central Illinois was April 1 or 15 to June 1. This season protected the nest-guarding bass in only about 6 years out of 10. There were no more young bass in years when bass nested early and were protected by the closed season than in years when they were still guarding eggs after June 1.

In general the controls imposed upon fishermen with the objective of benefiting the fish were far from realistic. Warm-water fish populations are generally controlled by interspecific competition and not by angling.

LITERATURE

1. * Adams, L., *Jour. Wildl. Mgt.*, 15(1), 13-19 (1951).
2. Allen, K. R., *N. Z. Jour. Sci. & Techn. Sec. B*, 35(6), 499-529 (1954).
3. Allen, K. R., *N. Z. Jour. Sci. & Techn. Sec. B*, 36(4), 305-334 (1955).
4. Barnickol, P. G., and Campbell, R. S., *Jour. Wildl. Mgt.*, 16(3), 270-274 (1952).
5. Bennett, G. W., *Ill. Nat. Hist. Surv. Bull.*, 23(3), 373-406 (1945).
6. Bennett, G. W., *Ill. Wildl.*, 1(2), 8-10 (1946).
7. Bennett, G. W., *N. A. Wildl. Conf. Trans.*, 12, 276-285 (1947).
8. Bennett, G. W., *Ill. Nat. Hist. Surv. Bull.*, 24(3), 377-412 (1948).
9. Bennett, G. W., *Ill. Nat. Hist. Surv. Bull.* 26(2), 217-276 (1954).
10. Bennett, G. W., and Childers, W. F., *Jour. Wildl. Mgt.*, 21(4), 414-424 (1957).
11. Bennett, G. W., Thompson, D. H., and Parr, S. A., *Ill. Nat. Hist. Surv. Biol. Notes*, 14, 1-24 (1940).
12. Bennett, G. W., and Weiss, G. F., *Ill. Wildl.*, 14(31), 8-9 (1959).
13. Bowers, C. C., and Martin, M., *Ky. Dept. Fish and Wildl. Res., Fish. Bull.*, 20, 1-13 (1956).
14. * Brown, C. J. D., and Ball, R. C., *Am. Fish. Soc. Trans.*, 72, 177-186 (1943).
15. Churchill, W., *Jour. Wildl. Mgt.*, 21(2), 182-188 (1957).
16. Cobb, E. S., *Prog. Fish-Cult.*, 15, 20-23 (1953).
17. * Cooper, G. P., *Am. Fish. Soc. Trans.*, 81, 4-16 (1952).
18. * Cooper, G. P., *Pap. Mich. Acad. Sci., Arts & Letts.*, 38, 163-186 (1953).
19. Cooper, G. P. and Latta, W. C., *Pap. Mich. Acad. Sci., Arts & Letts.*, 39, 209-223 (1954).
20. * DeLury, D. B., *Biometrics*, 3(4), 145-167 (1947).
21. * DeLury, D. B., *Jour. Fish. Res. Bd. Can.*, 8(4), 281-307 (1951).
22. Eschmeyer, R. W., *Tenn. Acad Sci.*, 17(1), 90-115 (1942).
23. * Fredin, R. A., *Iowa St. Jour. Sci.*, 24(4), 363-384 (1950).
24. Hansen, D. F., *Ill. Nat. Hist. Surv. Bull*, 25(4), 211-265 (1951).
25. Hansen, D. F., Bennett, G. W., Webb, R. J., and Lewis, J. M., *Ill. Nat. Hist. Surv. Bull.*, 27(5), 345-390 (1960).
26. * Jackson, C. H. N., *Jour. Animal Eco.*, 8(2), 238-246 (1939).
27. James, M. C., Meehean, O. L., and Douglas, E. J., *U.S.D.I.F.W. Serv. Bull.*, 35, 1-22 (1944).
28. Kimsey, J. B., *Cal. Fish & Game*, 43(2), 111-118 (1957).
29. * Krumholz, L. A., *Pap. Mich. Acad. Sci., Arts & Letts.*, 29, 281-291 (1944).
30. Kuhne, E. R., *Tenn. Acad. Sci. Reelfoot L. Biol. Sta.*, 3, 46-53 (1939).
31. Kuhne, E. R., *Tenn. Acad. Sci. Reelfoot L. Biol. Sta.*, 3, 54-60 (1939).
32. Lagler, K. F., and DeRoth, G. C., *Pap. Mich. Acad. Sci., Arts & Letts.*, 38, 235-253 (1953).
33. Lagler, K. F., Hazzard, A. S., Hazen, W. E., and Thompkins, W. A., *N. A. Wildl. Conf. Trans.*, 15, 280-303 (1950).

* References having to do with population estimations.

34. Latta, W. C., *Dissertation Abstracts,* **XVIII** (5), 1905 (1958).
35. Lux, F. E., and Smith, L. L., Jr., *Amer. Fish. Soc. Trans.,* **89**(1), 67-79 (1960).
36. Martin, R. G., *Ann Conf. S. E. Assoc. Game & Fish Comm. Proc.,* **11**, 76-82 (1958).
37. Minckley, W. L., and Craddock, J. E., *Prog. Fish Cult.,* **23**(3), 120-123 (1961).
38. Murphy, G. I., *N. A. Wildl. Conf. Trans.,* **15**, 235-251 (1950).
39. Olson, D. E., *Am. Fish. Soc. Trans.* **87**, 52-72 (1958).
40. * Omand, D. M., *Jour. Wildl. Mgt.,* **15**(1), 88-98 (1951).
41. Paloheimo, J. E., *Jour. Fish. Res. Bd. Can.,* **15**(4), 749-758, (1958).
42. Plančić, J., *Deutsche Fischerei-Zeitung,* **3**(12), 373-375 (1956).
43. * Ricker, W. E., *Jour. Am. Statistical Assn.,* **32**, 349-356 (1937).
44. * Ricker, W. E., *Jour. Fish. Res. Bd. Can.,* **5**(1), 43-70 (1940).
45. * Ricker, W. E., *Invest. Ind. Lakes & Streams,* **2**, 215-253 (1942).
46. * Ricker, W. E., *Copeia,* **1944**(1), 23-44 (1944).
47. Ricker, W. E., *N. A. Wildl. Conf. Trans.,* **10**, 266-269 (1945a).
48. Ricker, W. E., *Ecology,* **26**(2), 111-121 (1945b).
49. * Ricker, W. E., *Invest. Ind. Lakes & Streams,* **2**, 345-448 (1945c).
50. * Ricker, W. E., *Jour. Fish. Res. Bd. Can.,* **11**(5), 559-623 (1954).
51. * Ricker, W. E., "Handbook of Computations for Biological Statistics of Fish Populations," Bull. 119, pp. 1-300, Queen's Printer and Cont. of Sta. Ottawa, Canada, 1958.
52. * Rose, E. T., *Am. Fish. Soc., Trans.,* **77**, 32-41 (1949).
53. Russell, E. S., "The Overfishing Problem—De Lamar Lectures," pp. 1-130, The University Press, Cambridge, 1942.
54. * Schaffer, M. B., *Fish. Bull., of the Fish & Wildl. Serv.,* **52**, 191-203 (1951).
55. Schäeperclaus, W., *Zietschr. f. Fischerei,* **5**(1-2), 3-59 (1956).
56. * Schnabel, Z. E., *Am. Math. Monthly,* **45**(6), 348-352 (1938).
57. Schoffman, R. J., *Jour. Tenn. Acad. Sci.,* **34**, 73-77 (1959).
58. * Schumacher, F. X., and Eschmeyer, R. W., *Jour. Tenn. Acad. Sci.,* **18**(3), 228-249 (1943).
59. Shetter, D. S., Whalls, M. J., and Corbett, O. M., *N. A. Wildl. Conf. Trans.,* **19**, 222-238 (1954).
60. Snieszko, S. F., *Prog. Fish-Cult.,* **20**(3), 133-136 (1958).
61. Starrett, W. C., and Fritz, A. W., *Outdoors in Ill.,* **4**(2), 11-14 (1957).
62. Starrett, W. C., and McNeil, P. L., Jr., *Ill. Nat. Hist. Surv. Biol. Notes,* **30**, 1-31 (1952).
63. Stroud, R. H., *Prog. Fish-Cult.,* **17**(2), 51-62 (1955).
64. Swingle, H. S., *N. A. Wildl. Conf. Trans.,* **21**, 298-322 (1956).
65. Swingle, H. S., and Smith, E. V., *Ala. Poly. Inst. Ag. Exp. Sta. Bull.,* **254**, 1-30 (1947).
66. Thompson, D. H., "A Symposium for Hydrobiology," pp. 206-217, Univ. of Wis. Press, Madison, Wis., 1941.
67. Van Oosten, J., *N. A. Wildl. Conf. Trans.,* **14**, 319-330 (1949).
68. Viosca, P., Jr., *Am. Fish. Soc. Trans.,* **73**, 274-283 (1945).
69. Wood, R., *Jour. Tenn. Acad. Sci.,* **26**(3), 214-235 (1951).
70. * Zippin, C., *Jour. Wild. Mgt.,* **22**(1), 82-90 (1958).

* References having to do with population estimations.

8 ～～～～

Fish Behavior and Angling

Water is so different from air in the conductance of light, sound, and chemical stimuli that the behavior and responses of fishes diverge considerably from those of terrestrial vertebrates. Thus, although the eyes, "ears," olfactory, and other sensory organs of the former are adjusted to function under water, the relative importance of these organs is not the same as for terrestrial animals.

These differences in the media of air and water can be appreciated by the skin diver. Near the surface of the lake, he can see at best but a few feet in fresh water, and can scarcely detect his outstretched hand in turbid water. Moreover, if he descends to depths greater than a dozen or more feet, he enters a twilight zone where he can see little, even when the water is clear. He cannot talk to his diving partner because of the mouth-blocking air hose, but even were he unencumbered, he could not be heard for more than a few inches. Although the diver's sense organs are of limited use to him when submerged, this does not mean that submerged vertebrates lack acute sensory perception, but rather that the organs of submerged animals are adapted to function under water, and the interrelationships of various types of sensory perception for aquatic animals are simply quite different from those of terrestrial ones.

An angler who has never been submerged often assumes that the sensory organs of fishes are similar in function to his own. Thus, if he sees a fish in the water, he may take it for granted that the fish views him as an upright land animal, or that it is too low in the vertebrate scale to recognize him as a potential danger (which probably is a mistake).

A nominal amount of research has been done on the sensory organs of fishes and their relationship to behavior. This chapter reviews these studies and attempts to integrate a reasonable concept of how each sensory organ functions in circumscribing the normal behavior of fishes.

VISION

Most fishes have eyes, which in many species are very functional. All of the so-called game fishes and pan fishes have well-developed ones and use them in finding and capturing their foods. Color vision has been tested in a number of species, and no fish is known to be without it.

COLOR VISION

Investigations of color vision in largemouth bass [16] indicated that bass vision was similar to that of a man looking at objects through a strong yellow filter, i.e., the yellow filter made it difficult for the man to separate colors at the blue end of the spectrum. Tests of color vision in bluegills using red and green lights at variable intensities demonstrated the ability of these fish to distinguish these colors. After 100 practice trials, bluegills made 94 correct selections out of 101 tests.[59] Other investigations indicated that various fishes differed in their ability to separate colors although they had little difficulty in separating colors from shades of gray of equal intensity. The elritze (a minnow) could distinguish blue from green but confused red with yellow. The stickleback could discriminate red from green, but not blue from yellow.[97]

Most of the kinds of fishes tested seemed to respond well to red, and either to shun or prefer it. In one series of experiments, untrained mud minnows and common shiners were stimulated by red. In daylight the mud minnows had a respiratory rate of 30 per minute. When a ruby glass was placed over the source of light, the fishes settled to the bottom, had fits of trembling, and more than doubled their rate of opercular movement. The common shiners "breathed" 60 times per minute in diffuse daylight, 85 times per minute when a carbon filament light was turned on in addition, and 150 times per minute when a ruby filter was placed over the light.

When trained to feed in response to a definite color, small fishes that were offered a whole spectrum on the wall of the aquarium gathered in the particular region of color to which they had been conditioned, and followed the movement of the spectrum. Carp were trained to give a positive response to a voilet disc but a negative one to a blue disc, and to move to a white triangle in preference to a white square. When confronted with a violet square and a blue triangle, these fish went to the violet square in preference to the blue triangle, suggesting that the stimulus of color was stronger than the stimulus of shape.

These laboratory experiments indicate the importance of color in the vision of fishes. Most fishermen are aware of the preferences shown by largemouth bass for red, orange, and yellow. In an Illinois lake, red and white casting baits had a catch rate for largemouth bass of 3.5 times that of the next most often listed color which was black.[26, 27] Among fly rod lures, yellow seemed to be the color most acceptable to the largemouths; white or combinations of white and other colors caught the second greatest number of fish. Black lures were important in both casting and fly rod sizes; some fishermen believe that fish strike black lures because they see these baits poorly and strike out of curiosity. Black plugs that create a disturbance at the waters' surface are often very effective for night fishing. Fish swimming below such a surface lure at night follow the water disturbance and may see the indefinite outline of the lure.

Underwater observations of the behavior of smallmouth bass in a quarry lake made by members of the Aquatic Biology staff of the Illinois National History Survey supported the idea that colors of lures were important. Smallmouths lying in several feet of water along a steep bank were presented with variously colored floating fly rod "poppers" of cork and hair, by a fisherman operating from a boat. A diver equipped with scuba * watched the behavior of fish as the "poppers" were moved overhead. Red and yellow "poppers" obviously excited the fish and even when they did not strike they often made short runs under the baits. They were particularly excited by "gantron" baits (covered with paints having high reflecting qualities) in very bright yellow. Poppers of blues, greens, white, and black apparently stimulated very little interest in these smallmouths living in the clear quarry water.

Underwater Vision

A description of a fish's underwater vision is given by Walls [97] as follows: "if a fish looks slantingly upward at the water surface, he cannot see through it, but instead sees mirrored upon it objects which are on the bottom at a distance (Figure 8.1). If he looks more directly upward, he sees into the air. In effect there is a circular window in the surface through which he can look. This window enlarges if he sinks, shrinks if he rises, but always subtends an angle of 97.6° (in fresh water) at his eyes (Figure 8.1B). If the bottom is distant, the surface outside the window is silvery with the reflection of the light scattered in the water, and this light of course always washes over and dilutes the image of the bottom, even when the latter is close enough to the surface to be seen reflected from it.

"Through his surface window the fish sees everything from zenith to horizon in all directions. This hemispherical aerial field is not narrowed or widened according to the size of the window and depth of the fish. It always contains everything above the plane tangent to the water surface at the rim of the window, but the distortion and brightness of objects

---

* Self-contained underwater breathing apparatus.

within it do vary. The objects seen proportionately largest are those directly overhead. If an object should swing down a semicircle from the zenith toward the horizon, along a meridian of the aerial hemisphere, it would get shorter and shorter in its meridional length and in its width measured parallel to the surface. Thus, even though its linear distance from the fish were constant, its apparent size would become smaller, the closer it approached the horizon. It would be seen more and more dimly, too, for light rays which make small angles with the water are largely

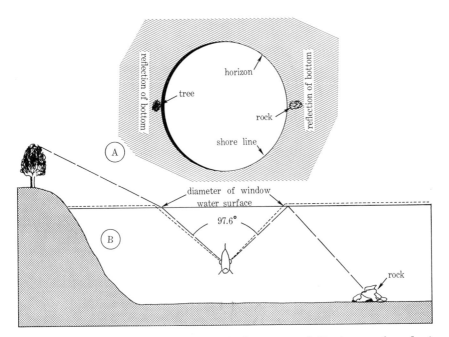

Figure 8.1. A. Visual field of a fish looking upward. B. As seen from horizontal view. [From Walls, G. L., "The Vertebrate Eye and Its Adaptive Radiation," Cranbrook Inst. of Science, Bull. 19, Bloomfield Hills, Mich., 1942]

reflected, and but little of such light is refracted down through the surface to enter the eye of a fish.

"The entire circumference of the 'horizon,' which a swimming man could see by treading water and rotating 360° on his axis, is, for the fish, contracted to the few inches or feet of circumference of his surface window. (Figure 8.1A and B.) It follows that a man standing on the bank of a pool is seen as a tiny doll by a fish which is a few yards away and only a few inches below the surface. Our tendency is to suppose that the fish will see us more poorly still; just as we see him less well, if he drops deeper in the water; but since dropping lower enlarges his window, it magnifies objects on the shore—magnifies them, that is, as compared with their apparent size when the window is smaller. To see the fishermen optimally, then, the fish must seek a depth from which the improvement of visibility through enlargement is not cancelled by the loss of light through the greater distance of water through which the rays must travel to his eyes. The poor fish is thus fated never to see us as we are—even through the flat glass side of an aquarium tank." (figure references in parentheses mine)

The eyes of most kinds of fish protrude enough and are located on the body in a position to give a full visual field. This is necessary because a fish has no neck, a situation that is not compensated for by his buoyancy and ability to rotate on his vertical axis.

CHANGING PIGMENTATION

Many years ago while stationed at the Rock Creek Hatchery in south central Nebraska, I observed some very large *black* rainbow trout in the small spring-fed rocky stream that meandered through the hatchery grounds. The hatchery superintendent told me they were blind "spawners" (fish used for stripping eggs and sperm in artificial trout propagation) that had been injured and later released in the creek. For something to do on a Sunday afternoon, four of us decided to catch one of these black trout; using two minnow seines, one above and below a fish, we tried to trap him in the bag of one or the other of the seines. He always escaped, usually by finding an opening under the seine when a rock caused a momentary lifting of the lead line. The fish was as capable of avoiding capture as if it had functional eyes, except that once it escaped the net it did not seek cover as a normal trout would do. The dark color of these trout is characteristic of fish that are totally blind.

The relationship of light to the intensity of a fish's pigmentation is described by Walls [97]: (1) When no light is striking a fish (with or without functional eyes) the melanophores (dark pigment cells) "contract." (2) When light strikes only the skin (whether the eyes are present or not) the melanophores "expand." (3) If more of any light entering the eye strikes the upper part of the retina, the melanophores "contract" despite the tendency mentioned in (2). (4) If more of the light entering the eye strikes the lower part of the retina, the inhibitory effect of the tendency given in (3) upon the tendency in (2) is ineffective and the melanophores expand. Thus the extent of pigmentation depends upon a combination of stimuli upon the skin and eyes. A fish that is completely blind darkens in the light because there is no functional eye to inhibit the innate tendency of the illuminated melanophores to expand. Fish taken from muddy water are usually light in color because they are exposed to limited light.

Direct Observation and Sun Orientation

According to Hasler, *et al.*,[52] the eyes of fishes are useful in orientation. These investigators demonstrated that white bass in Lake Mendota (Wisconsin) moved in a definite direction when transported from one part of the lake to another on clear days, but when displaced on cloudy days, or if blinded by eye caps, they moved at random. These investigators demonstrated in laboratory experiments that the sun was a source for orientation (whether the "sun" was natural or artificial) and that the fish had a biological "clock" that operated in combination with the sun to allow compensation of movement for different times of day.

In some earlier experiments, Hasler [48] had discovered that the elritze (a European minnow) used minute marks on the wall and floor of its tank for orientation rather than the presence of an artificial "sun." It was only after removing all visible marks in the tank during training over a long period of time that these fish were taught to associate a 90° angle of a "sun" to a feeding position.

With a combination of sun orientation and/or the demonstrated ability of a fish to orient through observation of inconspicuous "landmarks" under water, it is little wonder that they show considerable ability to return to "home" territory after having been displaced. As will be described later, other sensory organs aid in "homing."

Light Sensitivity

The eyes and other light-sensitive organs of fishes control to some extent the relative position of fish in a body of water. Fish placed in a tank containing a light gradient selected the level of illumination most satisfying to them and were restricted in their movements by light above a certain intensity.[106] This light intensity selection is upset by hunger, season, and by sex stimulation during the spawning period. Reaction to light also may change as a fish grows from fry to adult size.[81] An important reason why electro-fishing at night is so much more efficient than in day time is because certain kinds and sizes of fishes usually found in deep water move into shallow water with the coming of darkness.

Many kinds of fishes show diurnal rhythms associated with the changing intensity of light. Elritze kept in a tank were active during the day and quiet at night, but their behavior was reversed if they were given hollow bricks in which to take cover and thus avoid bright light.[61] When cover was available, they were active at sunrise and sunset. Minnows kept in continuous darkness showed no rhythm of locomotor activity. Blinded minnows responded to daily variations in light intensity and were more active at night than during the day. These and many other laboratory experiments demonstrate the high light-sensitivity of most kinds of fishes.

Some species prefer semi-darkness and are so sensitive to light that they exhibit extreme agitation if forced to swim in illuminated clear water.

Walleyes in Lake Gogebic (Michigan) were so sensitive to an automobile floodlight at close range that they would collide with rocks or beach themselves in their attempts to escape.[30]

Fingerling channel catfish being reared in turbid river water in wooden hatchery troughs, exhibited extreme fright when clear water was turned on them while the troughs were being cleaned. When black bullheads are placed in an aquarium in strong light they tend to pile-up, each fish trying to hide under the others. Smallmouth bass, red-ear sunfish, and grass pike in laboratory tanks have been observed to die of shock when the lights in the aquarium room were turned on at night.

HEARING

Laboratory experiments using modern equipment have established that all species studied have the ability to hear. The range of tone perception is believed to vary from 8 to 22,000 cycles per second. The "ears" of fishes are internal and consist of a sacculus and lagena (*pars inferior*) believed to be responsible for hearing, and a utriculus and semi-circular canal system (*pars superior*) concerned with equilibration. In some species the *pars superior* may take part in the perception of tones. In the Ostariophysi (examples are gold fish and yellow bullhead), the connection of the air bladder with the "ear" by Weber's ossicles increases the ability of fish to hear. Perception of very low frequencies is generally attributed to sensory organs in the skin.

Various species of common warm-water fishes have different ranges of sound perception; for example, the range of the bluegill is 35 to 8960 cycles per second [94] while that for the carp is 8 to 22,000.[82] These ranges cover a part of the range of human speech, but a great deal of intensity is lost between air and water, so that it would be difficult for a fish to hear a fisherman talking. This is not true for vibrations transmitted through the bottom of a boat or from walking with "heavy feet" along the water's edge. The disturbance caused by rowing or paddling where the oarsman is careless about letting oars or paddle hit or scrape the edge of the boat is undoubtedly heard by fishes.

Sound Location

Fish learned to distinguish between tones of different intensities and were able to distinguish a change in frequency (one-fifth of an octave) in a continuously sounding source.

According to Kleerekoper and Chagnon,[62] creek chubs were able to locate a source of vibration and move toward it along curved pathways which probably represented fields of higher intensity such as are produced by the crests of interfering waves or by a standing wave.

SOUND PRODUCTION

Among freshwater fishes known to produce sounds are the sheepshead or drum, several kinds of minnows (Cyprinidae),[25, 101] and the catfishes. Others probably produce noises or vibrations of various frequencies.

Records of sounds produced by freshwater drum were made in Lake Winnebago (Wisconsin) using a Type H-11 hydrophone (U. S. Navy).[84] The sheepshead started "drumming" in early May and continued at a decreased intensity until the end of August. Drumming began about 10 A.M. and continued until sunset; highest drumming activity occurred during the afternoon. Sounds were produced by sexually mature males only and appeared to be for communication during the spawning season.

The drumming sound of the sheepshead is produced by muscular contractions which actuate a tendonlike structure across the swim bladder. The frequency spectrogram of the sounds produced covered a broad range of frequencies between 150 and 2000 cycles per second with the largest relative amplitudes within the range of 250 to 400 cps.

In the blacktail shiner and the red shiner only the ripe females produced sounds. These sounds were useful in attracting ripe males of their own species.[25] The satinfin shiner is reported to make a sound similar to the sound made when one strikes wood with his knuckles. These sounds were produced when males fought and when males and females courted. Isolated females also produced fainter, less frequent knocks than males, so that it was impossible to positively identify the source of the sound when males and females were together. Males also made a purring sound when actively courting females.[101]

Many species of marine fishes are known to produce sounds, and some deep sea forms are believed to use their sound-producing apparatus to engage in echo-sounding.[42]

ODOR PERCEPTION AND TASTE

Fishes demonstrate an ability to taste and "smell" substances dissolved in water. In fact the sense of "smell" appears to be very highly developed and probably has many functions other than that of food finding. Terrestrial animals are able to detect an odor when (according to one theory) minute particles of a substance are dissolved on membranes associated with sensory cells of olfactory nerves. These minute particles are carried on air currents and are, in some instances, subject to dessication. One modern theory of odor perception suggests that substances having odor interfere with enzyme-catalysed reactions in the receptors. The fact that enzymes are affected in their action by minute amounts of many substances may explain the wide range of compounds that possess odors (to humans). The ability of an animal (or human) to recognize faint odors in the presence of a constant strong odor is explained by the rapid reversability of inhibitory effects on enzymes of odors continuously applied at a constant level. The strong odor of a soy bean processing plant (while not unpleasant to many people) does not obscure a weaker but more delectable odor of broiling steak.

There is no indication that the acuity of olfaction in fishes is any less than that of terrestrial animals.

LOCATION OF TASTE ORGANS

In many species, taste buds occur on the outer surface of the body as well as in the mouth. This is often demonstrated by lowering a piece of raw meat on a string into an aquarium so that it approaches the tail of a black bullhead. The fish will immediately turn and grasp the meat. Experiments have shown that taste buds are most abundant in the barbels of the bullhead but lesser numbers are scattered over the surface of the body and tail.[56]

This wide distribution of taste buds is characteristic of fishes that normally live in turbid waters such as bullheads, other catfishes, carp, and some of the other fishes that live and feed on the bottom. Fishes such as bass or sunfish (Centrarchidae) that feed primarily by sight have less well developed and less widely distributed taste buds. However, observations substantiate a general hypothesis that the outer surfaces of most fishes are sensitive to a variety of mild chemical stimuli.

Bullheads and other fishes that have taste organs scattered over the outer surface of the body use their olfactory organs for locating food at a distance.[47] Tests of bullheads with barbels removed (taste) and others with olfactory tracts severed (odor perception) demonstrated that odor perception was more important than taste in locating earthworms in a cheesecloth sack.

Olmsted [76] tested bullheads with many natural substances to determine which ones proved stimulating to them. Using 30 pairs of fish throughout a fairly long period of time he charted the number of bites made by each pair during trials extending for one-half hour. Materials used for testing the fish were graded by using an arbitrary scale from 100 to 0; most stimulating materials were rated near 100 and lesser ones accordingly lower. In these experiments he discovered that human saliva rated below earthworms and liver, but was rather high in its over-all rating. Thus the custom of "spitting on one's bait" is apparently more than a superstition.

Some Uses of Odor Perception

Odor perception is less limited by water than is vision and hearing. For this reason the olfactory organs of fishes are highly developed and extensively used for many purposes.

Schooling. Wrede [107] discovered that schools of elritze were held together by a substance in the mucus of that species; the introduction of mucus from these minnows into a part of an aquarium would cause the minnows in the aquarium to congregate there. Vision appeared to be important in schooling during daylight hours, but the stimulus of odor held the schools together in darkness. "Both blinded and hind-brain-extirpated fish could be trained to these substances, indicating chemoreception, although animals with nose intact responded best."[107] Schools of young silver salmon in an aquarium remained intact as long as the room was lighted, but when the light was extinguished and infrared substituted, dispersal of the school was complete in a matter of a few seconds, indicating that in this case, schooling depended entirely upon vision.[3]

Fright Reaction. Blinded elritze that did not respond to pike mucus, were placed in an aquarium with a pike that captured some of them. When those remaining were tested with a combination pike and elritze odor, they gave a severe fright reaction. Thus when these minnows show a reaction to odors of several other fishes, it may be that the reaction is due to past experience with these fishes rather than an innate response.

In a long series of experiments von Frisch [32] tested a substance exuded by an injured elritze minnow which he called "Schreckstoff" (alarm substance). This material would cause an alarm reaction (Schreck-reaktion) when released in a school of uninjured minnows. Quantitatively, when 100 ml of this solution was poured into aquaria of 25- to 150-liter capacity, the minnow gave pronounced fear reactions. The alarm-causing material was mostly in the skin, because extracts from minnow intestine and liver gave no reaction and extracts from gills, muscle, and ovaries were from one-tenth to one-hundredth as active as skin extracts. Minnows with severed olfactory nerves would not respond to the substance; for this reason von Frisch concluded that the alarm substance was odoriferous. Huttel [60] pointed out that the alarm substance of the elritze was a purin- or pterin-like substance.

That the alarm reaction may be transmitted by sight alone was demonstrated by Verheijen [96] when he placed two aquaria containing elritze side by side and dropped tissue juice into one aquarium to produce typical fright reactions. Minnows in the adjacent aquarium eventually huddled together in a tight "fright" school, but were about 10 seconds slower in their reaction than were the minnows stimulated with "fright" juice.

Identification of Common and Uncommon Odors. Fisheries researchers at the University of Wisconsin [47] demonstrated that blinded bluntnose minnows, after a training of 2.5 months, were able to distinguish between odors of milfoil, *Myriophyllum exalbescens,* and coontail, *Ceratophyllum demersum,* when rewarded with food and punished with electric shock. These minnows were able to detect a water rinse of a sprig of an aquatic plant diluted 1:10,000. Hasler and Wisby [53] found that bluntnose minnows could detect phenols at concentrations of 0.01 ppm and could discriminate between phenol and p-chlorophenol at concentrations of 5×10^{-4} ppm.

These studies suggest that olfaction in fishes (at least in some species) may be as important in the routine of day to day existence as is olfaction in dogs. Fish may not be so obvious in their use of the sense of smell as are dogs, but there is little doubt that they may recognize a "home" environment, identify individual fishes of their kind as well as those of other kinds, and perform other functions through the use of olfactory organs. Further experiments indicate that some fishes are "blood hounds" in their use of the sense of smell. This is particularly true of fishes that make long migrations.

Odor as an Aid in Migration. Biologists have long searched for an explanation for the return migration of salmon to a specific location in a home stream. These fish are spawned in fresh water streams, usually many miles from the oceans. After spending several months in the stream where they were spawned, they gradually work seaward, finally leaving fresh water, for a period of several years in the ocean. When they reach sexual maturity, they return to the stream system where they were spawned, migrate upstream always selecting the right branch or tributary until they return to the location of their origin where they in turn spawn. Hasler and Wisby [54] have postulated that salmon must find the way back to their place of origin through their retention of olfactory impressions of the stream. In order for such a hypothesis to be true, investigators would have to be able to give an affirmative answer to the following questions:

(1) Do streams have characteristic odors to which fish can react, and, if so, what is the nature of the odor?
(2) Can salmon detect and discriminate between such odors if they do exist?
(3) Can salmon retain odor impressions from youth to maturity?

They began by testing unconditioned salmon fry with odoriferous substances [102] to find ones that the salmon fry gave evidence of liking or disliking. Salmon fry were placed in a central waterfilled compartment of an apparatus and a test substance was introduced into one of four tributary arms through which water flowed to supply the center compartment. Gates at the openings of the tubes were opened and the fry were allowed to enter the tubes of their choice. Their distribution after the test was recorded and compared with the distribution obtained when no odor was introduced.

Many organic odors were tested in this manner. None was found which would attract salmon, but morpholine seemed to fit the necessary requirements—soluble in water permitting accurate dilutions, detectable in very low concentrations (easily detected at 1×10^{-6} ppm) making the treatment of large volumes of water feasible, and chemically stable under stream conditions. At low concentrations morpholine was neither an attractant or repellent, so that salmon could be conditioned to it in either direction. Thus salmon fry which hatched in a stream treated with a low concentration of morpholine should associate that odor with the spawning site when they returned several years later. This would give the stream a characteristic odor [and satisfy condition (1)]. Salmon have already shown evidence of detecting this odor at concentrations as low as 1×10^{-6} ppm [condition (2)] and if they are able to retain odor impressions from youth to maturity they should have no difficulty in arriving at the original spawning site. A further and a very crucial test would be an attempt to decoy the salmon conditioned to morpholine up the wrong stream branch by treating that branch with morpholine. If the salmon entered the wrong branch, it would be certain proof that they were migrating entirely by odor impressions. However, if they did not enter the wrong branch, the odor theory would not necessarily be disproved because the odor impression of the "home" stream might consist of a complex of odors including morpholine, and the salmon might not have accepted the other components making up the odor complex (excluding morpholine) of the wrong stream branch. Salmon could be expected to enter a "wrong" stream branch when the odor impression for morpholine completely subordinated other stream odors. Field tests to measure the possibilities given above have not been completed.

In further experiments on odor recognition in salmon, sexually ripe coho salmon were captured in each of two branches of the Issaquah River in Washington, marked and returned downstream below the junction of the two branches to remake the upstream run and reselect the correct branch.[103] In one half of the fish the nasal sac was plugged with cotton. Most of the normal fish repeated their former stream choice upon reaching the fork while the plugged-nose fish selected one or the other of the branches in nearly random fashion. While the pressure of the cotton plugs in the nasal sacs of the plugged-nose salmon may have influenced their behavior (and no similar pressure was applied to the normal fish), the experiment is indicative of the importance of the olfactory system in the migration of these fish.

Brett and MacKinnon [15] made a series of tests to explore the sense of smell in migrating coho and spring salmon. When dilute solutions of various chemicals were introduced in the path of salmon moving up a fish ladder, they caused no significant change in migration rate. However, a dilute rinse of mammalian skins had a distinct repellent action suggesting that the salmon may have been conditioned against this odor.

These experiments with salmon indicate that the olfactory organs are very important in orientation and migration of these fishes. The long migrations of salmon are necessary in order that the fish complete its life cycle; therefore one might expect that sensory development of organs useful in making the long journey might be more highly developed in salmon than in fishes living a fairly localized existence.

Odor as an Aid in Homing. Homing, home range, and territoriality of fishes will be discussed later in Chapter 8. Displaced fishes find their way back to home areas by using a combination of sensory organs. However, Gunning [43] was able to show that odor orientation was more important than vision in the rapid return of a fish to its home area. In fact, blind fishes with unimpaired olfactory organs were able to return to a home range, after being displaced experimentally, as quickly and accurately as control (normal) fishes.

More detailed and technical information on the functioning of the sensory organs of fishes may be found in the book "The Physiology of Fishes," Vol. 2, edited by Margaret E. Brown.[17]

TEMPERATURE PERCEPTION AND RESPONSES

The body of a fish is almost uninsulated from the cold or warm water surrounding it, presumably because fishes do not maintain a constant body temperature. This does not mean that they are insensitive to temperature changes or cannot be killed by high or low temperatures. Fishes frequently expire through exposure when they are moved from extremes of heat and cold within the north-south range of a species. For example, red-ear sunfish transferred from northern Texas to central Illinois lived during the summer but died over the first winter, in all probability from the cold. There is also a likelihood that bluegills from northern Michigan would die from high water temperatures if moved to southern Alabama or Georgia. However, through a series of transplants, gambusia, a live-bearing top minnow indigenous to the southern United States, was purposely moved northward from its normal range nearly 700 miles during a period of about 20 years. This was accomplished in 4 or 5 stages: Offspring of the fishes that survived one or more winters at one stage were in turn moved northward to the next stage until they were thriving in southern Michigan.[64] These fish are now being successfully established as far north as Winnipeg, Manitoba, Canada.[90]

Sensitivity to Temperature Change

Although there appears to be no specialized temperature receptors in a fish's skin, there is little doubt that fish are capable of feeling relatively slight changes in temperature. Sullivan [95] describes an experiment in which fish were fed at the same time that the temperature was slightly raised so that feeding became associated with small rises in temperature.[18, 19] After a training period, a temperature rise as small as 0.03° to 0.1°C would produce a feeding reaction. By the direct approach, employing electrophysiological equipment, it has been demonstrated that a rising temperature (within the range of 4° to 17°C) increased the frequency of rhythmatic impulses in trunk lateral line nerves, with about a two-fold increase in frequency for each 4° temperature rise.

After fish were shown to be sensitive to small changes in temperature, the next approach was to see how they were affected by rapidly increasing temperature. There was no response until a specific "response temperature" of 27°C (80.6°F) was reached, when the fish suddenly began vigorous swimming movements.[83] In reverse, fish plunged into cold water reacted immediately with violent bursts of activity followed by benumbed inactivity.[14]

Changes in temperature of a few degrees C, with time for the body of the fish to equilibrate with the water (20 minutes), resulted in a little movement at low temperatures, increasing as the temperature was raised to a peak which occurred at the temperature that the species normally selected in a temperature gradient. If the temperature were raised further, activity decreased reaching a second low several degrees below the lethal level.[14] If the temperature were increased further, movement again increased to a second peak after which activity stopped abruptly and the animal died. These experiments demonstrate the relationship of temperature to activity levels in fishes. Peaks of activity were modified to some extent by exposure to low or high temperatures for extensive periods prior to testing.

Mortalities Caused by High Temperatures

Fishes are seldom killed by high temperatures alone when out-of-doors in natural waters (see Chapter 3, p. 46) although Bailey [4] recorded such a mortality of fishes in a part of Bass Lake, Livingston County, Michigan, that had become separated from the main lake by a gravel ridge. At the time of the kill the pond was about one-fourth acre with a maximum depth of 5 inches.

On the afternoon of July 12, 1952 the water in this pond reached a temperature of 38°C (100.4°F) and fish began to die without showing symptoms of oxygen shortage. Not all of the fishes died and several days later there were still live killifish, and gambusia (a southern species) as well as bluegill, pumpkinseed, longear and green sunfish, all in apparent good condition. Most of the mud minnows, chubsuckers, and several species of minnows, i.e., golden shiner, blacknose shiner, blackchin shiner, sand shiner, and bluntnose minnow were all dead, as were the brown and yellow bullheads, stonecats, madtoms, and Iowa darters. The smaller individuals of some species survived while the larger ones died; this was true of the minnows, catfish and madtoms.

The problem of lethal temperatures is very complicated because it is dependent upon the previous acclimation of test animals, and is affected by diet, length of photoperiod and probably other factors related to the physiology of the fish. Thermal deaths may be complicated by oxygen and carbon dioxide tensions, mineral content, and salinity of the water.[34] Therefore, when high temperature mortality occurs out of doors as described by Bailey above, one can hardly explain why some fish died and some survived.

TEMPERATURE ACCLIMATION

Fish in pools that are drying up may die of high water temperatures, or high or low dissolved oxygen tensions, although these deaths usually go unnoticed. The temperature at which a fish dies (both high and low) is affected by the temperature to which the fish was acclimated prior to exposure. Brett [14] lists upper and lower lethal temperatures for a number of freshwater fishes when these fishes previously had been acclimated to various temperatures. Lethal temperatures for three warm-water fishes listed by Brett are given in Table 8.1.

The changes in a fish's ability to tolerate low or high temperatures resulting from a change in acclimation temperature, probably does not have a great deal of survival value under natural conditions. It has been shown by Brett and others that the rate of increase in ability to tolerate higher temperatures is relatively rapid, requiring 24 hours at temperatures above 20°C (68°F). Conversely the loss in this increased tolerance to high temperatures, and a gain in resistance to low temperatures is much slower, requiring as much as 20 days to approach complete acclimation in some species. Thus, sudden drops in air temperatures that cause rapid and abnormal cooling of natural waters might cause the death of fishes acclimated to warm waters, while warm-air temperatures resulting in rapid and abnormal warming of cold waters might have little effect because the fish could become acclimated to higher temperatures almost as fast as the water temperature could increase.

The relationship between acclimation temperatures and lethal temperatures in fishes is undoubtedly a factor in the survival of fishes transported overland in tanks, particularly where fish are cooled abnormally through the use of ice or refrigerated tanks.

TABLE 8.1 LETHAL TEMPERATURES FOR THREE WARM-WATER FISHES.

	High Temperatures	Low Temperatures
Largemouth Bass	Acc. Temp. Lethal Temp. 20°C(68°F)–32.5°C(90.5°F) 25°C(77°F)–34.5°C(94.1°F) 30°C(86°F)–36.4°C(97.5°F)	Acc. Temp. Lethal Temp. 20°C(68°F)–5.5°C(41.9°F) 30°C(86°F)–11.8°C(53.2°F)
Bluegill	Acc. Temp. Lethal Temp. 15°C(59°F)–30.7°C(87.3°F) 20°C(68°F)–31.5°C(88.7°F) 30°C(86°F)–33.8°C(92.8°F)	Acc. Temp. Lethal Temp. 15°C(59°F)–2.5°C(36.5°F) 20°C(68°F)–5°C(41°F) 25°C(77°F)–7.5°C(45.5°F) 30°C(86°F)–11.1°C(51.9°F)
Yellow Perch	Acc. Temp. Lethal Temp. 5°C(41°F)–21.3°C(70.3°F) 10°C(50°F)–25°C(77°F) 15°C(59°F)–27.7°C(81.9°F) 25°C(77°F)–29.7°C(85.5°F)	Acc. Temp. Lethal Temp. 10°C(50°F)–1.1°C(34°F) 25°C(77°F)–3.7°C(38.7°F)

PREFERRED TEMPERATURES

Anglers have shown considerable interest in the preferred temperatures of sport fishes of various species during summer months because they believe this knowledge will help in locating these fishes, which, of course, is the first step in catching them. Ferguson [31] made laboratory studies of the preferred temperature of yellow perch and compared his results with preferred temperatures for perch and other species as recorded by other fishery biologists. He used the definition of preferred temperature of Fry [33]: "the region, in an infinite range of temperature, at which a given population will congregate with more or less precision—a temperature around which all individuals will ultimately congregate, regardless of their thermal experience before being placed in the gradient."

The level of thermal acclimation influences the preferred temperature. In general, the preferred temperature is considerably higher than the acclimation temperature for fish that are acclimated to low temperatures. The differences decrease up to the final preferendum where both coincide. In nature a fish may be prevented from selecting its true preferred temperature by light, feeding routines, social behavior and dissolved gases.

Table 8.2 shows the preferred temperatures of some sport fish. This table represents a part of a table given by Ferguson.[31] Preferred tempera-

TABLE 8.2 FIELD OBSERVATIONS OF SOME SPECIES OF SPORT FISH AND TEMPERATURES ASSOCIATED WITH THEM. AUGUST DISTRIBUTIONS AND TEMPERATURES WERE USED WHEREVER POSSIBLE. (FROM FERGUSON,[31] 1958.)

Species	Temperature		Water	Location	Author
	°C	°F			
Largemouth Bass	26.6-27.7	79.9-81.9	Norris Reservoir	Tenn.	Dendy, 1948
Spotted Bass	23.5-24.4	74.3-75.9	Norris Reservoir	Tenn.	Dendy, 1948
Walleye	20.6	69.1	Trout Lake	Wis.	Hile and Juday, 1941
Walleye	22.7-23.2	72.9-73.8	Norris Reservoir	Tenn.	Dendy, 1948
Rock Bass	14.7-21.3	58.5-70.3	Lakes	Wis.	Hile and Juday, 1941
Yellow Perch	21.2	70.2	Lake Opeongo	Ontario	Ferguson, 1958
Yellow Perch	21.0	69.8	Costello L.	Ontario	Ferguson, 1958
Yellow Perch (small)	12.2	54.0	Muskellunge L.	Wis.	Hile and Juday, 1941
Yellow Perch (larger)	20.2	68.4	Muskellunge L.	Wis.	Hile and Juday, 1941
Yellow Perch	20.2	68.4	Silver Lake	Wis.	Hile and Juday, 1941
Yellow Perch	21.0	69.8	Nebish Lake	Wis.	Hile and Juday, 1941
Smallmouth Bass	20.3-21.3	68.5-70.3	Nebish Lake	Wis.	Hile and Juday, 1941
Brook Trout	14.2-20.3	57.6-68.5	Moosehead L.	Maine	Cooper and Fuller, 1945
Brook Trout	12.0-20.0	53.6-68.0	Redrock L.	Ontario	Baldwin, 1948
Lake Trout	10.0-15.5	50.0-59.9	Cayuga L.	N.Y.	Galligan, 1951
Lake Trout	14.0	57.2	White L.	Ontario	Kennedy, 1941

tures for four species have been collected from two or more investigations often widely separated. For example, the preferred temperatures of walleyes in Norris Reservoir, Tennessee, are several degrees higher than those for walleyes in Trout Lake, Vilas County, Wisconsin—more than 1000 miles farther north. This is probably true also for largemouth and spotted bass although no information is at hand for bass in more northern locations. Fishes shown in table 8.2 are arranged in order of descending (higher to lower) temperature preferences.

There are a number of records of fish acclimated to low temperatures invading warm water in spite of a lethal effect; [38,44] also, a record of a concentration of fish (mostly white crappies) where the temperature gradient was only 1 to 2°F.[44]

Rising water temperatures in spring and early summer would eventually force species of fish preferring cool waters out of the upper layers of a lake. For example, the lake trout and walleyes of Trout Lake, Vilas County, Wisconsin, had always left the surface waters by the time spring was well advanced and successful fishermen caught these species after May by trolling with baits at depths of 25 to 100 feet.

BEHAVIOR PATTERNS

Fishes have many behavior patterns that are well known, partly because they are common to many species. Other behavior patterns of a more specific nature are familiar to many because the fish are common and widely distributed. Each group of fishes has its own characteristic reproductive pattern, but reproductive behavior will be omitted from this chapter in favor of more general types of activities. Some of these are described below.

Some Types of Behavior Patterns

Fishes are so often referred to as "schooling," that one may be led to believe that this is the normal social grouping for these animals. Although not all fishes show schooling tendencies, the subject of social behavior involves all of them and is, therefore, a logical subject with which to begin.

Social Groupings. Breder [13] recognized four degrees of social groupings among fishes: solitary, aggregating, schooling, and podding. Some kinds of fishes show more than one of these grouping classifications in relation to seasonal or sexual behavior. Breder's grouping classifications are defined as follows:

1. *Solitary.* Fishes that show zero or negative attraction toward others of their kind.

2. *Aggregating.* Fishes attracted to their kind by favorable temperature, local abundance of food or other environmental detail, but which show no particular polarity as a group, nor is the group capable of any specific directional movement. These fish are oriented without reference to other individuals.

3. *Schooling.* Fishes sufficiently attracted to one another to impel them to swim in substantially similar paths and perform as a troupe of like-acting individuals in which independence of action is reduced to near the vanishing point. Such a group of fishes is polarized and capable of forward movement as a unit.

4. *Podding.* Fishes packed so closely in groups as to leave no swimming clearance, i.e., these fish are actually in contact with one another. The individuals may or may not be polarized.

Among warm-water species, solitary and aggregating fishes are more common than schooling or podding fishes. Most species of Centrarchids (sunfishes) are solitary or aggregating, although crappies might be considered as schooling under certain conditions. White bass and many kinds of minnows show well-defined schooling, as do bullheads, although under certain conditions the latter form pods. Aggregations, schools, and pods are, in general, without leadership and may shift first in one direction and then in another. Leadership may be evident in schooling fish representing a female followed by a number of males. Schooling may have survival value in that the "confusion effect" of a large school of fishes may reduce the precision of a predator's attack.

Seasonal Rhythm. Most warm-water fishes have a fairly constant seasonal rhythm of activities. Being adapted to warm water their movements tend to be inhibited by low water temperatures. Some forms such as the smallmouth bass spend the winter in a quiescent state in schools or groups. Others, such as the northern pike, are quite active in winter and move about constantly. Greenbank [39] set trap nets facing in both directions across the opening into Target Lake, a backwater area of the Mississippi River (Wisconsin) during 40 days of winter and caught 3328 fish, most of which were black crappies, yellow bullheads, and bowfin. He found a positive correlation between total fish movement and the amount of snow cover on the ice. This movement was more related to reduced light conditions than to current, temperature, or dissolved oxygen.

Breder [12] in his treatise on the reproductive habits of North American sunfishes (Centrarchidae) stated that "hibernation" in most species was broken up at about 10°C (50°F) with a general movement from deep water to inshore areas. But not all of the Centrarchids are quiescent in winter. Hansen [45] found that the crappies in Lake Decatur in central Illinois were more readily trapped in nets in fall, winter, and spring than in summer. The poorest trapping season for crappies in this lake was from about mid-July to late September. Other warm-water fishes also show a tendency to be less active during the hottest part of the summer than in spring and fall.

Daily Activity. There are many records of daily activity patterns of warm-water fishes. Carlander and Cleary [21] describe three types of diurnal movements of fishes that they observed through the use of gillnets: (1) more activity at night than in the day time; (2) more activity in daylight than in darkness; (3) activity that resulted in movement from one habitat to another at different periods of the day. These authors listed walleyes and tullibee as being more active at night than in day time, and perch and northern pike as being more active in the day time. They stated that common suckers moved into shallow waters at night and into deep water during the day, while carp and yellow bass moved into shallow waters during the day time and into deep water at night. Spoor and Schloemer [91] had previously reported an inshore and offshore movement of common suckers at Muskellunge Lake, Vilas County, Wisconsin, associated with darkness and daylight (No. 3 above). They could demonstrate no such directional movement in rock bass, but the peaks of activity (catches) for this species were at dusk and dawn, with considerable activity during the night.

Hasler and Bardach [51] discovered an interesting daily migration of the perch in Lake Mendota (Madison, Wisconsin) beginning about the end of May and continuing into October. These fish moved toward shore in certain areas in the hours before sunset and, to a lesser degree, before sunrise. Once they reached the 18-foot (6-meter) contour they changed direction and cruised along parallel to shore. With the coming of darkness these fish appeared to disperse rather suddenly. Fish caught at sunset were gorged with freshly ingested water fleas (*Daphnia*), which suggested that this movement may have been a feeding migration.

The difference in activity periods of closely related species is illustrated by laboratory experiments of Childers [23] using white and black crappies. These two species were placed in separate large aquaria and supplied with a known number of minnows. As the minnows were eaten, they were recorded and others were added to replace them. Both kinds of crappies consumed more minnows during the 2-hour dusk period than they did during the 2-hour dawn period and more food was consumed at night than during the day, but while the black crappies ate 2.5 per cent of their food during daylight hours, the white crappies consumed 14.8 per cent of their food in daylight. A similar difference in feeding habits of the two kinds of crappies is suggested by a trapping study conducted by David H. Thompson [45] in which 31 per cent of the white crappies netted in

Meredosia Bay (Illinois) were caught during the day and 69 per cent at night. By comparison 11 per cent of the black crappies were caught during the day and 89 per cent at night. "Night" included dusk, darkness and dawn.

RESPONSES TO SPECIFIC STIMULI

Many instances of fish activity resulting from a combination of stimuli have been recorded in fishery literature. Eschmeyer [29] found that when the fall drawdown of Norris Reservoir was begun in September (1942), the white bass, yellow bass, and sauger migrated upstream from Watts Bar Reservoir into the mouth of the Clinch River and upstream to Norris Dam. These fishes represented the larger individuals of the 1942 year class (the first) produced in Watts Bar Reservoir. The distance from Watts Bar Dam to Norris Dam is about 118 miles by water (river channel, 38 miles to the mouth of the Clinch and about 80 miles up the Clinch), and several weeks elapsed after the drawdown was begun before these fishes appeared below Norris Dam. Apparently the stimulus for this unusual migration was the arrival of cooler water at Watts Bar Reservoir. Later on largemouth bass appeared in considerable numbers. A few largemouth bass were present in the river between the reservoirs, but white bass, yellow bass and saugers were relatively scarce.

Fishes are sometimes stimulated to move by violent storms or in spring by the entrance of warm surface water into cold ponds or lakes. For example, wing nets set on March 9, 1942, in Fork Lake (Illinois) caught few fish until a warm rain of about 1 inch fell during the night of March 16. When this water drained into the pond, the fish were stimulated to move and when the wing nets were raised on March 17, they contained many more than the March "quota" of bluegills and some were released.[7]

Wood [105] assigns to Dr. C. M. Tarzwell the observation that largemouth bass move into newly-flooded backwater areas with rising waters in less than 48 hours after flooding has begun and are the first to leave when waters begin to fall.

Whitmore, Warren, and Doudoroff [99] used a "channeled avoidance tank" to test the reaction of small largemouth bass, bluegills, and several kinds of juvenile salmon to various levels of oxygen tension. Marked avoidance of 1.5 mg/l dissolved oxygen was observed in tests of largemouth bass and some avoidance reaction was evident even with dissolved oxygen as high as 4.5 mg/l. In bluegills avoidance reactions were definite at oxygen concentrations of about 1.5 and 3.0 mg/l, although the latter was not very pronounced. These experiments furnish proof that warm-water fishes are capable of adjusting their movements to avoid low concentrations of dissolved oxygen in the aquatic habitat. Pearse and Achtenberg [79] were able to show that perch would enter deep stagnant waters of Lake Mendota where dissolved oxygen was very low.

HYPERACTIVITY AS A LETHAL FACTOR

Under certain conditions death may follow violent muscular activity, such as struggling of fishes in a live box, responding to vigorous chasing, swimming through swift passages of water, or struggling on a trolling line.[10] While death from exertion is more characteristic of trouts and salmon than of warm-water fishes, it may occur in certain of the more sensitive warm-water fishes such as gizzard shad, some minnows, and occasionally smallmouth bass.

The precise cause of death is unknown, but it is likely that the main cause is a severe acid-base disturbance following a large accumulation of lactic acid. The acid concentration becomes great enough to reduce the oxygen-combining power of the blood, reduce its alkali reserve or carbon dioxide-combining capacity, and alter the shape and probably the volume of the red cells.

Mortalities of fishes resulting from hyperactivity during handling and transportation might contribute to oxygen deficiencies in holding basins and tank trucks. This precludes the value of a tranquilizer in reducing oxygen requirements during fish-moving operations.

"STAY AT HOME" FISH

Bass were reported to rove over the entire water area of Third Sister Lake (Michigan) and showed almost no tendency to remain in one location.[5] In contrast some other fishes showed strong tendencies to remain within a very small area. About 60 per cent of tag returns for bluegills were taken within 30 yards of the point of original capture.[5] The same was true of bullheads where 39 per cent were recaptured within 15 yards of the point of release and 81 per cent within 100 yards. In other tests all of the bullheads recaptured more than once were taken at the same location each time, even though the time intervals between recaptures were several weeks or months.[88] Walleyes in Gogebic Lake (Michigan) remained close to the original point of capture during and after the spawning season; in fact 115 marked walleyes were retaken in the same net in which they were originally captured.[30] Walleyes may be less restricted in their movements later in the season, although fishermen have discovered that these fish are often found in about the same locations day after day.

Newly-stocked fish may or may not move about, depending on the kind of fish and various other factors. Smallmouth bass (from ponds) stocked in a stream showed tendencies to either "stay put" or move upstream.[67] Stocked northern pike moved to all parts of 3643-acre Clear Lake (Iowa) within 6 months.[22]

HOMING AND HOME RANGE

In general terms, homing is the ability of an animal to return, when displaced, to an area which may be considered its home range.[37, 55] This home range may or may not be the location where the fish was spawned. The return of smallmouth bass to home pools in Jordan Creek (Illinois) is an example of a generalized type of homing.[66] Marked smallmouths were moved by tank truck to locations upstream and downstream from their home pools and many of them were able to find their way back to the pool from which they were taken originally. Some bass were even moved from their home stream into another tributary of the same river system several miles distant. At least one fish found its way back to its home pool although to do so required that it move down the stream in which it was released until it reached the larger river, then up this river to the mouth of the home creek, and finally up stream to its home pool. Once the fish reached the larger river it might be possible for it to identify the odor of water flowing from the home creek because the mouth of the creek to which it was taken was down stream from the home stream.

Displaced longear sunfish returned readily to home locations in an Indiana stream.[43] They moved both upstream and downstream to return to their home ranges, although those released in the stream below returned more rapidly than those released upstream from their home ranges. As mentioned previously, further tests demonstrated that olfactory organs were more important than vision in the homing of longears released downstream from their home pools.

Investigations of homing of fishes in streams have brought to light the presence of a roving population that apparently does not show homing tendencies.[35, 37, 66, 68] These roving fish are important in repopulating streams that have lost their fish populations through temporary but lethal pollution, or through severe drought. There is also some evidence for the presence of homing and roving populations in lakes.[77, 78] Parker [77] found that approximately 31 per cent of the smaller Centrarchids (sunfishes) and 18 per cent of the largemouth bass in Flora Lake (Wisconsin) "homed," as did 25 per cent of the bass in nearby Dadik Lake.

Gerking [37] compiled a table of the species of marine and freshwater fishes that have shown homing capabilities. In the reproduction of this table (Table 8.3) marine fishes have been omitted.

There is a great deal of evidence that a fish which shows homing tendencies recognizes the area in which it lives and orients itself accordingly. Some fish also show territoriality, represented by an area which it will defend, and hierarchy or peck-order among its closest associates. These hierarchies develop very quickly with sunfish in aquaria.[40] According to Gerking [37] species which exhibit marked aggressive tendencies will show sedentary populations. Both Larkin [69] and Miller [72] recognize the importance of space requirements in determining population density and growth.

TABLE 8.3   SPECIES OF FISH KNOWN TO HAVE RESTRICTED MOVE-MENT NOT ASSOCIATED WITH SPAWNING. (FROM GERKING [37] 1959, AND OTHERS, BUT INCLUDING ONLY FRESH-WATER FISHES.)

Species	Reference
Salmonidae: Salmon family	
Brown trout	Schuck,[85] Allen,[2] Stefanich [93]
Brook trout	Shetter,[87] Stefanich,[93] Newman [75]
Rainbow trout	Stefanich,[93] Holton,[57] Newman [75]
Cutthroat trout	Miller [71]
Coregonidae: Whitefish family	
Mountain whitefish	Stefanich [93]
Catostomidae: Sucker family	
Golden redhorse	Gerking [36]
Hog sucker	Gerking [36]
White sucker	Stefanich [93]
Ictaluridae: Catfish family	
Yellow bullhead	Shoemaker,[88] Ball,[5] Funk [35]
Channel catfish	Harrison [46]
Percidae	
Fantail darter	Winn [100]
Iowa darter	Winn [100]
Rainbow darter	Winn [100]
Orangethroat darter	Winn [100]
Greenside darter	Winn [100]
Centrarchidae: Sunfish family	
Bluegill	Ball [5]
Longear sunfish	Gerking,[36] Funk [35]
Rock bass	Scott,[86] Gerking,[36] Funk [35]
Green sunfish	Greenberg,[40] Gerking [36]
Largemouth bass	Parker and Hasler [78]
Smallmouth bass	Larimore,[66] Gerking,[36] Funk [35]
Spotted bass	Gerking [36]
Pumpkinseed	Shoemaker [88]
Spotted sunfish	Caldwell, Odum, and Hellier [20]

Some investigators wish to set aside the use of the term "homing" for the homing movements of those fishes which make long migrations to spawn in locations where they themselves were hatched. Well known examples are the salmon and the eel. This point of distinction based on distance is probably not wholly justified.

Parts of home ranges may be considered territories which are defended against the encroachment of all fish except those much larger than the defender. This is particularly true during the spawning season among fishes that build nests.

No one has yet been able to define the roles of hearing, the sensory perception of semicircular canals, the kinesthetic senses, and the lateral line senses in orientation or homing, although auditory organs and the lateral line organs are believed to supplement vision and olfaction in helping to locate objects at a distance. These objects may be moving and thereby create mechanical disturbances or their presence and location may be perceived and accurately computed from the time relations of reflected water waves set up by the swimming movements of the fish itself. In moving water the presence of deflecting objects is readily recorded. This type of sensory perception is extremely important in turbid water where vision is impaired.

THEORIES OF MIGRATION IN FISHES

It has been shown that vision and olfactory senses have a role in orientation and home-range recognition. Hasler, *et al.*,[52] have modified the classification of Griffin [41] to define the types of abilities required by fish that return home from varying distances:

Type I: The ability of an animal to find its way home by relying on local landmarks within familiar territory and the use of exploration in unfamiliar areas.

Type II: The ability to maintain a constant compass direction in unfamiliar territory.

Type III: The ability to head for home from unknown territories by true navigation. This involves a "sextant" type of mechanism.

The homing movements of displaced warm-water fishes are operative over relatively short distances as compared with the spawning (homing) migrations of such fishes as salmon, eel, and some other marine fishes. These fishes are able to migrate many thousands of miles and return with some precision to specific spawning locations where they themselves were hatched. Such migrations may involve the three types of homing abilities listed above: for identifying local landmarks and exploring, for maintaining a fixed direction in unfamiliar territory, and for true navigation.

The migrations of the salmon have been studied more than any other fishes and serve to illustrate the complexity of these spawning movements. Salmon are spawned in cold-water streams tributary to the oceans and move downstream into salt water where they spend 2 to 7 years at sea depending on the species. When they reach sexual maturity, they return to the same rivulet so consistently that populations in streams not far apart follow distinctly separate lines of evolution. Salmon belonging to the genus *Oncorhyncus* die after spawning, while those belonging to the genus *Salmo* may return to the home stream on several annual spawning trips.[49] Many salmon have been marked, either as young on their seaward migrations or as adults at sea. A few have been marked in the home stream, caught and remarked at sea, and then recaptured in the home stream.[11, 58, 80] These tag returns show that some salmon may migrate 1200 to 1700 miles to return "home."

A salmon approaching sexual maturity and stimulated by an urge to spawn is confronted by two problems: (1) finding the mouth of the river to which the salmon's home rivulet is tributary, and (2) finding the actual location in the rivulet that will satisfy the homing urge.

The theory of odor recognition may be adequate to explain an upstream migration to specific spawning grounds, but it can hardly be very useful for finding the mouth of a home river from a distance of hundreds of miles. However, the fact, that on sunny days white bass were able to return to their spawning area in Lake Mendota after having been caught in fyke nets, tagged, and released at one of several release stations, indicates that some kinds of fishes have a type of sun-orientation ability.[52] On cloudy days the white bass swam randomly. Perhaps salmon are also capable of finding their way by sun orientation (Type II, a method for maintaining fixed direction). Yet some observations have been made that suggest true navigation. Salmon are known to migrate at night in the sea and gill net fishermen make night sets for them. Hasler [50] reports an observation of Clifford Barnes (University of Washington) who saw salmon migrating at night at right angles to his oceanographic research vessel. Because of a luminescent sea, this school of large salmon was easily observed. The fish swam on a fairly straight course until out of sight.

The migration of salmon and other migratory species over long distances of open ocean certainly demands an ability to navigate. How else could fishes keep from becoming "lost" and how else could they pinpoint the mouth of a specific river along a thousand miles of shoreline?

No warm-water fish shows migration habits and abilities for homing comparable to that of some marine fishes. The objective of summarizing homing in the salmon is to illustrate the extent of development of the sensory organs in fishes and to emphasize the complexity of their instinctive behavior patterns.

RESPONSES OF FISH TO ANGLING

Angling is a mortality factor along with natural predation, diseases, senile degeneration and other things that may cause the death of fishes (Chapter 7). Angling might be called unnatural predation: A natural predator (man) causes the death of a fish through the degradation of a natural function of that fish (the fish engulfs an insect larva containing a hook and is caught, or strikes an artificial lure that imitates some natural food, and is hooked). This seems like a method of predation that is fool proof, i.e., the fish does not know that it is being attacked until it is on the hook and therefore has less than the usual warning that a predator is attacking.

Why then are not all fish of desirable kinds and sizes removed from heavily fished waters?

In part, the answer lies in the ability of all living organisms to develop greater or lesser resistance to forces in their environment that would cause their death. Thus, in spite of the fact that angling is a "refined" mortality factor in fishes, many of the fishes subjected to angling are able to adjust to this factor and avoid being caught.

Why do fish attempt to capture a natural or artificial bait or lure? No one except a fish can know exactly, but we fishermen assume that they bite because they are hungry or because they become "angry," or they are inquisitive, or they are protecting a home territory, a nest, or a hierarchy that is broken by the audacious action of a plug.

Why then do fish refuse to bite? They may fail to come within striking distance of the bait, may be unconvinced that the bait is a natural food organism, or be frightened by unusual noises made by the fisherman or by the bait. There is evidence also that fish may become conditioned to avoid a bait through seeing one of their members being caught,[24] much as minnows are observed to give a fear reaction to pike after one of their members has been captured and eaten.

In this chapter I have attempted to describe the limits of sensory perception in some freshwater fishes and a few behavior patterns related to their success as animals inhabiting an aquatic environment. In the next few pages I will attempt to establish a relationship between fishermen and certain factors that are believed to influence the rate of catch of fish.

FACTORS THAT INFLUENCE BITING

Factors that influence the angler's rate of catch can be conveniently divided into several categories: (1) physical—those such as climate, season, time of day, etc., that influence the general and nonspecific behavior of fish in their contacts with fishermen; (2) human—those, such as degree of care in presenting baits, that are controlled almost entirely by the fisherman; (3) fish response—factors controlled almost entirely by specific fish behavior patterns; and (4) combinations of two or more of these categories.

Water Temperatures. Changes in water temperature associated with the cycle of seasons affect the response of fish to the feeding stimulus.

As water temperatures drop below 18.3°C (65°F) warm-water fishes become slow-moving and sluggish and their rate of digestion becomes proportionately slowed.[70] However, the fact that most species of warm-water fishes may be caught in winter through the ice suggests that they do not stop feeding, even though the digestion of any food material ingested may require days. Because of a sluggishness of movement and a tendency to congregate in deep water, the fish may be difficult for the winter angler to find. Once a concentration of fish is located, they are often caught at a relatively high rate and fishermen tend to congregate at points where a few good strings of fish have been taken.

For some unknown reason the catch of fish through the ice is usually more rewarding in fish per man-hour during late January and February than during the early part of winter. It has been conjectured that fat stored during fall may be reduced by the latter part of winter so that the fish become more interested in taking food.

Of all the warm-water fishes, the crappies are more associated with early spring fishing than any other kinds. Hansen[45] showed that the larger white crappies in Lake Decatur (Illinois) reached peak weight in fall, winter, or early spring and lost weight during the spring months. The period of good crappie fishing was usually correlated with the period of weight decline.

Largemouth and smallmouth bass will begin to feed actively in early spring when the water is at a temperature below 15.6°C (60°F) but their movements are so sluggish that an artificial lure moved at "normal" speed for summer bass fishing is too "fast" for the bass to capture. This is also true for various pan fish—bluegills, red-ears, pumpkinseeds, and warmouths. Yellow perch and yellow bass are often taken in numbers in early spring, and they are active at colder water temperatures than are most sunfish.

Walleyes, northern pike, and muskellunge are quite active during early spring when the water is still relatively cold.

Except for the high rate of catch sometimes recorded for ice fishing the catch rate for most anglers' species is highest in the spring months, beginning in March in the south, in late April and early May in the mid-states, and in late May and early June in the northernmost states and southern Canada. The phenomenon of good spring fishing is probably due to a combination of factors including a warming of waters, a sex stimulus, and a scarcity of small fish upon which to feed. This high catch rate may continue until spawning is completed and summer weather temperatures are attained. At this time a maximum of foods is available both in quantity and variety and surface water temperatures that exceed 23.9 to 26.9°C (75 to 80°F) cause fish to seek locations where they may find cooler temperatures and adequate oxygen.

Most small ponds and lakes are thermally stratified during summer months (see Chapter 2, p. 3). The warm upper layer of water is often above the optimum for warm-water fish; but cooler water may be found at greater depths. When a fish moves downward from the warm upper epilimnion into the transition zone (metalimnion), it gradually enters cooler water and the amount of dissolved oxygen decreases until at some level it may disappear entirely. The optimum temperature-oxygen relationship may be at a level where the water is as cool as possible but with enough dissolved oxygen for the fish to carry on respiration without discomfort. Here the fish may remain, except during periods of active feeding. If a fisherman can locate this level and keep his bait (whether artificial or natural) within this stratum of water, he may often catch fish when others fishing the surface or at other depths may catch little or nothing. Even bluegills may be caught by trolling a worm in this stratum when the shore shallows are devoid of them.

Some improvement in feeding activity and rate of catch occurs during fall months, but less fishing is done in fall than during any other season. There are some exceptions—most active fishing for muskellunge takes place after waters have cooled from summer temperatures.

Thus, water temperatures are important in affecting the behavior of fishes and the successful angler adjusts his fishing operations to conform to these temperature effects.

Water Transparency. Most game and pan fishes important for angling find their food more through sight than through taste. This is why artificial lures are very effective in taking these fish. Thus, within limits there is a positive correlation between an increasing clearness of water and increasing catch. This was demonstrated at Fork Lake (Illinois) using surface fly rod lures for bass and bluegills. When the transparency of this pond (Secchi disk) was 0.5 to 2.0 feet the catch rate was 2.4 fish per man-hour; with transparencies of 2.1 to 2.5 feet the catch rate was 2.86 fish per man-hour, and at 3.5 to 4.5 feet the catch was 6.59 fish per man-hour.[9]

In most waters, turbidity is caused by suspended particles of clay or silt stirred up by the action of bottom-rooting fishes or wind or carried into the lake with inflowing water. Turbidity may also result from a "bloom" of plankton algae stimulated by fertilization of the water. This nonsilt type of turbidity has less of an effect upon rate of catch than turbidity caused by clay or silt particles. In lakes and ponds containing carp, suckers, or bullheads, a more-or-less constant turbidity may result from the rooting and stirring action of these fish on the bottom. Impoundments that are "muddy" during periods of dry weather are often kept so by these fish, and this type of turbidity is usually as bad for angling as is silt brought in on floods.

In most small lakes and ponds fishing is poor if the transparency of the water is less than two feet (Secchi disk). Fly casting is probably best when the transparency of the water ranges between 3.5 to 6.0 feet. When the transparency is greater than 6.0 feet, fish are able to see the angler for some distance and unless long casts are made to place the angler beyond the fishes' vision, or extreme care is taken to shield his movements from the fish, the rate of catch will decrease as the water becomes clearer.

The late Professor W. P. Flint of the University of Illinois and the Illinois Natural History Survey, trained the bluegills around his boat dock at the Sunset Cliff Club Pond (an abandoned stripmine where the water was very clear), to feed upon bread crumbs tossed to them. He also taught them to scatter when anyone appeared with a moving fly rod, and he took great pleasure in demonstrating that although these fish behaved like pets when being fed on bread, they were nearly immune to fishing.

Diurnal Effects. Alternate periods of darkness and daylight affect the feeding and therefore the catch rate of fishes. Often diurnal movements of certain species develop in certain lakes and these movments are usually associated with feeding. Such movements [23, 51] have been described on p. 231.

It is impossible to say that the stimulus for feeding is entirely one of the changes in light intensity even though periods of feeding in many lakes appear to be associated with dawn and dusk.

Rising and Falling Water Levels. Most artificial lakes are built to store water temporarily during heavy runoff from the watershed. This storage capacity respresents the vertical distance within the lake basin between a lower normal spillway crest and a higher large surface floodway. Once the lake level rises to the crest of the floodway, several hours may elapse before the stored water has time to pass over the lower normal spillway outlet to bring the lake back to "normal" level. This capacity for storage reduces the size (and cost) of spillway structures and assures that sudden rises in water level in the lake are common. The extent of these rises may vary, but in most artificial lakes the range of vertical distance for storage between the normal spillway crest and the flood spillway crest is from 1 to 6 feet.

A sudden inflow of water may stimulate fish to move and feed, particularly in early spring when runoff water from a warm rain may bring in water at a temperature above that of the lake. Fish may feed actively as long as silt brought in by the runoff does not cause the lake to become turbid.

Channel catfish are always stimulated to feed on rising water levels; in fact, it is almost the only time they bite well in lakes.

Flood waters almost always carry a load of silt, and the fishes that depend upon sight for feeding may have difficulty in finding food. This was illustrated during the 1943 early summer flood on the Salt Fork of the Vermilion River (east central Illinois) when the river overflowed the stripmine lakes owned by the South Pollywog Association. Club members who fished the stripmine lakes during the flood period of several weeks caught almost nothing. After the high water had subsided, so that it no longer entered the lakes, and these lakes had an opportunity to clear, largemouth bass were caught in large numbers in all parts of the area. This very unusual fishing lasted for about a week; after this length of time, bass fishing dropped to the "normal" low rate of catch. The exceptional fishing was probably due to the fact that bass had trouble finding sufficient food in the highly turbid flood waters.

During the months of May, June, July, and August, the catch of fish per fisherman-day in Lake Chautauqua, a 3600-acre lake in the flood plain of the Illinois River (Illinois), paralleled rather closely the highs and lows of the lake level (Figure 8.2).[92] Here the catch was composed largely of yellow bass, black and white crappies, bluegills, channel catfish and freshwater drum, and all of these species apparently were stimulated to bite by a rise in lake level. This was not true for largemouth bass where the situation was reversed, i.e., greater numbers were caught when the lake level was low than when high.

Barometric Pressures and Fishing Tables. There is a great deal that is inexplicable about the biting of fishes, and it is natural that man should develop a wide variety of theories to supply himself with answers. So far, none of these theories has passed scientific testing.

Several years ago fishermen were interested in barometric pressures because fish were supposed to bite best on a rising or high barometer and poorest on a falling or low barometer. In order to test this theory Dr. David H. Thompson compared a 10-year fishing record of the Rinaker Lake Fishing Club near Carlinville, Illinois, with barometric records from two nearby weather stations. Fishermen making the record were not aware that the fish were supposed to be influenced by barometric pressures. Thompson found periods of high, intermediate, and low rates of catch, but they could not be correlated with any levels or changes of barometric pressures. He concluded that the change in pressure on a fish moving from the surface to the bottom of a pond was so many times greater than the effect of changes of atmospheric pressure that the latter certainly might be hidden. However, stormy weather (usually with a low barometer) might keep fishermen from going out on large lakes.

Tests of the Solunar Tables theory of John Alden Knight [63] showed that catches made with hook-and-line and with gill nets [89] were not demonstrably better during solunar periods than at other times.[28]

Several investigators have tested the effect of moonlight on rate of catch of fish,[73, 74, 108] and their reserved conclusions were that fishing usually was better in darkness.

Other fishing tables and fads have come and gone without serious damage to fish populations or the fishing public; there is no danger in them and they add interest and theory to the age-old question of why fish bite when they do and why they do not bite at other times.

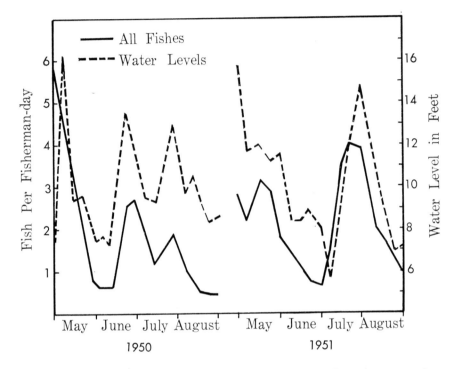

Figure 8.2. Weekly average water levels and corresponding average catches of fish per fisherman-day (all species) at Lake Chautauqua during May, June, July, and August of 1950 and 1951. [From Starrett, W. C., and McNeil, P. L., *Ill. Nat. Hist. Biol. Notes*, 30 (1952)]

Resistance of Fish to Being Caught. All living organisms show ability to counter decimating forces in their environments by developing resistance or immunity (to disease), by instincts, or by learned avoidance reactions. In angling, the fish may be confronted by a food item presented in a particular manner (worm on a hook), by an object that is supposed to look and act like some natural food (crippled minnow lure) or an object that attracts because of its movements and lack of identifying characteristics (the fish is supposed to strike to find out what the object is). The fish has the choice of striking or ignoring the bait. Whether or not he strikes depends upon the behavior of the fish.

Laboratory experiments at the Illinois Natural History Survey, Urbana demonstrated that fish were quite capable of learning and that certain species were more easily taught than others. Mr. Lynn Hutchens and later Dr. Arthur Witt [104] tested the ability of common warm-water fish to learn to avoid an earthworm impaled upon a hook; at the same time these fish were being fed on free earthworms. Largemouth bass learned quickly, but were sometimes somewhat brash when they evidently realized they would be hooked. Bluegills learned quickly and were much less bold than were the bass. Warmouths were difficult to impress with the danger of being hooked and learned very slowly. Even an electric shock applied to the warmouth when it bit the hooked worm did not always deter it from biting the next one presented. The fish that "learned" to avoid being caught retained this learning for several days.

Lagler and DeRoth [65] discovered that the bass in Lower Lach Alpine (Michigan) could not be "fished out." When the population of this lake had been reduced to 6 legal bass per acre the rate of catch was 0.04 legal fish per hour (25 hours to catch one legal fish). At this time the fishermen had the impression that the lake was "fished out."

Westman, Smith, and Harrocks [98] describe a "die-away curve" in fishing success for largemouth bass which was the same when the fish were returned to the water as when the fish were removed from the water.

The largemouth bass of Ridge Lake (Illinois) always exhibited resistance to being caught (Figure 7.3).[8] In 1949, for example, the lake contained 1027 marked bass large enough to catch. These fish were returned to the lake basin after the lake was drained in March and a small amount of water had collected behind the dam. By June 1, when the lake was opened to fishing, it had refilled only to the 11-acre contour (lake area at spillway crest about 18 acres). Thus, all of the larger bass that had developed in 18 acres were concentrated in a much smaller volume of water supporting subnormal populations of small fish and crayfish (because they had been removed or lost on the March drainage). In spite of these adverse conditions for bass, after 220 hours of angling per acre, fishermen were only able to catch 595 bass or only 67.1 per cent of the weight of bass returned.

The experience at Onized Lake (Illinois) where 275 bass were present in a 2-acre pond after more than 3000 hours of angling points up the futility of fishing for bass after they have become "conditioned" to angling.[6]

Aldrich [1] describes some observations made on largemouth bass at Spavinaw Lake (Oklahoma): By sitting quietly and flipping pebbles into the water dozens of bass were attracted to the boat. Minnows flipped overboard were seized at once and "the congregated bass remained to see how long our generosity would last." A fly or spinner flipped among them resulted in a strike immediately, but once the unlucky individual was hooked, the rest vanished. Continued casting was useless until the boat was moved to a new location. This type of observation could be made almost anywhere on Spavinaw Lake on days when few fishermen were present.

"Records reveal that on days of heavy fishing, Friday, Saturday, and Sunday, the catch per person was very low. This poor catch is not the result of an abundance of poor or mediocre fishermen. The best anglers have learned that they cannot always catch fish, particularly bass, when there is a crowd on the lake. Everyone reports seeing plenty of bass, but few catches are made on weekends."

Ciampi,[24] after testing fish at the Shedd Aquarium (Chicago), concluded that the largemouth bass demonstrated the highest level of "intelligence" in avoiding artificial baits, with the smallmouth bass following close behind. Along with the muskellunge, they were the only species that would not take an artificial bait after any other fish in the same tank had hit it. On the basis of his experiments, Ciampi ranks the "intelligence" of fish studied in the following order: (1) largemouth bass, (2) smallmouth bass, (3) muskellunge, (4) northern pike, (5) trout, (6) bluegill, (7) crappies, (8) gar.

Fisherman "Know-how." A fisherman must realize (if he is to be successful in catching the more wary fish) that he must introduce himself and his fishing lure into the fishes' environmental background without causing undue alarm. At this point many would-be fishermen are failures, because they assume that they are operating mostly in one medium (air), while the fish are operating in another, and because they cannot see, hear, smell, or feel the presence of fish in the water below, that the fish cannot see, hear, smell, or feel their presence above. Usually a fish is made wary of impending danger or at least of an abnormal addition to its environment before the lure has even been presented. Under these conditions a fisherman places himself under a severe handicap that must be overcome before he can expect a strike. A quiet fisherman in a slow-moving boat propelled by quiet oars in well-oiled oarlocks, or a sculling paddle, may bring himself within casting distance of a bass without alerting the fish to his presence. On heavily fished waters where noisy fisherman are the rule rather than the exception, a quiet approach may catch a fish "off guard."

Creel records on heavily fished waters have shown that more than 80 per cent of the fish are caught by less than 50 per cent of the fishermen—in the case of largemouth bass the catch usually is made by about 25 per cent of the fishermen.

The best way to learn how to fish is to go fishing with a successful angler and try to copy his methods. There are experts in all types of fishing, from trotliners to fly fishermen. These anglers have special methods that usually bring results and often they are unwilling to divulge their secrets to anyone except their closest friends.

Underwater observations of the behavior of bass in relation to lures presented to them has led us to believe that there are rather small differences in the way a bait is "fished" which determine whether a bass strikes or simply follows without striking. The successful fisherman knows how to give the lure that extra something that makes the difference.

LITERATURE

1. Aldrich, A. D., *Am. Fish. Soc. Trans.*, **68**, 221-227 (1939).
2. Allen, K. R., *Fish. Bull., Wellington, N. Z.* **10**, 1-231 (1951).
3. Anon., *Prog. Fish-Cult.*, **18**(3), 142 (1956).
4. Bailey, R. M., *Ecology*, **36**(3), 526-528 (1955).
5. Ball, R. C., *Am. Fish. Soc. Trans.*, **74**, 360-369 (1947).
6. Bennett, G. W., *Ill. Nat. Hist. Surv. Bull.*, **23**(3), 373-406 (1945).
7. Bennett, G. W., *Ill. Nat. Hist. Surv. Bull.*, **24**(3), 377-412 (1948).
8. Bennett, G. W., *Ill. Nat. Hist. Surv. Bull.*, **26**(2), 217-276 (1954).
9. Bennett, G. W., Thompson, D. H., and Parr, S. A., *Ill. Nat. Hist. Surv. Biol. Notes*, **14**, 1-24 (1940).
10. Black, E. C., *Jour. Fish. Res. Bd. Can.*, **15**(4), 573-586 (1958).
11. Blair, A. A., *Jour. Fish. Res. Bd. Can.*, **13**(2), 225-232 (1956).
12. Breder, C. M., Jr., *Zoologica*, **21**(1), 1-48 (1936).
13. Breder, C. M., Jr., *Am. Mus. Nat. Hist. Bull.*, **117**(6), 393-482 (1959).
14. Brett, J. R., *Quart. Rev. Biol.*, **31**(2), 75-87 (1956).
15. Brett, J. R., and MacKinnon, D., *Jour. Fish. Res. Bd. Can.*, **11**(3), 310-318 (1954).
16. Brown, F. A., Jr., *Ill. Nat. Hist. Surv. Bull.*, **21**(2), 33-55 (1937).
17. Brown, M. E., "The Physiology of Fishes," Vol. 2, Chapt. 2, p. 121-210, Academic Press, Inc., New York, 1957.
18. Bull, H. O., *J. Mar. Biol. Assoc. U.K.N.S.*, **15**(I), 485-533 (1928).
19. Bull, H. O., *J. Mar. Biol. Assoc. U.K.N.S.*, **21**(VII), 1-27 (1936-37).
20. Caldwell, D. K., Odum, H. T., and Hellier, T. R., Jr., *Am. Fish. Soc. Trans.*, **85**, 120-134 (1957).
21. Carlander, K. D., and Cleary, R. E., *Am. Midland Nat.*, **41**, 447-452 (1949).
22. Carlander, K. D., and Ridenhour, R., *Prog. Fish-Cult.*, **17**(4), 186-189 (1955).
23. Childers, W. F., *Uni. Ill. Lib., Masters Th.* 1-24 (1956).
24. Ciampi, E., *Sports Illus.*, **15**, 35, 48 (1961).
25. Delco, E. A., Jr., *Tex. Jour. Sci.*, **12** (1 & 2), 48-54 (1960).
26. Durham, L., and Bennett, G. W., *Ill. Wildl.*, **4**(2), 10-13 (1949).
27. Durham, L., and Bennett, G. W., *Ill. Wildl.*, **6**(2), 5-7 (1951).
28. Elser, H. J., *Md. Dept. Res. & Ed., Solomons Mimeo*, 1-12 (1954).
29. Eschmeyer, R. W., *Jour. Tenn. Acad. Sci.*, **19**(1), 31-40 (1944).
30. Eschmeyer, P., *Mich. Inst. Fish. Res. Bull.*, **3**, 1-99 (1950).

31. Ferguson, R. G., *Jour. Fish. Res. Bd. Can.*, **15**(4), 607-624 (1958).
32. Frisch, K. Von, *Naturwiss*, **291**, 321-333 (1941).
33. Fry, F. E. J., *Ont. Fish. Res. Lab.*, **68**, 1-62 (1947).
34. Fry, F. E. J., *L'Annee Biologique*, **33**(3d), 205-219 (1957).
35. Funk, J. L., *Am. Fish. Soc. Trans.*, **85**, 39-57 (1957).
36. Gerking, S. D., *Ecology*, **34**, 347-365 (1953).
37. Gerking, S. D., *Biol. Rev.*, **34**, 221-237 (1959).
38. Graham, J. J., *Univ. Toronto Stud.*, *Biol. Ser.*, **62**, 1-43 (1956).
39. Greenbank, J., *Copeia*, **3**, 158-162 (1956).
40. Greenberg, B., *Physiol. Zool.*, **20**, 269-299 (1947).
41. Griffin, D. R., *Amer. Sci.*, **41**, 209-244 (1953).
42. Griffin, D. R., *Pap. Mar. Biol. and Oceanography*, **3**, 406-417 (1955).
43. Gunning, G. E., *Invest. Ind. Lakes & Streams*, **5**(3), 103-130 (1959).
44. Hancock, H. M., *Okla. Agric. Mech. Coll. Res. Found. Pub.*, **58**, 1-104 (1954).
45. Hansen, D. F., *Ill. Nat. Hist. Surv. Bull.*, **25**(4), 211-265 (1951).
46. Harrison, H. M., *Proc. Iowa Acad. Sci.*, **60**, 636-644 (1954).
47. Hasler, A. D., *Jour. Fish. Res. Bd. Can.*, **11**(2), 107-129 (1954).
48. Hasler, A. D., *Zeitschrift fur Vergleichende Physiologie*, **38**, 303-310 (1956).
49. Hasler, A. D., *Science*, **132** (3430), 785-792 (1960a).
50. Hasler, A. D., *Sonderdruck aus. Ergebnisse der Biologie*, **23**, 94-115 (1960b).
51. Hasler, A. D., and Bardach, J. E., *Jour. Wildl. Mgt.*, **13**(1), 40-51 (1949).
52. Hasler, A. D., Horrall, R. M., Wisby, W. J., and Braemer, W. B., *Limnology & Oceanography*, **3**(4), 353-361 (1958).
53. Hasler, A. D., and Wisby, W. J., *Amer. Fish. Soc. Trans.*, **79**, 64-70 (1950).
54. Hasler, A. D., and Wisby, W. J., *Amer. Nat.*, **85**, 223-238 (1951).
55. Hayne, D. W., *Jour. Mammal.*, **30**, 1-18 (1949).
56. Herrick, C. J., *Bull. U.S. Fish. Comm.*, **22**, 237-271 (1903).
57. Holton, G. D., *Jour. Wildl. Mgt.*, **17**, 62-82 (1953).
58. Huntsman, A. G., *Science*, **95**, 381-382 (1942).
59. Hurst, P. M., Jr., *Prog. Fish-Cult.*, **15**(2), 95 (1953).
60. Huttel, R., *Naturwiss*, **29**, 333-334 (1941).
61. Jones, F. H. H., *Jour. Exp. Biol.*, **33**(2), 271-281 (1956).
62. Kleerekoper, H., and Chagnon, E. C., *Jour. Fish. Res. Bd. Can.*, **11**(2), 130-152 (1954).
63. Knight, John Alden, "The Solunar Theory" in "The Fisherman's Encyclopedia," pp. 244-248, Stackpole and Heck, N. Y. and Harrisburg, 1950.
64. Krumholz, L. A., *Copeia*, **2**, 82-85 (1944).
65. Lagler, K. F., and DeRoth, G. C., *Pap. Mich. Acad. Sci., Arts & Letts.*, **38**, 235-253 (1953).
66. Larimore, R. W., *Ill. Nat. Hist. Surv. Biol. Notes*, **28**, 1-12 (1952).
67. Larimore, R. W., *Jour. Wildl. Mgt.*, **18**(2), 207-216 (1954).
68. Larimore, R. W., Childers, W. F., and Heckrotte, C., *Amer. Fish. Soc. Trans.*, **88**, 261-285 (1959).
69. Larkin, P. A., *Jour. Fish. Res. Bd. Can.*, **13**, 327-342 (1956).
70. Markus, H. C., *Amer. Fish. Soc. Trans.*, **62**, 202-210 (1932).

71. Miller, R. B., *Jour. Fish. Res. Bd. Can.*, **14**, 687-691 (1957).
72. Miller, R. B., *Jour. Fish. Res. Bd. Can.*, **15**, 27-45 (1958).
73. Mottley, C. M., *Am. Fish. Soc. Trans.*, **67**, 212-214 (1938).
74. Mottley, C. M., *Jour. Am. Stat. Assoc.*, **37**(217), 41-47 (1942).
75. Newman, M. A., *Physiol. Zool.*, **29**, 64-81 (1956).
76. Olmsted, J. M. D., *Amer. Jour. Physiol.*, **46**, 443-458 (1918).
77. Parker, R. A., *Uni. of Wisc. Dissertation Abstr.*, **16**(11), 2248-2249 (1956).
78. Parker, R. A., and Hasler, A. D., *Copeia*, **1**, 11-18 (1959).
79. Pearse, A. S., and Achtenberg, H., *Bull. U.S. Bur. Fish.*, **36**, 294-306 (1920).
80. Pritchard, A. L., *Fish. Res. Bd. Can. Progr.*, **57**, 8-11 (1943).
81. Privol'nev, T. L., *Voprosy Ikhtiol.*, **6**, 3-20 (1956).
82. Rough, G. E., *Copeia*, **3**, 191-194 (1954).
83. Rubin, M. A., *Jour. Gen. Physiol.*, **18**, 643-647 (1935).
84. Schneider, H., and Hasler, A. D., *Zeitschrift fur Vergleichende Physiologie*, **43**, 499-517 (1960).
85. Schuck, H., *Am. Fish. Soc. Trans.*, **73**, 209-230 (1943).
86. Scott, D. C., *Invest. Ind. Lakes*, **3**, 169-234 (1949).
87. Shetter, D. S., *Am. Fish. Soc. Trans.*, **66**, 203-210 (1937).
88. Shoemaker, H. H., *Copeia*, **2**, 83-87 (1952).
89. Sieh, J. G., and Parsons, J., *Iowa Acad. Sci.*, **57**, 511-518 (1950).
90. Smith, D. L., *Mosquito News*, **20**(1), 55-56 (1960).
91. Spoor, W. A., and Schloemer, C. L., *Am. Fish. Soc. Trans.*, **68**, 211-220 (1939).
92. Starrett, W. C., and McNeil, P. L., Jr., *Ill. Nat. Hist. Surv. Biol. Notes*, **30**, 1-31 (1952).
93. Stefanich, F. A., *Amer. Fish. Soc. Trans.*, **81**, 260-274 (1952).
94. Stover, R. E., *Prog. Fish-Cult.*, **15**(2), 94-95 (1953).
95. Sullivan, C. M., *Jour. Fish. Res. Bd. Can.*, **11**(2), 153-170 (1954).
96. Verheijen, F. J., *Experientia*, **12**(5), 202-204 (1956).
97. Walls, G. L., "The Vertebrate Eye and Its Adaptive Radiation," Cranbrook Inst. of Sci., Bloomfield Hills, Mich., *Bull.*, **19**, 1-785, 1942.
98. Westman, J. R., Smith, R. K., and Harrocks, A. W., *N.J. Cons. Dept. Mimeo Rept.*, 1-14 (1956).
99. Whitmore, C. M., Warren, E., and Doudoroff, P., *Am. Fish. Soc. Trans.*, **89**(1), 17-26 (1960).
100. Winn, H. E., *Ecol. Monogr.*, **28**, 155-191 (1958).
101. Winn, H. E., and Stout, J. F., *Science*, **132**, (3421), 222-223 (1960).
102. Wisby, W. J., *Uni. Wisc. Lib. Ph.D. Thesis Abst.* (1952).
103. Wisby, W. J., and Hasler, A. D., *Jour. Fish. Res. Bd. Can.*, **11**(4), 472-478 (1954).
104. Witt, A., Jr., Uni. of Illinois, Lib., Master's Thesis, 1-60 (1948).
105. Wood, R., *Jour. Tenn. Acad. Sci.*, **26**(3), 214-235 (1951).
106. Woodhead, P. M. J., *Jour. Exp. Biol.*, **33**(2), 257-270 (1956).
107. Wrede, W. L., *Z. Vergl. Physiol.*, **17**, 510-519 (1932).
108. Wright, S., *Am. Fish. Soc. Trans.*, **73**, 52-58 (1945).

9 〰〰〰

Commercial Aspects of
Sport Fishing

Many outdoorsmen look with distaste upon the commercialization of outdoor recreation. These people search for solitude in the out of doors—an opportunity to get away from machines and man-made irritations. In the 1930's, during the time when Aldo Leopold was Professor of Game Management at the University of Wisconsin, he acquired a piece of land near Baraboo, Wisconsin, where he and his family could go to escape from the frustrations and noise of a mechanized environment. There, in a rustic cabin, they slept in straw-filled bunks and cooked in kettles hung above an open hearth. The situation was primitive, but Professor Leopold found that it provided a wholesome counterbalance to everyday living.

However, few people are willing to dispense with the comforts of their mechanized niches to follow a homesteader's routine. Also, it is difficult to escape from a human-dominated environment unless one searches out the poorest and roughest land areas of the East, or travels west of the Mississippi. Many people have lived a lifetime without getting away from clipped lawns and paved highways. Their children deface the woodlands when they visit state parks or forest preserves, because they have never learned to appreciate a natural environment and to them an untrimmed and uncultivated landscape "doesn't belong to anybody."

Recently more urban people are fulfilling "basic" urges by camping out. Living in a tent and cooking over a camp stove is so much less expensive than patronizing motels and restaurants, that campers can afford to go to places previously considered unattainable. Others, who have more money to spend, camp out because they want to break from the stereotyped pattern of living or because their children would rather travel that way. Moreover, campers have more money for boats, trailers, outboard motors, and fishing tackle.

Supervisors of state and national forests are well aware of this rather sudden interest in outdoor living and are frantically expanding camping sites in an attempt to keep up. One forest supervisor estimated that the numbers of campers using state- and federally operated camp sites increased 10- to 20-fold in the period from 1955 to 1960.

Concurrent with the interest in outdoor living has been the recent, sudden, and widespread enthusiasm for power boats and associated activities. In 1960 the State of Wisconsin made a survey of Wisconsin boat owners, their needs, and problems.[4] More than 200,000 boats were licensed in that state, 130,000 by residents, 20,000 by nonresidents, and 50,000 by boat livery operators. Ninety-three per cent of all of these licensed boats were propelled by outboard motors of which about 60 per cent exceeded 10 horse-power. Owners often used their boats for several activities, such as fishing, water skiing, and general boating.

The uses of boats in aquatic activities were as follows:

Fishing	81.5 per cent
General boating	55.6 per cent
Water skiing	25.5 per cent
Hunting	16.6 per cent
Overnight cruises	4.0 per cent
Sailing	1.5 per cent
Skin diving	1.1 per cent
Racing	1.0 per cent
Commercial	0.6 per cent

They were taken out an average of 32.5 days per year, and about half of the owners hauled them around on trailers.

The Wisconsin tax on the gasoline used in boats amounted to $670,000 in 1960. As less than 10 per cent of this tax was refunded, more than 90 per cent was going into the state highway fund.

This study for Wisconsin illustrates the interest in boating there and in other lake states where many waters are available. However, even in Wisconsin there are problem waters where the number of boats exceeds use facilities. The most important needs listed by Wisconsin boat owners were: (1) more launching ramps, (2) more auto and trailer parking space, (3) improved launching ramps, (4) toilet facilities, (5) camping areas near mooring facilities, and (6) more piers and docks. Ten other categories were considered of lesser importance.

Whether the campers, power boaters, and water skiers will continue to place a strain upon available facilities is a question only time can answer. There is little doubt that the fishermen will continue to be as numerous as they have been in the past. Fishing gives opportunity for mild exercise out-of-doors in surroundings that are highly appealing to the average individual regardless of his age. Moreover, the equipment is not exacting and may vary from the least expensive pole-and-line to the most elaborate and expensive rods, reels, and artificial lures.

INTEREST IN ANGLING

Some idea of the interest in fishing may be obtained from the 1955 and 1960 National Surveys of Fishing and Hunting sponsored by the U. S. Department of Interior.[1, 3] The 1955 survey was made by Crossley, S-D Surveys, Inc. of New York City, a firm specializing in large-scale sampling censuses. The survey of 1960 was conducted by the Bureau of Census, U. S. Department of Commerce. In both surveys, each of the 48 or 50 states was included in the sample; house calls at 18 to 20 thousand households containing a total of 45,000 or more persons 12 years of age or older yielded about 6500 interviews with fishermen and more than 3500 interviews with hunters. The 1960 Survey found that of 130 million persons 12 years of age and over, 25,323,000 fished (23 per cent). Two out of every five persons went fishing or hunting or both. They spent almost 2 billion seven hundred million dollars ($2,690,872,000) for fishing tackle, camping gear, special clothing, automobile expense, food, lodging, boats, motors, and licenses. Of this amount $376,000,000 was spent for travel expenses, $52,743,000 for licenses, $1.3 billion for equipment, $573,000,000 for bait, guide fees, and other trip expenses but not including food and lodging. These people traveled 7.5 billion miles by automobile to fish in fresh-water lakes and streams. In 1960 the typical fisherman (median fisherman) spent $27.09, took 7.6 trips, for 9.0 days, and drove 216 miles to and from fishing locations. However, the over-all average (mean) expenditure including all fishermen was $106.26 for 16.3 trips representing 743.8 miles by automobile. Quite obviously there were big spenders and people who had lots of time to fish at the top of this mountain of fishermen, who were responsible for making the average costs look less representative than median costs.

SUPPLYING THE NEEDS OF THE SPORT FISHERMAN

These surveys point up that sport fishing is important not only for recreation but also in the commercial provision of the goods and services required. If we assume that 4 per cent would be a reasonable yield from such a capital outlay, we can assign a minimum capital value of $67.5 billion to the sport fishery resources which currently generates $2.7 billion of annual income. Stroud,[15] using the statistics from the 1955 survey and from "Current Business for July 1956," showed that Americans spent almost twice as much money for fishing as for dental care, medical care, hospitalization insurance, personal legal services, higher education, or even for funeral and burial expenses. This is believed to be true for 1960 also.

Of some interest were the relative expenditures for things fishermen buy: tackle made up about 11 per cent; camping equipment, outboard motors, boats and trailers an additional 37 per cent; food and lodging accounted for about 10 per cent; automobile expenses and cost of gasoline and oil represented approximately 14 per cent. The remaining 28 per cent went for miscellaneous items such as licenses, fees, live bait, etc.

Costs Assigned to an End Product, Usually Fish. It is impossible to measure in dollars the intangible benefits of fishing, such as mental relaxation, exercise, and "change of pace." Therefore some biologists have assigned values to the end product of fishing, namely the fish themselves, on the assumption that the fish caught were worth what the fisherman was willing to pay in tackle expense, travel, meals, lodging, and other costs, in order to catch them. This method of assigning values was not acceptable to many economists because it was not a measure of the value of the intangible benefits. A family may travel to a Canadian lake ostensibly to fish, but the reason for their going may be more related to the climate and to the aesthetic attractiveness of the summer landscape than to the fish that are brought to creel. While they probably would not go to the Canadian lake if they could not fish, it is still unreasonable to balance the large costs of the trip to Canada against the fish that they may or may not catch.

More justifiable is the assignment of costs of fishing to the end product of fishing when this activity is done on a local basis. When one goes fishing in a nearby reservoir where the climate has nothing unusual to offer and the aesthetics are more commonplace, an angler's main interest must be in a "change of pace" and in the fish that he catches; also his expenses for this type of activity may be very comparable to those for other forms of local recreational activity. Several estimates of recreational values assigned to fish have been published [5], [6] (U.S. F. and Wildlife Serv. Manual of Instructions, River Basin Studies). In these the value of largemouth bass has ranged from $2.00 to $8.66 per pound, with pan fish valued at a lesser figure.

Still another method of assigning recreational values to fishing and hunting is to allow them to assume the value of lands or waters upon which these activities may be followed with some assurance of success. This idea may have originated from practices followed by U.S. Engineers in their land appraisals for benefits from flood-control projects. For example, in an early flood control report for the Illinois River (Illinois) certain bottom land lakes that were to be made into corn-producing fields through the construction of levees and through pumping were given, in their natural state, a recreational value of one dollar per acre. Yet these same lakes included some of the most important duck-hunting lands in the Midwest, and were excellent for fishing. At the present time, duck marshes in the Illinois valley that were not included in drainage districts and are still in existence have become nearly unpurchasable, while corn continues to be in glut supply. Happily, the U.S. Engineers now have given recognition to recreation as a value of considerable importance and equal to other less intangible values.

What are reasonable recreational values for productive fishing waters? Here again the answers are variable. In one instance an annual value of a lake for bass fishing was proposed (on the basis of what fishermen were willing to spend) of $162.10 per acre.[6] If we assume 4 per cent is a reasonable yield from a capital outlay generating an annual product equal to $162.10 per acre in goods and services, then the lake must have a value of $4052.50 per acre. This is several times the per-acre cost of the lake.

About 48 per cent of a fisherman's expenditures go into camping equipment, tackle, outboard motors, boats, and trailers. This is almost one half of 2.7 billion dollars or about 1.3 billion annually. The manufacture and retailing of these items is big business of a very specialized nature.

One of the "little businesses" connected with fishing is the live-bait industry which actually represents thousands of small businesses when one includes all of the "worm farm" operators along with a smaller number of minnow raisers and the retailers of these products.

Supplying Fishermen's Baits. Not too many years ago a fisherman who planned to use live bait on a fishing trip had to reserve the time necessary to collect his bait—either the day before if it were not too perishable or on the way to the lake or stream if it were. Collecting one's own bait was a matter of digging, hand collecting, or seining, and most fishermen kept well-informed on where certain kinds of live baits were to be found.

Today few people bother to collect their own bait because bait dealers are available wherever there are fishing waters, and their products can be purchased without loss of time.

Many people engage in the part-time avocation of raising some kind of live bait for fishermen. Some bait raisers sell these products locally but many advertise in newspapers and magazines and ship by mail, express, or truck.

Earthworms and Other Invertebrates. Baits sold to fishermen for freshwater angling include earthworms, insects and their larval stages, crustacea, "minnows," and sometimes frogs. The extent of interest in the propagation and sale of earthworms and other baits was evidenced by the "for sale" ads in a recent issue of a leading hunting and fishing magazine. These ads, which exceeded twenty per cent of the space devoted to all sportsmen's items, were largely for "red wigglers" or "hybrid red wigglers" or for information on how to raise them. Other live baits for sale were crickets, gray crickets, grubs, meal worms, "mousie" grubs (rat-tailed maggots), brownnose worms, wax worms, and Giant African crawlers. Only one ad offered night crawlers (*Lumbricus terrestris*) for sale, presumably because they cannot be raised without special refrigeration equipment, and are perishable in shipment. Prices for red worms varied from $3.00 to $3.50 per 1000; crickets, both common and gray, were $7.50 per 1000; African night crawlers were $8.00 per 1000. Other grubs and larvae ranged in price between red worms and crickets.

The propagation of manure worms (*Helodrilus spp.*) and other annelids for fish bait is sufficiently common to make them available in most cities and towns through local bait dealers who either raise their own or buy from a wholesaler supplying several outlets. In winter these same dealers may handle the larvae of various insects used for ice fishing. The large night crawler worms are usually captured and sold locally, and may bring as much as four or five cents each because of their desirability and the effort required in catching them. Most state fish and game departments have leaflets on raising various kinds of live baits.

Minnows. The raising and retailing of minnows has become a very specialized operation and is often done on a very large scale. However, small operators having one or several small minnow ponds may sell wholesale to local distributors. There are a number of comprehensive bulletins on minnow propagation available and one of the best is U.S. Fish and Wildlife Service Circular 12.[8]

Some commercial dealers seine their minnows from shallow prairie lakes that often are subject to winterkill. If these are stocked with a few minnows in spring, they usually will produce a good crop large enough to sell by fall.

Within recent years some states have restricted the transportation of minnows across state lines. This restriction protects licensed minnow breeders within these states from excessive competition and reduces the spread of fish diseases and parasites. There may also be restrictions on the sale and use of carp, goldfish and suckers for fish bait, to prevent contamination of lakes and ponds with these undesirable species.

FISHING FOR SALE

When fishing was entirely free it was valueless, a time-wasting activity not to be followed by the ambitious, an activity fraught with some secrecy, not only because good fishing "holes" were private knowledge, but because over-indulgence might brand one as a "loafer." Now that fishing activity is more limited, the opportunity to fish has become quite valuable, and the status of the fisherman is one to create envy among his friends. With this change of public attitude toward fishing has come the commercialization of certain types of fishing. Some of the more common types are described in the following pages.

"Executives" Fishing and Hunting Clubs

There are a small number of hunting and fishing clubs that cater to the executives of businesses and corporations. Membership is frequently in the name of the corporation; a small group of executives purchases group membership and operates more or less as a unit. These clubs must furnish exceptional hunting and fishing for their members. Pheasants, mallard ducks, wild turkeys, Hungarian partridges, bobwhite quail, and sometimes deer are the hunter's game. Fishing may be done in streams and artificial lakes for brook and rainbow trout, largemouth and smallmouth bass, walleyes, northern pike, and muskellunge. Usually ringneck pheasants and mallard ducks carry the weight of hunting and the trouts and basses that of fishing. Members pay an annual hunting and fishing license fee and are billed for individual items of game and fish that they kill. These are picked (skinned or scaled), drawn, and perhaps quick frozen by the time the member is ready to leave after a day of field sport. Cost is much less important than services in the operation of this type of club, and members expect an abundance of game and fish that can be taken with a minimum of effort. All of the game birds are hatchery produced and pen reared, but in such a way that they develop strong wings and are able to fly well. Fish are reared in hatcheries and stocked for put-and-take fishing; they are fed artificial food or live minnows and thereby are held in good condition in spite of high concentrations.

The clubs are usually located near large cities or are supplied with air service so that members may reach them without time-consuming travel. These are used extensively for "quick" fishing or hunting trips or for entertaining clients or out-of-town guests, often providing hotel accommodations. A member may leave for the club with a guest in midafternoon, shoot or fish until dark, stay overnight and then, after an early morning fishing or hunting period, return to his office by 10 or 11 a.m.

Fishing-Lake Investments

Occasionally a few individuals who wish to make an investment and are interested in fishing will pool their resources, purchase a site, and build an artificial lake. Sometimes individual owners divide up the lake shore and build permanent homes or summer cottages; other group owners or a company owner may build a community lodge to be used by all families or employees when they are at the lake. Where several investors go together, ownership in the property may be in the form of an investment, to be sold to a new party at any time such a sale is agreeable to the other owners. Group owners are usually incorporated for their own protection against individual law suit.

Sportsmen's clubs are frequently organized in a similar manner. Low-cost membership among a large group usually will not furnish sufficient income for lake construction, but incorporated sportsmen's clubs may solicit donations or engage in money-raising activities to obtain money for a "building fund" to be used for building lakes, club houses, and other facilities. Ownership of these lakes and physical plants resides in the sportsmen's club organization.

Sometimes these sportsmen's groups may purchase an abandoned gravel pit, a flooded quarry, or stripmine, instead of building an impoundment. Usually these properties increase in value because of the increasing demand for recreational real estate.

The legal aspects of corporation ownership of lake property make it imperative that legal advice be obtained by any group contemplating the construction or purchase of a pond or lake.

Trespass-rights Fishing

Owners of ponds or lakes retaining control of their waters who wish at the same time to receive an income from them, may for a fee give right of trespass of the surrounding lands to a limited number of individuals on an individual basis for one or more years. When permission is granted, the owner may specify that certain rules and regulations must be followed by the users with the penalty stipulation that should the rules be broken, the lessee loses his right of trespass without the return of his original payment.

Experience has shown that where such "trespass leases" are available within reasonable driving distance of urban centers, owners of waters managed to produce angling at an average rate of one or more fish per man-hour, can often make a larger net cash return from an acre of such water than from an acre of productive farm land given over to row crops.

Rules for trespass-fishing lakes usually specify that anyone who fishes must fill out a creel card each time that he terminates a fishing period. At the end of the fishing season a tabulation of the creel cards will furnish the lake owner with the total annual fish yield in kinds, numbers, and pounds, and also the rate of catch in number and pounds of fish per man-hour. These records are of interest to those who fish because they indicate whether or not the anglers are receiving a satisfactory return for their money.

This type of operation has another advantage in that the lake owner is able to select only fishermen who are entirely dependable and honest.

With selected individuals using his property, he is required to spend a minimum of his time for general supervision.

Recreational facilities other than adequate roads into the area and parking lots are minimal. A creel station where fishermen weigh, measure, and record their catches is, of course, a necessity, and picnic areas are desirable.

Income from trespass-fishing may vary with size of the water area, the facilities available, the location, and type of fishing.

CATCH-OUT PONDS

Catch-out ponds, or pay-as-you-fish ponds, are small heavily-stocked bodies of water. As fish are caught, anglers pay a small fee at so much per pound or inch. In 1959, a general survey was made of the catch-out ponds in the United States through a questionnaire sent to the conversation departments of each of the (then) 49 states.[14] There were about 1500 of these ponds in operation with Pennsylvania (238 ponds) in the lead. Not all states had catch-out ponds; in those that had them, many had been in operation for less than 10 years. However, in some western states, catch-out ponds for trout had been in existence for a much longer period, for example, more than 58 per cent of the catch-out ponds in Colorado exceeded a 10-year operation period.[7]

Most states have passed special legislation to cover the licensing and operation of these pay fish ponds. In some states, both the fisherman and the operator of the pond must have a license; in others, such as California, no fishing license is required (Dr. Leo Shapovalov: personal communication). Pond-owner licenses usually varied from $5.00 to $25.00 per year.

In the survey,[14] 55 per cent of the pond owners used trout only, 16 per cent used warm-water species only, and 29 per cent used both. Trout usually were rainbows or brooks, rather than browns because the latter were more difficult to catch. Some ponds contained all three trout species. Warm-water fishes were largemouth bass, bluegill and miscellaneous sunfishes, channel catfish, black, yellow or brown bullheads, flathead cat, carp, and drum. A few pond owners offered pike, muskellunge, perch, and walleye.

All of the trout came from private hatcheries or ponds as did some of the warm-water fish. Bullheads, catfish, carp, and drum were purchased from commercial fish dealers.

The amount of net income from a catch-out pond must be directly related to the number of fishermen who will pay to patronize the facility, minus the cost of the fish to keep it stocked. A satisfactory supply of fishermen are to be found near most medium and large-sized centers of population. The least expensive source of fish is through direct purchases from commercial fish dealers who handle large quantities of live fish and supply a number of catch-out pond operators all located within a limited area. In the operation of a catch-out pond, the margin of profit is small, even if all fish arrive in good condition. If a substantial percentage of the fish are injured in the catching or hauling process, the profit may be less. For this reason it is expedient to purchase fish from dealers who know where to obtain live fish that have been carefully handled in seining, and who know how to truck them without injury.

Dr. Albert Hazzard (personal communication) stated that catch-out ponds in Pennsylvania have been of considerable interest to fishermen, particularly since 1950. In at least one instance, large lake sturgeon were stocked in small numbers in a catch-out pond. The lucky angler who caught one could either keep the fish (if able to bring it in successfully) or return it to the pond and receive a reward of $50.00. Blue and flathead catfish exceeding 25 pounds each, are sometimes used in the same way, e.g., as a "come-on" fish to induce fishermen to purchase fishing permits.

Dr. Hazzard described a trout project where one may fish to his heart's content with barbless artificial flies and return all of the fish that he catches. A season license to fish such a pond is $100 or a daily license may be secured for about $5.00. Surprisingly enough, these particular ponds were paying off well.

From the biological standpoint there are several probabilities that make the operation of catch-out ponds a financial risk. Not only are fish easily injured in handling and hauling, but when they are stocked in ponds at poundage levels above the natural capacities of these ponds to support fish, the total weights of the populations move progressively downward until they approach carrying-capacity poundages (see Chapter 4). If all of the fish are of adult sizes, there is little or no chance of their preying upon one another; instead, all will lose weight. Suppose, for example, a one-acre catch-out pond were stocked with 2250 bullheads weighing one third of a pound each or a total of 750 pounds. If the normal carrying capacity of this pond for bullheads were 300 pounds and fishermen removed only 1000 of the 2250 fish originally released, the average weight of those remaining at the end of the season (provided there was no natural mortality) would be 0.24 pound, a weight reduction of more than 25 per cent. These bullheads would probably be so thin that they would scarcely interest anglers or fish buyers. Although artificial feeding might help to maintain their weight, the high oxygen demand of the increased organic waste might jeopardize the actual survival of the fish. Moreover, fish foods are expensive and if the margin of profit were small to begin with, the operation might not stand the added cost.

The constant threat of disease and parasites in catch-out ponds is very real because the fish may come from many sources, and because fish are "piled up" above the carrying capacity of these ponds. Parasites brought in on new fish often have an easy time infesting fish already in the pond, and diseases may be transmitted directly and quickly.

Diseases and heavy infestations of parasites may kill the fish outright or cause them to become so emaciated that they either will not bite or else will provide an unacceptable catch. Once the fish in a catch-out pond become sick or heavily parasitized, one would be foolish to introduce additional stock. The best procedure is to kill the fish (and take the loss), sterilize the pond, and then restock with "healthy" fish.

In view of these biological problems associated with the mechanics of operating catch-out ponds, it is reasonable to drain the ponds in the fall after the fishing season and dispense with the remaining fish. Ponds should be allowed to remain dry during winter and the pond bottom should be treated with quick lime.

Ponds that cannot be drained should be seined at the end of the season and the fish sold, either alive or dressed. If there is no evidence of disease or parasites, the fish that escape the seining operation may be left in the pond over winter. If fish are diseased or heavily parasitized, the pond should be treated to eliminate all remaining fish and then sterilized.

PONDS IN WHICH FISH ARE ARTIFICIALLY FED

Several attempts have been made to improve fishing through artificial feeding which increases the poundage of fish a body of water may support. Fish may be fed live food if such food is available, or prepared food if the species of fish receiving support can be trained to eat it.

For a number of years the chain of fishing lakes (15.9 acres) on the Fin 'n Feather Club near Dundee, Illinois, containing largemouth bass, smallmouth bass, bluegills, and some green sunfish were fed emerald shiners seined from Lake Michigan and released alive in the lakes at the rate of about 1000 pounds per acre. These shiners were released in February and March and some of these minnows were still present in July and August, although, at that time, they appeared to be badly emaciated.

No draining census was made of the fishes in these lakes, but records of the catch for 1956 and 1957 were analyzed by Dr. D. Homer Buck (unpublished). In these years, the catch was almost entirely of largemouths. In 1956, 46 man-hours of fishing per acre produced a yield of 45.6 pounds of largemouths per acre at the rate of 0.99 pound per hour. In 1957, 34.8 man-hours of fishing per acre produced a yield of 60.6 pounds of bass per acre at the rate of 1.74 pounds per hour. These statistics indicate that the bass fishing in the lakes was very exceptional; it would be wholly unsafe to estimate the standing crop of bass in the lakes during these years, except to guess that it may have been between

100 and 200 pounds per acre. A part of the exceptional fishing must be attributed to the fact that the fishing pressure was so low and intermittent that the bass probably had little opportunity to become "hook-wise." The Supervisor of Fisheries for the Club believed that crayfish ingested by bass imparted a musty flavor to bass flesh; therefore it was thought that the addition of minnows not only increased the poundage of bass in the lakes, but also improved their flavor. He believed that the bass were eating minnows in preference to crayfish, because the former were always readily available. These assumptions could not be verified at the time the catch records were tabulated.

Channel catfish have been used as a subject for feeding experiments. Swingle [16] developed a procedure for feeding channel catfish fingerlings on prepared food and was able to build up populations of 2000 or more pounds per acre of fish of useful sizes. Before experiments were begun, fingerling channel catfish used for stocking were treated for external and internal parasites and inspected for disease.

Following these production experiments, Prather [13] tested the sport-fishing potential of these high-poundage channel catfish populations. In the first experiment, a 2.2-acre pond was stocked in spring with 1000 channel catfish fingerlings per acre, fertilized with seven applications of 8-8-0 at the rate of 100 pounds per acre per application and fed with fish food (Auburn No. 1 containing 42 per cent protein and composed of peanut oil meal, soybean oil meal, fish meal, and distillers dried solubles) at the seasonal rate of 2236 pounds of feed per acre. In September, when the catfish averaged 1.0 pound each, the lake was opened to public fishing at $1.00 per fisherman per day, with a catch limit of 3 fish. Fishing success was poor and few people were able to catch their limit. Between September 17 and October 14, sixty-four people caught an average of 1.25 catfish each at a rate of 0.3 pound of fish per hour. When the pond was drained in December, it contained 868 channel catfish, weighting 882.3 pounds per acre. This experiment was considered a failure from the standpoint of fishing, although the production was more than 800 pounds per acre.

In a second experiment a 12.4-acre pond was stocked in February, 1958 with 2000 3-inch channel catfish fingerlings, 1000 fathead minnows, and 66 largemouth bass fingerlings per acre, fertilized with 4 applications of 100 pounds of 8-8-0 per acre, and fed 5423.9 pounds of Auburn No. 2 fish food (like No. 1, but with peanut cake instead of peanut oil meal) per acre between April 1 and October 3.

This pond was opened to public fishing during the latter part of September when the catfish weighed 0.7 pound each. In this first fishing period (September 24 to December 8) permits were $1.00 for a limit of 3 catfish and 3 bass. The fishing season for the next year began March 14,

1959, and continued until October 6, and 5 catfish and 3 bass represented a limit for a permit. Feeding in 1959 was continued at a somewhat lower rate than in 1958 (16 pounds per acre per day in 1959 as compared with an average of about 20 pounds in 1958). Fishing in March, 1959 was poor, but it picked up in April and was very good in May and June. Late in June the fishing again became poor and remained so for the rest of the season.

In the experiment extending from September of 1958 to October of 1959, 579 fishermen per acre caught 1241 channel catfish weighing 1292.5 pounds per acre, plus an additional poundage of bass and miscellaneous other fish, making a total of 1356.4 pounds per acre. The rate of catch of channel catfish by months ranged from 0.58 to 0.08 pound per hour, averaging about 0.30 pound per hour (about the same as in the first experiment). When the pond was drained in December, it contained 180 additional channel cats per acre, weighing 391.2 pounds. Bass, bluegills, and other fish raised the total to 508.3 pounds per acre.

Fishing permits furnished income of $593.37 per acre. Sale of dressed catfish remaining (234.7 pounds dressed weight at $.60 per pound) was $140.82, making a total income of $734.19. Total cost for fertilizer, feed, and fingerlings was $481.46, leaving a return of $252.73 per acre for labor and capital.

Some possibilities for the spread of diseases and parasitic infestations are present in ponds where fish are fed artificially, but they probably are not as great as in catch-out ponds. In both types of ponds the concentration of fishes is abnormally high. However, fish receiving artificial food are well-nourished and are not under the stresses of adjustment to a lower carrying capacity; therefore they might be expected to show greater resistance to some diseases, and to the effects of heavy parasitic infestations.

FLOATING FISHING DOCKS

Floating fishing docks that are heated in winter have revolutionized winter fishing on many of the large reservoirs, particularly in the southwest. These docks originated in the 1950's on 46,000-acre Grand Lake O' The Cherokees and on 92,000-acre Lake Texoma in Oklahoma where there are now more than 100 of these enterprises.[10]

A floating fishing dock (Figure 9.1) usually consists of a rectangular floating barge with a rectangular opening in the center surrounded by a waist-high railing. The entire barge is covered by a structure which completely encloses it. Windows along the sides and ends let in light during the day. At night electric lights are turned on, and during cold weather the pier is heated. Some barges are supplied with television and lunch counters to serve the guests. Fishermen stand, or sit on upholstered

A. Exterior view.

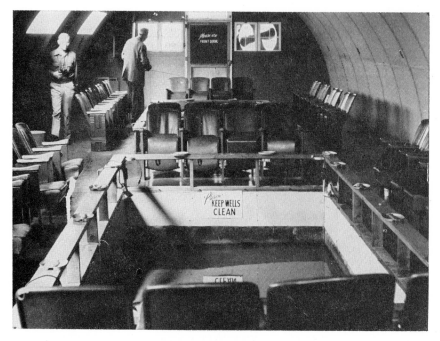

B. Interior view.
Figure 9.1. Enclosed fishing dock.

seats around the open rectangle in the center, as they fish over the guard railing.

Fish are attracted to these floating barges by brush piles of evergreens suspended below them. Some are baited through the use of cottonseed cake and other types of bait. Dock operators usually sell live bait, fishing tackle, and snacks.

Charges of about $1.00 per day are customary, and these fishing docks are very popular with people who would hesitate to go out in small boats, and who would probably not fish at all in winter.

"An estimated 60,000 fisherman-days were recorded in fishing docks on 19,000-acre Fort Gibson Reservoir, Oklahoma, in the period January through March, 1956." [9] This was probably as much as 90 per cent of all of the winter fishing on the lake. The catch was mostly of crappies and continued year-round, representing 37 per cent of the fishing on Fort Gibson.

The effectiveness of these fishing docks is related to their location on a reservoir over natural concentrations of fishes.

FISH FOR SALE

Private hatcheries selling warm-water fishes are in many states. They operate under state fish breeders licenses and sell their products to private lake and pond owners for release in their waters.

In some states these hatchery-reared fish are not subject to state regulations: Fishermen using private lakes stocked with commercially-raised fish do not need to have a state fishing license. In other states a license is necessary, even if the fish caught were purchased from a fish breeder. However, these fish may not be subject to the same restrictions (length limits, closed seasons, and creel limits) enforced for "wild" fish of the same species in that state.

Most warm-water fishes are raised in ponds. Adults of bass and other centrarchids are allowed to nest in ponds; afterward young may be removed to growing ponds, or the adult spawners seined from the spawning ponds. Fishes from which eggs can be removed by stripping may be hatched in jars inside the hatchery building and counted numbers stocked in growing ponds. Most of the hatchery techniques for raising fish are standard, although each operator makes modifications for his specific situation.

Hatcheries selling game fish for stocking may arrange to ship them by air in sealed plastic bags or transport them by truck, since many lake owners have no tank-truck equipment. The fish sold are rarely heavier than large fingerlings, and are, of course, not big enough to catch. These hatcheries are not patronized by catch-out pond owners because the fish are small and too expensive. Fishes sold are large- and smallmouth bass, muskellunge, northern pike, walleyes, channel catfish, panfish, and hybrid sunfish. Often live delivery is guaranteed. Much of the business of these hatcheries is with lake and pond owners who know nothing of lake-management techniques and who expect stocking to answer all of their fishing problems. Consequently, their money and the fish are often wasted.

Sometimes marshes and low swampy areas can be converted to fish farming by killing aquatic plants and by raising and controlling water levels. Most kinds of young fishes may be carried through the first summer in relatively shallow waters, even if they cannot be held over winter. The largest problem is that of moving the small fish from these shallow areas at the end of summer. If the areas may be drained, fish may be concentrated and seined in deeper channels near the outlet or caught in a Wolf weir below an outlet. In the South where winters are mild, fish may be allowed to winter in the same shallow areas used for summer growing of fish.

Within the early 1950's, some rice farmers in the Mississippi delta (Arkansas) discovered that they could alternate crops of rice with crops of fish.[2] After the rice was harvested, fields were reflooded and planted with carp, buffalo, and channel catfish. After two years the fields were drained and the fish crop (commercial) harvested. The results were so promising that the practice expanded rapidly and research was begun in an attempt to improve and perfect the rice-fish crop rotation. While this was primarily a commercial food-fish-production operation, it did show some possibilities for sport fishing and sport fish production. Rice-fish farming has spread from Arkansas into parts of Texas, Mississippi, and Louisiana, but is still centered in the state of Arkansas.

Delta land cleared of trees, leveed and brought into rice cultivation is very fertile, producing about 100 pounds of rice per acre the first season. However, in each successive year the crop decreases until by the fourth it is so low that the land must be fallowed or planted to some other crop.[11] A good part of this problem is related to the encroachment of native grasses and weeds which compete with rice for nutrients and light.

Rice fields used for fish production range in size from 10 to more than 600 acres, but about 40 acres or less is considered optimum. Maximum water depth is usually less than 5 feet—shallowest water depth is 18 inches. Where buffalo fish are used, yields of 500 pounds per acre are common. Buffalo fingerlings are stocked at the rate of 125 per acre in order to produce fish with an average weight of about 5 pounds.

The sport-fishing aspects of rice-fish farming appeared when largemouth bass fingerlings were stocked with the buffalo fish in order to control other undesirable fish that might gain entrance. Buffalo fish grew fast enough to prevent predation by bass. At the end of the 2-year fish-growing period, the fields supported 20 to 125 pounds per acre of marketable-sized largemouths in addition to the buffalo fish. Where bass could be sold legally, they brought 15 to 25 cents per pound dressed and somewhat more when sold alive for stocking in private lakes and catch-out ponds. Assuming a 500-pound-per-acre yield of buffalo fish at 12 cents per pound and an 80-pound-per-acre yield of bass at 15 cents, a grower could receive $72 per acre for each 2-year rotation. Probably less than 40 per cent or $13.50 per acre per year would represent net income.[11] Frequently, lease of trespass rights or the sale of daily permits to fish and to shoot waterfowl exceeded the commercial sale of fish; this represented additional income.

Rice-field reservoirs cannot be constructed everywhere this crop is grown, but as fields must hold water for its production, additional heights added to levees at a cost of $10 to $60 per acre may allow a rice-fish rotation, with further potential use for bass fishing and duck hunting.

Fish Management Service

Perhaps the newest commercial operation associated with sport fishing —and one very badly needed in some regions—is fish and lake management service. King [12] reports that five years is the average "productive life" of a pond without renovation and restocking.

Since on large country estates artificial ponds and lakes continue to present diverse problems to their owners, this service may involve any and/or all of the management operations described in this book. More common needs, however, are chemical treatment for the control of algae and obnoxious rooted aquatic vegetation, or the renovation through chemical treatment of lakes that have become contaminated with undesirable fish and their restocking with desirable ones.

In some states a limited amount of this type of extension service has been furnished to private clubs and individuals by state-employed fishery biologists. However, as more state-owned reservoirs are built for public recreation, state biologists will have less time to devote to the problems of private lake owners.

As with most businesses, working capital and training are necessary for a start. The latter may be obtained at universities giving courses in fishery biology and management, as well as basic courses in zoology, botany, physics, and chemistry.

Conceivably, one might set up a lake management service office in one's own home, but much of the equipment used (boats, trailers, pumps, seines, etc.) is rather bulky and requires a large storage space, usually lacking in the average yard or its accessory buildings. Moreover, ponds are useful for holding a supply of fish while one is engaged in a lake-renovation operation or in stocking a new lake. Thus, a physical situation is required that either furnishes or has the potential to provide office and laboratory space, fish-holding tanks and ponds, and buildings to store bulky equipment.

LITERATURE

1. Anon., *U. S. Fish & Wildlife Serv. Circ.*, **14**, 1-50 (1955).
2. Anon., *Prog. Fish-Cult.*, **18**, 134 (1956).
3. Anon., *U. S. Fish & Wildlife Serv. Circ.*, **120**, 1-73 (1961).
4. Anon., "Pleasure Boating in Wisconsin," pp. 1-17, Wis. Dept. Resource Devel., Madison, Wis. (1961).
5. Bellrose, F. C., and Rollings, C. T., *Ill. Nat. Hist. Surv. Biol. Notes*, **21**, 1-24 (1949).
6. Bennett, G. W., and Durham, L., *Ill. Nat. Hist. Surv. Biol. Notes*, **23**, 1-16 (1951).
7. DeWitt, J. W., Jr., *Prog. Fish-Cult.*, **16**, 147-152 (1954).
8. Dobie, J. R., Meehean, O. L., and Washburn, G. N., *U. S. Fish & Wildlife Serv. Circ.*, **12**, 1-113 (1948).
9. Houser, A., and Heard, W. R., *Okla. Acad. Sci. Proc.*, **38**, 137-146 (1958).
10. Jenkins, R. M., *Spt. Fish. Inst.*, 1-22 (1961).
11. Johnson, M. C., *Prog. Fish-Cult.*, **21**, 154-160 (1959).
12. King, Willis, *U. S. Fish & Wildlife Serv. Cir.*, **86**, 1-20 (1960).
13. Prather, E. E., *S. E. Ass. G. & F. Comm.*, **13**, 331-335 (1959).
14. Schoumacher, R., University of Mich. Lib., Master's Thesis (1959).
15. Stroud, R. H., *Spt. Fish. Inst. Bull.*, **59**, 1-8 (1956).
16. Swingle, H. S., *S. E. Ass. G. & F. Comm.*, **12**, 63-72 (1958).

Appendix

Common and Scientific Names of Fishes Referred to in Text

With a few exceptions, the common and scientific names listed below are those accepted by the American Fisheries Society, Committee on Names of Fishes,* published in 1960. One exception is the common name of redear, for *Lepomis microlophus* (G), which is invariably read as "re-dear," presumably because both the prefix "re-" and the word "dear" are more commonly seen in print than are the words "red" and "ear." Other exceptions are the names of a few fishes not native to the United States and Canada.

Common names vary from place to place, and exact identification of any fish must be associated with an accepted scientific name. As most readers will be unfamiliar with the scientific names, and will look first for common names, the Appendix has been arranged with the common *family* names in alphabetical order. Under each family is listed, in alphabetical order, the common names of the species mentioned in the text, and opposite each common name is its corresponding scientific name.

Basses (Sea)   Serranidae
    Bass, Striped   *Roccus saxatilis* (W)
    Bass, White   *Roccus chrysops* (R)
    Bass, Yellow   *Roccus mississippiensis* (J & E)
    Perch, White   *Roccus americanus* (G)

Bowfins   Amiidae
    Bowfin   *Amia calva* L

Catfishes   Ictaluridae
    Bullheads   *Ictalurus* spp
    Bullhead, Black   *Ictalurus melas* (R)

* Baily, R. M., *et al.*, "A List of Common and Scientific Names of Fishes from the United States and Canada," American Fisheries Society Special Publication 2, 1-102 (1960).

Catfishes (*cont.*)
  Bullhead, Brown
  Bullhead, Yellow
  Catfish, Channel
  Catfish, Flathead
  Madtoms
  Stonecats

Ictaluridae (*cont.*)
  Ictalurus nebulosus (Le S)
  Ictalurus natalis (Le S)
  Ictalurus punctatus (R)
  Pylodictis olivaris (R)
  Noturus spp
  Noturus flavus R

Drums
  Drum, Freshwater

Sciaenidae
  Aplodinotus grunniens R

Gars
  Gars, Garfishes

Lepisosteidae
  Lepisosteus spp

Herrings
  Shad
  Shad, Gizzard
  Shad, Threadfin

Clupeidae
  Dorosoma spp
  Dorosoma cepedianum (Le S)
  Dorosoma petenense (G)

Killifishes
  Killifishes

Cyprinodontidae
  Fundulus spp

Lampreys
  Lamprey, Sea

Petromyzonidae
  Petromyzon marinus L

Livebearers
  Gambusia, Mosquitofish
  Guppy

Poeciliidae
  Gambusia affinis (B & G)
  Lebistes reticulatus (P)

Minnows and Carps
  Carp
  Chub, Creek
  Dace, Northern Redbelly
  Elritze (European)
  Goldfish
  Minnow, Bluntnose
  Minnow, Flathead
  Shiner, Blackchin
  Shiner, Blacknose
  Shiner, Blacktail
  Shiner, Emerald
  Shiner, Golden
  Shiner, Red
  Shiner, Redside
  Shiner, Sand
  Shiner, Satinfin

Cyprinidae
  Cyprinus carpio L
  Semotilus atromaculatus (M)
  Chrosomus eos C
  Phoxinus phoxinus L
  Carassius auratus (L)
  Pimephales notatus (R)
  Pimephales promelas R
  Notropis heterodon (C)
  Notropis heterolepis E
  Notropis venustus (G)
  Notropis atherinoides R
  Notemigonus crysoleucas (M)
  Notropis lutrensis (B & G)
  Richardsonius balteatus (R)
  Notropis stramineus (C)
  Notropis analostanus (G)

Mouthbreeders
    Tilapia (Asiatic pondfish)

Chromides
    Tilapia mossambicus P

Mudminnows
    Mudminnow (Central)

Umbridae
    Umbra limi (K)

Perches
    Darter, Fantail
    Darter, Greenside
    Darter, Iowa
    Darter, Orangethroat
    Darter, Rainbow
    Perch, European
    Perch, Yellow
    Sauger
    Walleye, Yellow Pike-Perch

Percidae
    Etheostoma flabellare R
    Etheostoma blennioides R
    Etheostoma exile (G)
    Etheostoma spectabile (A)
    Etheostoma caeruleum S
    Perca fluviatilis R
    Perca flavescens (M)
    Stizostedion canadense (S)
    Stizostedion vitreum vitreum (M)

Pikes
    Muskellunge
    Pickerel
    Pike, Northern

Esocidae
    Esox masquinongy M
    Esox spp
    Esox lucius L

Porgies
    Sheepshead

Sparidae
    Archosargus probatocephalus (W)

Smelts
    Smelt (American)

Osmeridae
    Osmerus mordax (M)

Sticklebacks
    Stickleback (Brook)

Gasterosteidae
    Eucalia inconstans (K)

Sturgeons
    Sturgeon
    Sturgeon, Lake

Acipenseridae
    Acipenser spp
    Acipenser fulvescens R

Suckers
    Buffalo
    Buffalo, Bigmouth
    Buffalo, Smallmouth
    Chubsucker, Lake
    Quillback
    Redhorse, Golden
    Sucker, Blue
    Sucker, Hog
    Sucker, White or Western White

Catostomidae
    Ictiobus spp
    Ictiobus cyprinella (V)
    Ictiobus bubalus (R)
    Erimyzon sucetta (L)
    Carpiodes cyprinus (Le S)
    Moxostoma erythrurum (R)
    Cycleptus elongatus (Le S)
    Hypentelium nigricans (Le S)
    Catostomus commersoni (L)

Sunfishes | Centrarchidae
Bass | *Micropterus* spp
Bass, Largemouth | *Micropterus salmoides* (L)
Bass, Rock | *Ambloplites rupestris* (R)
Bass, Smallmouth | *Micropterus dolomieui* L
Bass, Spotted | *Micropterus punctulatus* (R)
Bluegill | *Lepomis macrochirus* R
Crappies | *Pomoxis* spp
Crappie, Black | *Pomoxis nigromaculatus* (Le S)
Crappie, White | *Pomoxis annularis* R
Pumpkinseed | *Lepomis gibbosus* (L)
Sunfish | *Lepomis* spp
Sunfish, Green | *Lepomis cyanellus* R
Sunfish, Longear | *Lepomis megalotis* (R)
Sunfish, Orangespotted | *Lepomis humilis* (G)
Sunfish, Red-ear | *Lepomis microlophus* (G)
Sunfish, Spotted | *Lepomis punctatus* (V)
Warmouth | *Chaenobryttus gulosus* (C)

Trouts and Whitefishes | Salmonidae
Ciscoes | *Coregonus* spp
Salmon | *Salmo, Oncorhynchus* spp
Salmon, Coho | *Oncorhynchus kisutch* (W)
Salmon, Spring (Chinook) | *Oncorhynchus tshawytscha* (W)
Trout | *Salmo* spp
Trout, Brook | *Salvelinus fontinalis* (M)
Trout, Brown | *Salmo trutta* L
Trout, Cutthroat | *Salmo clarki* R
Trout, Lake | *Salvelinus namaycush* (W)
Trout, Rainbow | *Salmo gairdneri* R
Tullibee (Nipigon cisco) | *Coregonus nipigon* (K)
Whitefish | *Coregonus clupeaformis* (M)
Whitefish, Mountain | *Prosopium williamsoni* (G)

Index

Achlya sp., 201
Age and sexual maturity, 96
Aging fish, 85
   origin of scale method, 5
Aggregating, of fishes, 230
Aldrich, A. D., 244
Aldrin, 148
Algae,
   as a basic food, 170
   control of, 172
   dangerous forms of, 171
   nuisance forms of, 171
   toxic substance from, 171
Allen, K. R., 118, 208
American Fisheries Society,
   meetings of, 4
Anabaena, 171
Angler relationships,
   with commercial fishermen at Reelfoot L., 199
Angling, public interest in, 251
Annuli,
   close spacing of, 87
   false, 87
   overlapping, 87
   skipped, 87
Annulus,
   summer ring, 85
   true, false, 85
   winter ring, 85
Aphanizomenon, 171
   flos-aquae, 176
Arrowhead Lake (Illinois), 65
Artificial fluctuation of water levels, 155
   drawdown to crowd fish, 155
   effects on fishes and other vertebrates, 159
   effects on invertebrates, 159
   effects on lake bottom, 158
   natural cycle of levels in Illinois River, 156-157

   on TVA lakes, 157
   reflooding after drawdown, 155
   types of drawdowns, 161
Au Sable River (Mich.), 208

Baccius, G.,
   carp-raising techniques, 2
Bachman, Dr. John,
   hatchery operation before 1865, 3
Balance, 125
   definition of Nicholson, 125
   definition of Swingle, 125
   harvestable-sized fish, 126
   sustained yield requirement of, 126
   untenable as applied to pond fish, 127
Ball, R. C., 64, 69, 106, 108, 118, 165
Ball, R. C. and Ford, J. R., 106
Ball, R. C. and Tait, H. D., 110
Barometric pressure, 242
Barnes, Clifford (U. of Wash.), 237
Barney, R. L.,
   aging fish from scales, 5
Barney, R. L. and Canfield, H. L., 6, 104
Barnickol, P. G. and Campbell, R., 190
Bass, alone,
   comparative population size of, 107
   method of stocking of, 107
Bass-bluegill combination,
   drawbacks of, 104
   in Illinois, 106
   in North Central States, 104
   in Northern United States and Canada, 106
   in Southeast, 104
   not recommended in New York and Montana, 106
   rates of stocking, 105
   stocking with adults, 105
   stocking intermediate-size lakes, 106
   theoretical basis for, 104

Bass-bluegill-warmouth-channel catfish combination, 108
Bass-bowfin-bluegill combination, 108
Bass-crappie-bluebill-bullhead combination, 108
Bass, largemouth,
  average number of eggs of, 92
  average number of fry in nest of, 93
  closed season for, 209
  color vision of, 213
  catch influenced by available food, 73
  competition with warmouths, 119
  condition of, 76, 77
  cost of fishing for, 252
  effects of drawdown on, 160
  effects of fluctuating levels on, 157
  feeding efficiency of, with minnows, 72
  fed artificially, in ponds, 259-260
  food competition with bluegills, 119
  growth in South Africa, 81
  "harvestable surplus" of, 193
  importation into South Africa, 81
  in catch-out ponds, 257, 258
  in minnow seine method, 136
  in net cropping experiment, 197
  in rice-fish rotation, 264
  in stripmine, with high sulfate, 45
  "intelligence" of, 244, 245
  interspecific predation with bluegills, 6
  length of life of, 202
  lethal temperatures for, 227
  low poundages with high bluegill poundages, 68, 69
  mortality rate of, 206, 207
  minimum useful size of, 71
  mortality rate in Ridge L., 205
  no overfishing of, 189
  predation on bluegill nests, 103
  preferred temperature of, 228
  production of, in Ridge Lake, 75
  rate of digestion, 72
  resistance to angling, 74
  resistance to capture of, 193
  sexual maturity of, 96
  sexual maturity, in Alabama, 96
  sexual maturity, in Illinois, 96
  shortage of prey for, 124
  sluggishness in spring, 239
  standing crop in pounds per acre, 64
  starvation of, 123
  stocking with bluegills, 104, 105, 106
  stocked with bowfin and bluegills, 108
  stocked to improve fishing, 110-111
  stocked with minnows, 108
  stocked with red-ear sunfish, 108
  stocked with warmouths, 108
  stocking after marginal poisoning, 152

  sudden abundance of food for, 85
  survival of fry, 199
  survival rate of fingerlings, 114
  survival rate of adults stocked, 114-115
  with green sunfish, 63
Bass-minnow combination, 108
Bass-red-ear sunfish combination, 108
Bass, rock,
  average number fry per nest, 93
  in tests with CO_2 variation, 49
  mortality rate of, 207
  preferred temp. of, 228
  standing crop of, in pounds per acre, 64
Bass, smallmouth, alone, 108
  annual turn-over of, 186
  color vision of, 214
  importation into S. Africa, 81
  inability to compete with warm-water fish, 108
  length of life of, 202
  maximum yield of, 73, 74
  mortality rate of, 207
  numbers of eggs of, 92
  preferred temp. of, 228
  sluggishness in spring, 239
Bass, spotted,
  importation into S. Africa, 81
  preferred temp. of, 228
Bass, striped,
  isolated by impoundment of Santee-Cooper Reservoir, 11
  introduction into Kentucky Lake, 11
Bass-warmouth combination, 108
Bass, white,
  introduction in reservoirs, 11
  length of life of, 202
  sun orientation of, 217
Bass, yellow,
  overfishing of, 190
Beckman, W. C., 152
Behavior,
  daily activity, 229, 231
  diurnal movements of fishes, 231
  social groupings of fishes, 229
  seasonal rhythm, 230
Bennett, G. W., 67
BHC, 148
Biological domination, by man of artificial lakes, 43
Biting,
  factors that influence, 238
  water temperatures, 238-239
Biting habits, seasonal, 194
Biting rate,
  diurnal effects, 241
  effect of moonlight, 243
  effects of rising and falling waters, 241

Biting rate (*Cont.*)
  effect of transparency, 240
  highest in spring, 239
  slowed by water too clear, 240, 241
  varies with water labels, 242
Bluegill,
  average number of fry per nest, 93
  capacity to grow after stunting, 81
  color vision of, 213
  condition of, 76, 77
  cycle of condition, 78
  effects of drawdown on, 160
  growth in S. Africa, 82
  importation into S. Africa, 81
  in carrying capacity experiments, 61, 62
  in catch-out ponds, 257, 258
  in minnow seine method, 136
  in net cropping exp., 197
  intraspecific competition of, 124
  killed by supersaturation of O_2, 55
  length of life of, 202
  lethal temperatures for, 227
  limited range of, 233
  minimum useful size of, 71
  mortality rate of, 207
  overfeeding of, 84
  sexual maturity of, 96
  sound perception of, 218
  standing crop in ponds per acre, 64
  total mortality of, 203, 204
Boats,
  needs of owners in Wisconsin, 250
  uses of in Wisconsin, 250
  Wisconsin survey, 250
Boat shocker,
  A.C. and D.C. uses, 139
  interrupted current, 139
  kind of sample taken by, 138
  requirements for, 138
  stomach collecting with, 139
Boroden, N.,
  fish aging from scales, 5
Bowfin,
  standing crop in pounds per acre, 64
Breder, C. M., Jr., 230
Brett, J. R., 226
Brett, J. R. and MacKinnon, D., 224
Brown, C. J. D., 106
Brown, W. H., 114
Brownian movements, 47
Buck, D. Homer, 259
Bigmouth buffalo,
  survived winterkill at Gale Lake, 53
Buffalo,
  in rice-fish rotation, 264
  standing crop in pounds per acre, 64

Bullheads,
  dominant year-class following winter-kill, 53
  in catch-out ponds, 257, 258
  limited range of, 233
  minimum useful size of, 71
  spawning time, 99
  standing crop in pounds per acre, 64
Bullheads, black,
  overfishing of, 190
  survived winterkill in Gale Lake, 53
  taste organs of, 220
Burr, J. G.,
  fish shocker, 5
Busch Memorial Wildlife Area (Mo.), 190
  ponds on the, 190, 191

Camping out,
  recent trends for, 249
Carbine, W. F., 8, 92
Carbon dioxide, 48
  effects of rapid change of, 48
  sudden changes, experimental testing of, 49
Carlander, K. D. and Cleary, R. E., 231
Carp,
  color vision of, 213
  competition for space, 120-121
  culture in Europe, 2
  importation into S. Africa, 81
  in catch-out ponds, 257, 258
  killed by supersaturation of O_2, 55
  reversion to wild type, 102
  sound perception of, 218
  standing crop of, 64
  survived winterkill in Gale Lake, 53
Carrying capacity,
  definition of, 59
  experimental testing of, 61
  function of surface area, 61
Catch, rate of,
  factors affecting, 195
  relationship of, to number of fish, 195
Catch-out ponds, 257
  "come-on" fish, 258
  kinds of fish used for, 257
  licensing of, 257
  margin of profit from, 258
  operational hazards of, 258
Catfish, channel,
  fed artificially in ponds, 260, 261
  in rice-fish rotation, 264
  standing crop in pounds per acre, 64
Catostomidae,
  restricted movement of, 235

Centrarchidae,
　restricted movement of, 235
Chautauqua L. (Illinois), 124
Childers, W. F., 231
Chlordane, 148
Chlorinated hydrocarbon insecticides, 148
Chlorothion, 148
Ciampi, E., 245
Clark, M., 111
Clay particles,
　neutralizer for electrical charges of, 47
Clear Lake (Lake Co., Calif.), 209
Clear Lake (Iowa), 124, 234
Combinations of fishes, 107
Commission, U. S. Fish,
　fish propagation duties in 1872, 3
Competition, 118
　for food, 118
　for specific habitats, 123
　inter- and intraspecific, 123
　on feeding and spawning grounds, 185
　for space, 119-120
　for space, experiments on, 120
　for space, inhibitory factor of Swingle,
　　120
　for space, substance destroys B_1, 121
Condition, 76
　coefficient of condition, K, 76
　conversion factors for, 78
　cycles of, 78
　factor of Cooper and Benson, R, 78
　factor of E. M. Corbett, C. F., 77
　index of condition, C, 76-77
　methods of measuring, 76
　uses in management, 79
　vs. rate of growth, 79
Coelosphaerium, 171
Cooper, G. P., 111
Copper sulfate,
　as an algicide, 172
　as a fish irritant, 135
Coregonidae,
　restricted movement of, 235
Costs of fishing, 252
Coyote Creek (Oregon),
　pollution, 47
Crappie,
　cycle dominated by, 8
　cycle in L. Senachwine, 124
　floating dock fishing for, 262, 263
　length of life of, 202
　number of eggs of, 92
　standing crop of, 64
　with bigmouth buffalo, 63
Crappie, black,
　activity periods of, 231
　cycle of, 124

killed by supersaturation of O_2, 55
　minimum useful size of, 71
　mortality rate of, 207
　overfishing of, 190
Crappie, white,
　activity periods of, 231
　cycle of condition of, 78
　disappearance of year class in summer,
　　55
　minimum useful size of, 71
　survived winterkill in Gale Lake, 53
Crayfish,
　as underwater scavengers, 201
Crowding,
　effect on number of eggs, 121
Culture, fish,
　as farm crop, 2, 3
　Chinese, 2
　classical, 2
　European pond-fish, 2
　relation to management, 2
Cycles,
　crappie-dominated, 8
　feeding of fish, 196
　in Lake Senachwine, 7
Cycles, fishing,
　of reservoirs, 196
Cycle, of use,
　of a resource, 208

Daily activity,
　in black and white crappies, 231
Dale Hollow,
　dam and outlet of, 36
Dale Hollow Dam,
　water release program of, 36
Dangers to ponds,
　crayfish and burrowing rodents, 56
Dangers to ponds and lakes,
　insecticides, 57
　wind action, 56
DDT, 148
　as a fish poison, 147
　toxicity of, 147
Deaths, natural,
　causes for, 199
　time of, 200
Deep Lake (Oakland Co.), Mich., 92
Derris, 142
Detergents,
　composition of, 44
　effects of, 44
　toxicity of, 44
Devonian Period, 91
Dieldrin, 148
Diet, maintenance, 123
Dipterex, 148

Drum,
  in catch-out ponds, 257
  sound production of, 219
  standing crop of, 64
Duck Pond (Illinois), 65
Dyche, L. L., 6, 104

Ellis, M. M., 10
Elritze,
  color vision of, 213
  observations of, 217
  odor perception of, 221
Endrin, 148
Environment,
  decrease in favorability of, 43
EPN, 148
Erie, Lake,
  soil conservation on water shed, 1
Escanaba Lake (Wisc.), 208
Eschmeyer, P., 103, 123
Eschmeyer, R. W., 6, 157, 232

Feeding migration, of perch,
  in L. Mendota, 231
Feeding stoppage,
  from overeating, 84
Ferguson, R. G., 227
Fertilization, lake, 162
  algae stimulated by, 163
  competition between filamentous and
    plankton algae, 163
  dangers of, 166, 167
  dosage of, for southeast, 163
  for starting new ponds, 168
  interference with sunfish nest building,
    165
  lime, 164
  manganese, 164
  nitrogen, 165
  no general recommendation for, 167
  phosphorous, 165
  potassium, 164
  standing crop increase in Illinois, 167
  sunfish nests and inorganic salts, 165
Fin 'n Feather Club (Dundee, Ill.), 259
Fish,
  cold-water species, 45
  desirable sizes of, 190
  exported to South Africa, 81
  for sale, 263
  no shortage of, 7
  relative plumpness of, 75
  useful sizes of, 70
  warm-water species, 45-46
Fish, death of,
  in spring, 201
  in summer, 201

Fish-eating birds,
  at Reelfoot L., 198
"Fished-out" lakes,
  contain wise fish, 131
Fish farming, 264
  carp, buffalo and channel catfish, 264
  in rice fields, 264
Fish "intelligence," 245
Fish management service, 265
Fish ponds, artificially fed, 259
  with emerald shiners, 259
  with prepared food, 260, 261
Fish population adjustment, 150
  partial poisoning, 150
  use of nets and seines, 150
Fish population removal, 140
  by draining, 140
  optimum time for, 141
  removing fish from water, 140
  by rotenone treatment, 142
  storing live fish, 141
Fishermen's baits,
  earthworms and other invertebrates,
    253, 254
  minnows, 254
  supplying, 253
Fishing,
  causes for poor, 7, 131
  changes in, 110
  publicity, for reservoirs, 12
  trespass-rights, 256
  year-round, in Norris Reservoir, 11
  year-round, in Tennessee and Ohio, 11
Fishing clubs,
  "executives," 255
  fishing-lake investments, 255
  organized sportsmen's clubs, 256
Fishing, commercial,
  effects of, 197
  an experiment in, 196, 197
  restricted by anglers, 198
Fishing docks, floating, 261
  on southwestern reservoirs, 261
  winter fishing on Fort Gibson Reser-
    voir (Okla.), 263
Fishing expenditures,
  relative amounts of, 252
Fishing lakes,
  recreational values of, 253
Fishing optimum,
  related to rapid growth and expanding
    population, 196
Fishing pressure,
  reaction of fishes to, 193
  seasonal, 191, 192
  types of, 193
Fishing pressure vs. yield, 190

Fishing for sale, 254, 255
Fleming, W. W., 176
Flint, W. P., 241
Food chain, 119
Food conversion, 72
Forage ratio, 118
Forbes, Prof. Stephen A.,
    fish, natural loss of, 4
Ford, J. R., 108
Fork Lake (Illinois), 65, 87, 110
von Frisch, K., 221
Fry, F. E. J., 46, 227
Fungi, aquatic,
    infestations of, 200
    toxins cause death of fish, 201

Gale Lake (Illinois),
    partial winterkill in, 53
Gambusia,
    appearance in S. Africa, 81
Garlick, Dr. Theodatus,
    hatchery operation before 1865, 3
Gerking, S. D., 234, 235
Glaeotrichia, 171
Goldfish,
    competition for space, 120
    release of, in lakes, 113
Gravel pit lakes,
    characteristics of, 24
    planning for recreation in, 24
Green, Seth,
    hatchery operation before 1865, 3
Greenbank, J., 230
Grid pattern
    for spreading rotenone, 145
Griffin, D. R., 236
Growing season, 69
Growth,
    abnormalities of, 89
    indeterminate, 79
    interpretation of, from scales, 85
    in new waters, 81
Growth, rate of, 82
    factors affecting, 82
    genetic potential, 82
    length of growing season, 82
Guppies,
    release of in lakes, 113

Habitat, aquatic,
    biological environment of, 42
    components of, 42
Hansen, D. F., 135, 230, 239
Hansen, D. F., Bennett, G. W., Webb,
    R. J., and Lewis, J. M., 195
Harvest, fish,
    increase in, for reservoirs, 12

"Harvestable surplus," of bass, 193
Hasler, A. D., 217, 237
Hasler, A. D. and Bardach, J. E., 231
Hasler, A. D. and Einsele, W. G., 167
Hasler, A. D., Horrall, R. M., Wisby,
    W. J., and Braemer, W. B., 217
Hasler, A. D. and Wisby, W. J., 222
Hatcheries,
    fish produced in, 5
    importance in minds of fish culturists, 5
    origin of, from Europe, 3
    "paper fish" of, 3
    purpose of introduction in U. S., 3
Hatchery, movement,
    success of, 5
Hayes, F. R. and Livingstone, D. A., 143
Hazzard, A. S., 258
Hearing, 218
    range of tone perception, 218
    of bluegills, 218
    of carp, 218
Hederström, H., 5
    growth rings on fish vertebrae in 1759,
    5
Heptachlor, 148
Hess, A. D. and Swartz, A. N., 118
Hey, D., 43
"Hibernation" of Centrarchidae, 230
Homing,
    definition of, 234
    fish that show, 235
    sensory perception as related to, 236
Homing and home range, 234
Houghton Lake (Mich.), 93
    predation on pike fry, 93
H.T.H. (calcium hypochlorite), 141
Hubbs, Carl L., 6
Hubbs, C. L. and Cooper, G. P., 85
Hutchens, Lynn H., 244
Huttel, R., 221
Hybridization,
    among sunfishes, 101
    in Cyprinids, pikes, and sunfish, 99
Hyperactivity as a lethal factor, 233

Ice fishing, 194
    extent of, 194
    more successful in January and February, 239
Ictaluridae,
    restricted movement of, 235
Illinois River (Ill.),
    commercial yield of fish in 1908, 3
Illinois State Fish Commission, 4
    fish, rescue operations, 4
Insecticides,
    toxicity to fish, 57

Irwin, W. H., 46
Issaquah River (Wash.), 223

Jackson, C. F., 166
James, Marian F., 123
James, M. C., Meehean, O. L., and
  Douglas, E. J., 45, 189
Jenkins, Robert M., 9, 108
Johannes, R. E. and Larkin, P. A., 118
Jordan Creek (Illinois), 234
Juday, C., Schloemer, C. L., Livingston
  C., 5
  fertilizers in water, 5

Keokuk, Lake, 9
King, Willis, 17, 265
Knight, John Alden, 242
Krumholz, L. A., 108, 110, 142

Lagler, K. F. and DeRoth, G. C., 111,
  189, 244
Lake,
  basis for separation from pond, 20
  definition of, 20
Lakes, artificial,
  kinds of, 15
  limited biota of, 15
  migration of biota into, 15
  motivation for construction of, 16
  multipurpose, 16
  planning of, 29
  water-control problems of, 30
Lake improvement, 6
  "The improvement of lakes for fish-
    ing," 6
Lamprey, sea, 185
  in the Great Lakes, 185
Langlois, T. H.,
  fish production in L. Erie, 1
Larimore, R. W., 89, 108, 119, 121
Larkin, P. A., 235
Lateral-levee reservoirs,
  characteristics of, 22
  origin of, 22
Learning to fish, 246
Learning,
  to avoid baited hook, 244
Legal restrictions,
  closed seasons, 209
  creel limits, 209
  size limits, 208
Leonard, J. W., 118, 142
Leopold, Aldo, 249
Lethal temperatures,
  for bass, bluegills, and yellow perch,
    227
Life span, of fishes, 201, 202

Light sensitivity, of fishes, 217
  preference for darkness, 218
Lindane, 148
Lonchocarpus, 142
Lux, F. E. and Smith, L. L., Jr., 195

Malathion, 148
Management, fish,
  definition of, 1
  early attempts at, 5
  "The improvement of lakes for fish-
    ing," 6
  integrated science of, 2
  manipulation of wild populations, 2
  master plan of, 1
  objectives of, 131
  techniques of, 140
  "wild" fish, 2
Management of sport fish,
  commercial fishing in, 196
Markus, H. C., 5, 72
Martin, R. G., 193
Median tolerance limit, 148
Mendota, Lake (Madison, Wisc.), 231
Meredosia Bay (Illinois), 232
Methoxychlor, 148
Methyl parathion, 148
Migration in fishes,
  theories of, 236
Migrations of salmons, 236, 237
Miller, R. B., 235
Minnows, bluntnose,
  odor sensitivity of, to phenols, 222
Minnow seine method,
  criticisms of, 136
  pond analysis critera, 136
Morpholine, 223
Mortality,
  as related to recruitment, 207
  of bass at Ridge Lake, 204-206
  rates of some game and panfish, 207
  various rates of, for Indiana bluegills,
    204
Mortality, fishing, 183
  angling vs. natural predation, 183
  unimportance in population dynamics,
    208
Mortality, natural, 183, 199
  calculation of, by returns of marked
    fish, 203
  definition of, 199
  problems of measuring, 202
  relation to fishing mortality, 203
Mortality, total,
  a combination of fishing and natural
    mortality, 187
  range of, in Indiana lakes, 203

Moyle, J. B., 39, 63
Mraz, D. and Cooper, E. L., 96, 121
Multipurpose reservoirs,
    conflicting uses of, 23
    fishing below dams of, 23
    mode of operation of, 23
Murphy, G. I., 209
Muskellunge, 108
    for control of overpopulation, 108
    length of life of, 202
    "intelligence" of, 245
    spawning temp. of, 98
Muskellunge Lake (Vilas Co., Wisc.),
    231

National surveys of fishing and hunting,
    1955 and 1960, 251
Navigation pools, 22
    origin of, 22
    sudden draining, danger of, 22
Nodularia, 171
Norris Reservoir,
    CO_2, rapid change of, 48
North, R.,
    carp culture, early, 2

Observation, direct,
    by elritze in tanks, 217
Odor perception,
    as aid in homing, 224
    as aid in migration, 222
    fright reaction to, 221
    hypothesis for migratory ability, 222,
        223
    identification of odors by, 222
    keenness of, for bluntnose minnows,
        222
    migration of salmon, 222
    schooling by, 221
    theory of, 220
    uses of, 221
Odor perception and taste, 219
Olmsted, J. M. D., 220
OMPA, 148
Oncorhynchus (salmon),
    die after spawning, 237
Onized Lake (Illinois), 74, 189, 244
Organic phosphorus insecticides, 148
Orientation,
    of white bass in L. Mendota (Wisc.),
        217
    sun, 217
Overfishing,
    definition of, 189
    example of, 189, 190
Overpopulation,
    of crappies self-perpetuating, 107

Overpopulation and stunting, 187
Oxidation ponds,
    sewage disposal in, 43
    stock waste disposal in, 43
Oxygen, 48
    as related to CO_2, 48
    deaths of fish caused by low and high,
        48
    tensions in bright sunlight, 48

Para-oxon, 148
Parathion, 148
Patriarche, M. H., 52
Patriarche, M. H. and R. C. Ball, 118
Pay-as-you-fish ponds, 257
Pearse, A. S. and Achtenberg, H., 232
Perch, European,
    importation into S. Africa, 81
Perch, yellow,
    feeding migration of, 231
    lethal temperatures of, 227
    preferred temperature of, 228
    spawning temperature of, 98
    standing crop of, 64
Percidae,
    restricted movement of, 235
pH
    causes for changes of, 45
    effects on fish, 45
    range of, 45
    sulfates in stripmine waters, 45
    variations of, 44
Pigmentation,
    changeability of, 216
    control mechanism of, 216
Pike-bluegill combination
    in Nebraska, 108
Pike,
    hybrids of, 99
    standing crop of, 64
Pike, northern,
    killed by supersaturation of O_2, 55
    length of life of, 202
    minimum useful size of, 71
    predation on fry in Houghton L., 93
    sexual maturity of, 96
    shortage of prey for, 125
    spawning temperature of, 98
    stocked with bluegills, 108
    see pike-bluegill combination
Plančić, J., 200
Plant die-offs, 173
Podding of fishes, 230
Poisoning, partial, 150
    restocking after, 152
    shoreline vs. sectional, 152
    shoreline treatment, 151

Poisoning, partial (*Cont.*)
 timing of, 151
 to relieve stunting, 153
 weakness of, 152
Poisoning, spot, 137
 methods of, 137
Ponds,
 carp, 2
 definition of, 20
Ponds, farm,
 number of, in U. S., 17
 planning of, 19
 purposes of, 17
 requirements of satisfactory, 18
 simplest aquatic habitat, 17
 water problems of, 19
Pond research unit,
 in Alabama, 8
Pond-season, 191
Pollution,
 chemical, 43
 organic waste, 43
 sewage as a pond fertilizer, 43
 silt, 43
Populations,
 as units, 7
 estimation of, 181, 182
 estimation of by effort-catch relationship, 182
 estimation of by recapture of marked
   fish, 181
 forces acting on, 182
 reducing undesirable fish in, 12
 Russell's interaction of factors, 182,
   183
Populations, roving,
 in streams and lakes, 234
Positive ions,
 for neutralizing elec. charges of clay
   particles, 47
Potamogeton foliosus, 176
Prather, E. E., 260
Predation,
 bass on bluegill eggs, 103
 effects of curtailment of, 117
 minor on 2+ fish, 200
 of crappies on bass, 107
 role in fish management, 115
Predators,
 behavior of, 116
 controlled by prey species, 117
 evolution of, 115
 of small fishes, 116
 types of, 116
Production, fish, 71
 as related to yield and standing crop,
   72, 73

 definition of, 71
 estimation of, 74
 loss of, from aquatic veg., 172, 173
 of smallmouth bass, 186
Productivity, biological
 alkalinity in, 38
 chemical indicators of, 38
 lake size in, 39
 nutrient material, function of, 38
 sulfates in, 39
Pumpkinseed,
 average number fry per nest, 93
 mortality rate of, 207
 standing crop of, 64

Quarry lakes,
 characteristics of, 27
 origin of, 27
Quillbacks,
 standing crop in pounds per acre, 64

Rawson, D. S. and Ruttan, R. A., 106
Recreational lakes,
 cost accounting of, 28
 development of, 29
Reelfoot Lake (Tenn.),
 history of commercial fishing in, 198
Reproduction,
 channel catfish unsuccessful in ponds,
   103
 flathead catfish unsuccessful in ponds,
   103
 potential of fishes, 92
Reproduction, competition, and predation,
 interrelationships of, 91, 124
Reproduction potential,
 natural production of young, 93
Rescue, of fish,
 on Illinois River, 4
 uselessness of, 4
Reservoirs,
 cycles of production, repeated, 11
 developmental future of, 13
 fishing cycle in, 10
 as aquatic deserts, 9
 early investigations of, 9
 management, and phases of operation,
   11
 renovation of, 10
 water supply, rotenoning fish in, 12
Responses of fish to angling, 189, 237,
   238, 243
Rice-fish farming,
 crop rotation, 264
 largemouth bass production in, 264,
   265

Ricker, Wm., 200, 203
Ridge Lake (Ill.), 67, 75, 93, 95, 204, 244
Rotenone,
  dosage for killing fish, 143
  first pond poisoning attempt with, 142
  method of application of, 143
  optimum temperature for treatment, 145
  properties of, 142
  removal of desirable fish before, 145
  residual toxicity, 147
  toxicity to fish, 143
  toxicity loss with kill of fish, 147
  used for collecting fish, 142
Rough fish,
  control, in reservoirs, 11-12
Russell, E. S., 182

Saila, S. B., 106
Salmo (salmon),
  several spawning migrations, 237
Salmon, spring or coho,
  repellent action of mammal skins, 224
Sampling, fish, 131, 132
  angling as a method of, 139
  boat shocking, 138
  minnow seine, 135-136
  reasons for, 131
  regular annual uses for, 137
  spot poisoning, 137
  with gill nets, 133
  with hoopnets, wing nets, and trap nets, 134
  with trammel nets, 133
Saran screen, M.S.-904, 140
Saturation point, 59
Scavengers, 201
  removal of carrion by, 201
Schäeperclaus, W., 200
Schloemer, C. L., 231
Schooling, of fishes, 230
Scuba, 214
Selection,
  intentional, of hatchery fish, 102
  through fishing, for least wary, 103
  unintentional, of hatchery fish, 102
Selective breeding, 101
Selective poisons,
  for fish, 147
Senachwine, Lake (Ill.), 124
Senility, in fish, 200
Sex characteristics, external, 97
Sex ratios, 96
Sewage, human,
  nitrogen content of, 44
  phosphorus content of, 44

Shad, gizzard,
  localized kills of, 56
  reduction of, in water supply reservoirs, 12
  standing crop of, 64
Shad, threadfin,
  stocked to improve food chain, 11, 112
Shapovalov, Leo, 257
Shetter, D. S., Whalls, M. J., and Corbett, O. M., 208
Shiner, blacktail,
  sound production of, 219
Shiner, golden,
  survived winterkill at Gale Lake, 53
Shiner, red,
  sound production of, 219
Shiner, satinfin,
  sound production of, 219
Size limit,
  on short-lived species, 208
  removal of, 209
Smelt,
  stocked to improve food for trout, 113
Snieszko, S. F., 200
Sodium cyanide, 149
  dangers of using, 149
  toxicity to fish, 149
Sodium sulfite,
  as a fish salvage, 149
Solitary fishes, 229
Solunar tables theory, 242
Sound location, 218
Sound production,
  of blacktail shiner, 219
  of drum, 219
  of red shiner, 219
  of satinfin shiner, 219
Spawning, 97
  length of season, 97
  related to season and water temperature, 98
Spawning, natural,
  deep lake studies, 8
  success, as compared to hatcheries, 8
Spawn production and number of spawners, 94
Standing crop,
  chemical basis for size of, 63
  definition of, 60
  effect of hard water on, 70
  effect of kinds of fishes on, 63
  factors affecting poundage of fish, 62
  fertilization increases, 63
  ranges of, 63
  relative abundance of species in, 60
  yield as related to, 185
Starrett, W. C., 20

Starrett, W. C. and McNeil, P. L., Jr., 124
Starvation, 123
  effects of, 81
  recovery from, 81
Statistics on fishermen, 251
"Stay at Home" fish, 233
Stickleback,
  egg production of, 92
Stimuli, specific responses to, 232
Stocking,
  bass-bluegill combination, 104
  causes for failures, 113
  compared to natural reproduction, 111
  corrective, 112
  dangers of, to improve food chain, 113
  failures of, 113-114
  following partial poisoning, 111
  for improvement of a population, 110
  in Michigan largely discontinued, 111
  objectives of, 103
  of a few individuals, 112
  of ponds containing fish, 110
  of reservoirs for improvement, 11
  smelt to improve trout growth, 113
  to improve a food chain, 112
  unauthorized, 110
Stream water,
  phosphorus content of, 44
Stripmine lakes,
  acid waters in, 26
  aging of, 27
  origin of, 26
Stroud, R. H., 115, 195
Stroud, R. H. and Jenkins, R. M., 36
Stunting,
  identification of, 189
Sturgeon, lake,
  in catch-out ponds, 258
Suckers,
  standing crop in pounds per acre, 64
Suckers, white,
  killed by supersaturation of O_2, 55
Sugarloaf Lake (Michigan), 204
Sullivan, C. M., 225
Summerkill, 54
  causes for, 55
Sunfish,
  hybrids, 99-101
  minimum useful size of, 71
  nesting habits of, 98-99
  nests, destruction of, 166
  number of eggs of, 92
  standing crop in pounds per acre, 6
Sunfish, green,
  effects of drawdown on, 160
  survived winterkill in Gale Lake, 53

Sunset Cliff Club Pond (Ill.), 241
Surber, E. W., 5
Survival rate,
  bass fry at Ridge Lake, 199
  of stocked fish, 114
Swingle, H. S., 120, 163, 185, 260
Swingle, H. S., Prather, E. E., Lawrence, J. M., 111, 152
Swingle, H. S. and Smith, E. V., 8, 61, 62, 69, 111, 167, 189, 195
Systox, 148

Tail water,
  temperature at Dale Hollow, 34
Tarzwell, C. M., 232
Taste,
  location of organs, 220
Temperature,
  effects of, on fish, 45
Temperature acclimation, 226
  survival value of, 226
Temperature, high,
  mortalities caused by, 225
Temperature, lethal,
  for brook trout, 46
  relationship to acclimation temperature, 226-227
Temperature perception and response, 224
  ability to distinguish minor changes, 225
  north-south acclimation, 224
  sensitivity to change, 225
  sudden changes of temperature, 225
Temperatures, preferred, 227
  of several species of sport fish, 228-229
TEPP, 148
Territoriality, of fish, 234-235
Thermal stratification,
  at Dale Hollow outlet, 34
  attempts to upset, 34
  bottom water outlets, 31
  characteristic types of, 31
  fall overturn of, 33
  inflowing water, temperature of, 36
  influence of, on reservoir outlets, 34
  influence of plankton blooms, 38
  in ponds, 32
  seasonal cycle of, 31
  temperature-caused wedge of water, 38
  variations in, 33
Thompkins, W. A. and Bridges, C., 135
Thompson, D. H., 72, 73, 124, 185, 231, 242
Thompson, D. H. and Bennett, G. W., 77
Thoreson, N. A., 106

Tilapia,
   competition between *T. mossambica* and *T. sparrmani*, 43
Toxaphene for lake renovation, 148
   dosages of, 149
   first use of, 148
   residual properties, 149
   selective toxicity of, 149
   toxicity as compared to rotenone, 149
   toxicity to aquatic invertebrates, 149
Trephosia, 142
Trout,
   below coldwater reservoir outlets, 34
   early production of in U. S., 3
   hatchery selection of, 102
   importation into S. Africa, 81
   in catch-out ponds, 257, 258
   maximum summer temperature for, 45
   standing crop in pounds per acre, 64
Trout, brook,
   lethal temperature of, 46
   preferred temperature of, 228
Trout, brown,
   restricted movement of, 235
Trout, lake,
   preferred temperature of, 228
Trout, rainbow,
   "black" trout, 216
   food competition with red-side shiners, 118
   pigmentation of, blind, 216
   restricted movement of, 235
Trout lakes,
   selective poisoning of, 143
Turbidity,
   colloidal clay in, 46
   effects of, 46
   effects on fishes, 47
   electrically charged clay particles, 47
   in Oklahoma ponds, 46

Underfishing, 187
   definition of, 187
U. S. Engineers, recreational values by, 252-253
U.S. F. and W. S.,
   Office of River Basin Studies, 11
U. S. Soil Conservation Service,
   origin of, 16
   pond sponsoring activities of, 8
Useful sizes,
   of fish, 70, 71

Vegetation, aquatic,
   competition for space, 169
   control with sodium arsenite, 177
   functions of, in lakes, 169
   movement into new waters, 168
   role in management, 176
   types of, 169
Vegetation control,
   herbicides for, 174-175
Ventura Marsh (Iowa), 125
Verheijen, F. J., 221
Viosca, Percy, Jr., 84, 110, 189
Vision, 213
   field of, 216
Vision, color,
   in largemouth bass, 213
   in bluegills, 213
   in elritze, 213
   importance of, in fishing, 213
   preferences for colors, 214
   stimulus of red, 213
Vision, underwater, 214-216

Walleye,
   dead eggs in Lake Gogebic, 103
   intraspecific competition of, 123
   killed by supersaturation of O_2, 55
   length of life of, 202
   limited range of, 233
   minimum useful size of, 71
   mortality rate of, 207
   preferred temperature of, 228
   shortage of prey for, 124-125
   spawning temperature of, 98
   standing crop in pounds per acre, 64
Walls, G. L., 214-216
Warmouth,
   competition with other species, 121-123
   growth affected by dragline, 89
   mortality rate of, 207
   number of eggs per fish, 93
Water levels,
   manipulation of, in lakes, 11
Water treatment,
   in drained lake basin, 141
Water-supply reservoirs, 20
   bottom-rooting fish in, 21
   eutrophic lakes, 21
   oligotrophic lakes, 21
   recreational uses of, 21
   use of rotenone in, 21
Weiss, G. F., 190
Westman, J. R., Smith, R. K., and Harrocks, A., 244
Whitmore, C. M., Warren, E., and Dondoraff, P., 232
Whitewood Creek (S. D.),
   pollution of, 47
Wiebe, A. H.,
   fertilizers in water, 5

Winter kill, 49
    aeration of water above ice, 51
    aeration of water under ice, 51
    changes of oxygen tension, 50
    circulation of bottom water, 52
    circulation of water having BOD, 52
    lamp black, 52
    partial kill, results of, 53
    pumping well water into pond, 51
    snow removal, 52
    transmission of light through ice, 50
Witt, Arthur, Jr., 244
Wittingau (Czechoslovakia)
    carp culture at, in 1358, 2

Wolf-type weir, 140
Wood, Roy, 232
Wrede, W. L., 221

Yashouv, A., 120
Year classes, intermittent, 186
Yield,
    annual replacement of, 186
    as related to growing season, 185
    as related to standing crop, 184
    Great Lakes, 1920-1947, 184
    maximum, 184
    relationship to carrying capacity, 185